INDUSTRIAL VENTILATION

A Manual of Recommended Practice

for Operation and Maintenance

Signature Publications

Copyright © 2007

by

American Conference of Governmental Industrial Hygienists (ACGIH®)

ISBN: 978-1-882417-66-7

ACGIH®
Kemper Woods Center
1330 Kemper Meadow Drive
Cincinnati, Ohio 45240-4148
Telephone: 513-742-2020 Fax: 513-742-3355
Email: Publishing@acgih.org
http://www.acgih.org

CONTENTS

FOREWORD

Since its first edition in 1951, *Industrial Ventilation: A Manual of Recommended Practice* (the Ventilation Manual) has been used by engineers and industrial hygienists to design and evaluate industrial ventilation systems. This Manual entitled *Industrial Ventilation: A Manual of Recommended Practice for Operation and Maintenance* (the O&M Manual) is a companion to the Ventilation Manual and is intended to complement its information. The Industrial Ventilation Committee considered several new chapters for inclusion in the Ventilation Manual. As the chapters developed, it became apparent that a reorganization of the Ventilation Manual and the proposed O&M Manual would make both volumes more readable. Consequently, the 26th edition of the Ventilation Manual will be entitled *Industrial Ventilation: A Manual of Recommended Practice for Design* (Design Manual) and will include several new chapters. The general organization splits the text between chapters that address design of an industrial ventilation system (Design Manual) and those that address operation and maintenance of ventilation systems (O&M Manual).

To facilitate navigation between the two volumes, an insert on the front, inside cover shows how the chapters are related. The two Manuals are divided into several topics, which generally follow the timeline for the development of an industrial ventilation system.

- Concept Design
  - Exposure Assessment – Design Manual – Chapter 1
  - Preliminary Design – Design Manual – Chapter 2
  - Ventilation Systems Costs – Design Manual – Chapter 12
- Detailed Design
  - Principles of Ventilation – Design Manual – Chapter 3 (Chapter 1 of 25th edition)
  - General Ventilation – Design Manual – Chapter 4 (Chapter 2 of 25th edition)
  - Design Issues – Systems – Design Manual – Chapter 5
  - Design Issues – Hoods – Design Manual – Chapter 6 (Chapter 3 of 25th edition)
  - Design Issues – Fans – Design Manual – Chapter 7 (Chapter 6 of 25th edition)
  - Design Issues – Air Cleaners – Design Manual – Chapter 8 (Chapter 4 of 25th edition)
  - System Design Calculations – Design Manual – Chapter 9 (Chapter 5 of 25th edition)
  - Supply Air – Design Manual – Chapter 10 (Chapter 7 of 25th edition)
  - Energy Issues – Design Manual – Chapter 11 (New chapter)
  - Specific Operations – Design Manual – Chapter 13 (Chapter 10 of 25th edition)
- Installation
  - Construction – O&M Manual – Chapter 1
- Commissioning
  - Commissioning – O&M Manual – Chapter 2
  - Air System Testing – O&M Manual – Chapter 3
  - Balancing – O&M Manual – Chapter 4
- Monitoring and Maintenance of a Ventilation System
  - M&M Ventilation Systems – O&M Manual – Chapter 5
  - M&M Air Cleaning Devices – O&M Manual – Chapter 6
- Managing Ventilation Systems
  - Troubleshooting – O&M Manual – Chapter 7
  - Change Management – O&M Manual – Chapter 8
  - Operator Training – O&M Manual – Chapter 9

Information provided as a guideline can be influenced by other factors in an industrial environment (material handling techniques, cross-drafts and replacement air, work practices, and housekeeping, etc.), therefore formulae developed in the laboratory and at other sites may need to be altered further for actual field conditions. In many cases, ranges of values are shown, leaving final selection to be based on the experience of the practitioner and appropriate field conditions. Hence, the practitioner should always evaluate the effectiveness of hoods and other parts of the system after installation and be prepared to make changes as needed. Indeed, due to process changes, work-practice changes, and to the effects of the aging of the system, practitioners should continually evaluate and modify systems throughout their life cycles.

This Manual is intended to be used as a guide, not as an official standard. It is designed to present current information with regard to the subject matter covered. It is distributed with the understanding that the Industrial Ventilation Committee and its members, collectively or individually, assume no responsibility for any inadvertent misinformation, for inadvertent omissions, or for the results in the use of this publication.

INDUSTRIAL VENTILATION COMMITTEE

G. S. Rajhans, GSR & Associates, Canada, Chair
K. M. Paulson, NFESC, California, Vice Chair
G. M. Adams, General Motors Corp., Michigan
R. Dayringer, MIOSHA, Michigan
N. Donovan, Editorial Consultant, Michigan
D. L. Edwards, KBD/Technic, Ohio
G. Grubb, MIOSHA, Michigan
S. E. Guffey, West Virginia University, West Virginia
J. F. Hale, Jackson-Hale Environmental Technologies, Inc., North Carolina

R. L. Herring, North Carolina Department of Health and Human Services, North Carolina
R. T. Hughes, Retired, Ohio
G. Q. Johnson, Health & Environmental Safety Alliance, Ohio
G. W. Knutson, Knutson Ventilation Consulting, Minnesota
G. A. Lanham, KBD/Technic, Ohio
J. L. Topmiller, NIOSH, Ohio
A. W. Woody, Ventilation/Energy Applications, Michigan

EXTERNAL CONTRIBUTORS

David Amrein, Fisher-Klosterman, Inc., Kentucky
Powell Maxfield, Münters Corporation, Massachusetts
W. Craig Jackson, Jackson-Hale Environmental Technologies, Inc., North Carolina
Richard Knight, RMT, Georgia
Dan Josephs, American Air Filter, Kentucky
Joe Klobucar, Dürr Environmental, Michigan
John Richards, Air Control Techniques, North Carolina
Loren G. Garner, Bio Reaction Industries, Oregon

ACKNOWLEDGMENTS

Industrial Ventilation is a true Committee effort. It brings into focus useful practical ventilation data from all parts of the world in one source. The Committee membership of industrial ventilation engineers and industrial hygienists represents a diversity of experience and interests that ensures a well-rounded cooperative effort.

From the First Edition in 1951, this effort has been successful as witnessed by the acceptance of the "Ventilation Manual" throughout industry, by governmental agencies, and as a worldwide reference and text.

As indicated in the Foreword, we now have two volumes of the Manual; the Operation and Maintenance (O&M) Manual and the Design Manual. We are extremely grateful to the external contributors listed at the end of the Foreword for their contributions to the sixth chapter of the O&M Manual.

We are also grateful for the faith and firm foundation provided by past Committees and members listed below. Special acknowledgment is made to the Division of Occupational Health, Michigan Department of Health, for contributing their original field manual, which was the basis of the First Edition, to Mr. Knowlton J. Caplan who supervised the preparation of the Manual and to Mrs. Norma Donovan, Secretary to the Committee, for her untiring zeal in our efforts.

To many other individuals and agencies who have made specific contributions and have provided support, suggestions, and constructive criticism, our special thanks.

INDUSTRIAL VENTILATION COMMITTEE

Previous Members

G.M. Adams, 2004-present
A.G. Apol, 1984-2002
H. Ayer, 1962-1966
R.E. Bales, 1954-1960
J. Baliff, 1950-1956; Chair, 1954-1956
J.C. Barrett, 1956-1976; Chair 1960-1968
J.L. Beltran, 1964-1966
D. Bonn, Consultant, 1958-1968
D.J. Burton, 1988-1990
K.J. Caplan, 1974-1978; Consultant, 1980-1986
A.B. Cecala, 1998-1999
G. Carlton, 1999-2002
W.M. Cleary, 1976-present; Chair, 1978-1984
M. Davidson, 1995-1998
R. Dayringer, 2004-present
L. Dickie, 1984-1994; Consultant, 1968-1984
T.N. Do, 1995-2000
N. Donovan, Editorial Consultant, 1950-present
D.L. Edwards, 2003-present
B. Feiner, 1956-1968
M. Flynn, 1989-1995
M. Franklin, 1991-1994; 1998-present
S.E. Guffey, 1984-present
J.F. Hale, 2004-present
G.M. Hama, 1950-1984; Chair, 1956-1960
R.P. Hibbard, 1968-1994
R.T. Hughes, 1976-present; Chair, 1989-2001
G.Q. Johnson, 2001-present

H.S. Jordan, 1960-1962
J. Kane, Consultant, 1950-1952
J. Kayse, Consultant, 1956-1958
J.F. Keppler, 1950-1954; 1958-1960
G.W. Knutson, 1986-present
G. Lanham, 1998-present
J.J. Loeffler, 1980-1995; Chair, 1984-1989
J. Lumsden, 1962-1968
J.R. Lynch, 1966-1976
K.R. Mead, 1996-present
G. Michaelson, 1958-1960
K.M. Morse, 1950-1951; Chair, 1950-1951
R.T. Page, 1954-1956
K.M. Paulson, 1991-present; Vice Chair, 1996-present
O.P. Petrey, Consultant, 1978-1999
G.S. Rajhans, 1976-1995; Vice Chair, 1994-1995; Chair, 2002-present
K.E. Robinson, 1950-1954; Chair, 1952-1954
A. Salazar, 1952-1954
E.L. Schall, 1956-1958
M.M. Schuman, 1962-1964; Chair, 1968-1978
J.C. Soet, 1950-1960
J.L. Topmiller, 2004-present
A.L. Twombly, 1986-present
J. Willis, Consultant, 1952-1956
R. Wolle, 1966-1974
A.W. Woody, 1998-present
J.A. Wunderle, 1960-1964

DEFINITIONS

Aerosol: An assemblage of small particles, solid or liquid, suspended in air. The diameter of the particles may vary from 100 microns down to 0.01 micron or less, e.g., dust, fog, smoke.

Air Cleaner: A device designed for the purpose of removing atmospheric airborne impurities such as dusts, gases, mists, vapors, fumes, and smoke. (Air cleaners include air washers, air filters, electrostatic precipitators, and charcoal filters.)

Air Filter: An air cleaning device that removes light particulate loadings from normal atmospheric air before introduction into the building. Usual range: loadings up to 3 grains per thousand cubic feet (0.003 grains per cubic foot). Note: Atmospheric air in heavy industrial areas and in-plant air in many industries have higher loadings than this, and dust collectors are then indicated for proper air cleaning.

Air Horsepower: The theoretical horsepower required to drive a fan if there were no losses in the fan; that is, if its efficiency were 100 percent.

Aspect Ratio: The ratio of the width to the length; AR = W/L.

Aspect Ratio of an Elbow: The width (W) along the axis of the bend divided by depth (D) in the plane of the bend; AR = W/D.

Blast Gate: Sliding damper.

Blow (throw): In air distribution, the distance an air stream travels from an outlet to a position at which air motion along the axis reduces to a velocity of 50 fpm. For unit heaters, the distance an air stream travels from a heater without a perceptible rise due to temperature difference and loss of velocity.

Brake Horsepower: The horsepower actually required to drive a fan. This includes the energy losses in the fan and can be determined only by actual test of the fan. (This does not include the drive losses between motor and fan.)

Capture Velocity: The air velocity at any point in front of the hood or at the hood opening necessary to overcome opposing air currents and capture the contaminated air at that point by causing it to flow into the hood.

Comfort Zone (Average): The range of effective temperatures over which the majority (50% or more) of adults feel comfortable.

Convection: The motion resulting in a fluid from the differences in density and the action of gravity. In heat transmission this meaning has been extended to include both forced and natural motion or circulation.

Deflagration: A propagation of a combustion zone that occurs at a velocity that is less than the speed of sound in the unreacted medium.

Density: The ratio of the mass of a specimen of a substance to the volume of the specimen. The mass of a unit volume of a substance. When weight can be used without confusion, as synonymous with mass, density is the weight of a unit volume of a substance.

Density Factor: The ratio of actual air density to density of standard air. The product of the density factor and the density of standard air (0.075 lb/ft^3) will give the actual air density in pounds per cubic foot; Density = df × 0.075 lb/ft^3 (the density of standard air).

Dust: Small solid particles created by the breaking up of larger particles by processes, i.e., crushing, grinding, drilling, explosions, etc. Dust particles already in existence in a mixture of materials may escape into the air through such operations as shoveling, conveying, screening, sweeping, etc.

Dust Collector: An air cleaning device to remove heavy particulate loadings from exhaust systems. Usual range of particulate loading: 0.003 grains per cubic foot or higher.

Entry Loss: Loss in pressure caused by air flowing into a duct or hood (inches H_2O).

Fumes: Small, solid particles formed by the condensation of vapors of solid materials.

Gases: Formless fluids which tend to occupy an entire space uniformly at ordinary temperatures and pressures.

Hood: A shaped inlet designed to capture contaminated air and conduct it into the exhaust duct system.

Hood Flow Coefficient: The ratio of flow caused by a given hood static pressure compared to the theoretical flow which would result if the static pressure could be converted to velocity pressure with 100 percent efficiency. *NOTE: This was defined as Coefficient of Entry in previous editons.*

Humidity, Absolute: The weight of water vapor per unit volume, pounds per cubic foot or grams per cubic centimeter.

Humidity, Relative: The ratio of the actual partial pressure of the water vapor in a space to the saturation pressure of pure water at the same temperature.

Inch of Water: A unit of pressure equal to the pressure exerted by a column of liquid water one inch high at a standard temperature.

Lower Explosive Limit: The lower limit of flammability or explosibility of a gas or vapor at ordinary ambient temperatures expressed in percent of the gas or vapor in air by volume. This limit is assumed constant for temperatures up to 250 F. Above these temperatures, it should be decreased by a factor of 0.7 since explosibility increases with higher temperatures.

Manometer: An instrument for measuring pressure; essentially a U-tube partially filled with a liquid, usually water, mercury or a light oil, so constructed that the amount of displacement of the liquid indicates the pressure being exerted on the instrument.

Micron: A unit of length, the thousandth part of 1 mm or the millionth of a meter (approximately 1/25,000 of an inch).

Minimum Design Duct Velocity: Minimum air velocity required to move the particulates in the air stream (fpm).

Mists: Small droplets of materials that are ordinarily liquid at normal temperature and pressure.

Plenum: Pressure equalizing chamber.

Pressure, Static: The potential pressure exerted in all directions by a fluid at rest. For a fluid in motion, it is measured in a direction normal to the direction of flow. Usually expressed in inches water gauge when dealing with air. (The tendency to either burst or collapse the pipe.)

Pressure, Total: The algebraic sum of the velocity pressure and the static pressure (with due regard to sign).

Pressure, Vapor: The pressure exerted by a vapor. If a vapor is kept in confinement over its liquid so that the vapor can accumulate above the liquid, the temperature being held constant, the vapor pressure approaches a fixed limit called the maximum or saturated vapor pressure, dependent only on the temperature and the liquid. The term vapor pressure is sometimes used as synonymous with saturated vapor pressure.

Pressure, Velocity: The kinetic pressure in the direction of flow necessary to cause a fluid at rest to flow at a given velocity. Usually expressed in inches water gauge.

Radiation, Thermal (Heat): The transmission of energy by means of electromagnetic waves of very long wave length. Radiant energy of any wave length may, when absorbed, become thermal energy and result in an increase in the temperature of the absorbing body.

Replacement Air: A ventilation term used to indicate the volume of controlled outdoor air supplied to a building to replace air being exhausted.

Slot Velocity: Linear flow rate of contaminated air through a slot, fpm.

Smoke: An air suspension (aerosol) of particles, usually but not necessarily solid, often originating in a solid nucleus, formed from combustion or sublimation.

Specific Gravity: The ratio of the mass of a unit volume of a substance to the mass of the same volume of a standard substance at a standard temperature. Water at 39.2 F is the standard substance usually referred to. For gases, dry air, at the same temperature and pressure as the gas, is often taken as the standard substance.

Standard Air: Dry air at 70 F and 29.92 (in Hg) barometer. This is substantially equivalent to 0.075 lb/ft^3. Specific heat of dry air = 0.24 BTU/lb/F.

Temperature, Effective: An arbitrary index which combines into a single value the effect of temperature, humidity, and air movement on the sensation of warmth or cold felt by the human body. The numerical value is that of the temperature of still, saturated air which would induce an identical sensation.

Temperature, Wet-Bulb: Thermodynamic wet-bulb temperature is the temperature at which liquid or solid water, by evaporating into air, can bring the air to saturation adiabatically at the same temperature. Wet-bulb temperature (without qualification) is the temperature indicated by a wet-bulb psychrometer constructed and used according to specifications.

Threshold Limit Values (TLVs®): The values for airborne toxic materials which are to be used as guides in the control of health hazards and represent time-weighted concentrations to which nearly all workers may be exposed 8 hours per day over extended periods of time without adverse effects (see Appendix).

Transport (Conveying) Velocity: See Minimum Design Duct Velocity.

Turn-Down Ratio: The degree to which the operating performance of a system can be reduced to satisfy part-load conditions. Usually expressed as a ratio; for example, 30:1 means the minimum operation point is 1/30th of full load.

Vapor: The gaseous form of substances that are normally in the solid or liquid state and that can be changed to those states either by increasing the pressure or decreasing the temperature.

ABBREVIATIONS

A . . . . .area
acfm . . . . .flow rate at actual condition
AH . . . . .air horsepower
AR . . . . .aspect ratio
A_s . . . . .slot area
B . . . . .barometric pressure
bhp . . . . .brake horsepower
bhp_a . . . . .brake horsepower, actual
bhp_s . . . . .brake horsepower, standard air
BTU . . . . .British Thermal Unit
BTUH . . . . .BTU per hour
C_e . . . . .hood flow coefficient
cfm . . . . .cubic feet per minute
CLR . . . . .centerline radius
D . . . . .diameter
df . . . . .overall density factor
df_e . . . . .elevation density factor
df_p . . . . .pressure density factor
df_t . . . . .temperature density factor
df_m . . . . .moisture density factor
ET . . . . .effective temperature
f . . . . .Moody diagram friction coefficient
F . . . . .degree, Fahrenheit
F_h . . . . .hood entry loss coefficient
F_{el} . . . . .elbow loss coefficient
F_{en} . . . . .entry loss coefficient
fpm . . . . .feet per minute
fps . . . . .feet per second
F_s . . . . .slot loss coefficient
ft^2 . . . . .square foot
ft^3 . . . . .cubic foot
g . . . . .gravitational force, ft/sec/sec
gpm . . . . .gallons per minute
gr . . . . .grains
h_h . . . . .hood entry loss
h_e . . . . .overall hood entry loss
h_{el} . . . . .elbow loss
h_{en} . . . . .entry loss
h_f . . . . .loss in straight duct run
HEPA . . . . .high-efficiency particulate air filters
H_f . . . . .duct loss coefficient
hp . . . . .horsepower
hr . . . . .hour
h_s . . . . .slot or opening entry loss

HV . . . . .humid volume (ft³ mix/lbm dry air)
HVAC . . . . .heating, ventilation, and air conditioning
in . . . . .inch
in^2 . . . . .square inch
"wg . . . . .inches water gauge
lb . . . . .pound
lbm . . . . .pound mass
LEL . . . . .lower explosive limit
ME . . . . .mechanical efficiency
mg . . . . .milligram
min . . . . .minute
mm . . . . .millimeter
MRT .mean radiant temperature
MW . . . . .molecular weight
ρ . . . . .density of air in lb/ft³
ppm . . . . .parts per million
psi . . . . .pounds per square inch
PWR . . . . .power
Q . . . . .flow rate in cfm
Q_{corr} . . . . .corrected flow rate at a junction
R . . . . .degree, Rankin
RH . . . . .relative humidity
rpm . . . . .revolutions per minute
scfm .standard cubic feet per minute
sfpm . . . . .surface feet per minute
sp gr . . . . .specific gravity
SP . . . . .static pressure
SP_{gov} . . . . .higher static pressure at junction of 2 ducts
SP_h . . . . .hood static pressure
SP_s . . . . .SP, system handling standard air
STP . . . . .standard temperature and pressure
TLV® . . . . .Threshold Limit Value
TP . . . . .total pressure
V . . . . .velocity, fpm
V_d . . . . .duct velocity
VP . . . . .velocity pressure
VP_d . . . . .duct velocity pressure
VP_r .resultant velocity pressure
VP_s . . . . .slot velocity pressure
V_s . . . . .slot velocity
V_t . . . . .duct transport velocity
W . . . . .watt
ω . . . . .moisture content (lbm H_2O/lbm dry air)
z . . . . .elevation in feet above sea level

Chapter 1

CONSTRUCTION AND PROJECT MANAGEMENT PHASE

1.1   INTRODUCTION

The construction and installation of the local exhaust system is often the User's initial introduction to the system hardware. The system has been designed and reviewed and is now being installed in the plant. Because most local exhaust ventilation systems also must meet environmental and safety and health regulations, the proper control and management of the construction process is the first important phase of operation and management.

1.1.1 *Organization of the Chapter.* The principals in a typical industrial ventilation construction project (both new work and renovations) include the Owner and the ***General Contractor*** (hereafter called Contractor), with the designer taking a less dominant role. This chapter focuses on activities of the General Contractor and the Owner's on-site representatives.

A diagram showing the relationship of all of the parties from concept and design through construction is shown in Figure 1-1. In this diagram, the Project Team takes a central role in the communication of design needs among all of the parties. Note that the 'team' may actually be one person for smaller projects but can have 20 or more members on complex projects and/or those impacting plant operations. Team members can include the Owner's own employees and/or outside consultants specifically hired for the project. Typical members include personnel with expertise in plant production requirements, maintenance, safety, permits, design, purchasing and operators. Details of the functions and tools for the operation of the Project Team will be further discussed in Chapters 2 and 4 of *Industrial Ventilation: A Manual of Recommended Practice for Design.*

1.2   GOALS AND OBJECTIVES DURING CONSTRUCTION

The primary objectives in the construction of the ventilation system are:

1) Meet ventilation system success criteria
2) Meet exposure control criteria
3) Meet building code and other regulatory criteria
4) Protect contractor and plant personnel during construction
5) Deliver project on time
6) Contain costs

1.2.1 *Meet Ventilation System Success Criteria.* From the Construction Contractor's perspective the project is a success if it meets the design requirements, i.e., correct airflow and capture velocity at the hoods, sufficient duct velocities in the branches and the main, appropriate fans and compliant air pollution control equipment. The testing, adjusting and balancing (TAB) agency must test both the exhaust and supply system and the relationship (balance) between the two systems. The TAB agency's role is to ensure that the mechanical system is operating as designed. TAB agencies typically do not conduct exposure monitoring.

1.2.2 *Meet Exposure Control Criteria.* The primary purpose for an industrial ventilation system is to protect workers from occupational stressors, typically in the form of airborne contaminants. Refer to Chapter 1 of *Industrial Ventilation: A Manual of Recommended Practice for Design*, entitled Exposure Assessment, to establish acceptable values. The facility Safety and Health Staff or an outside contractor can determine if the industrial ventilation system is controlling the stressor. Occasionally industrial ventilation alone cannot fully control the stressor. Facility management must employ other methods of contaminant control.

1.2.3 *Meet Building Code and Other Regulatory Criteria.* Because local exhaust ventilation systems transport materials that could be hazardous, system construction and operation are subject to numerous regulations ranging from local community building codes to national consensus codes such as National Fire Protection Association (NFPA), American National Standards Institute (ANSI), and Sheet Metal and Air Conditioning Contractors National Association (SMACNA). Most countries have a set of standards that they use as the industrial facility design and operation basis. Many standards are codified into the local community codes. Communities will adopt others, such as the International Mechanical Code and American Society of Heating, Refrigerating and Air Conditioning Engineers (ASHRAE) codes or standards in whole or in part.

The air pollution control system is considered part of the industrial ventilation system. Since the material is conveyed away from the worker and potentially deposited to the outdoors, environmental protection regulations are a critical part of the project. Obtaining environmental permits is a critical task that should be initiated as soon as possible in the project's lifecycle.

1.2.4 *Protect Contractor and Plant Personnel During Construction.* Unfortunately, the construction industry has one of the highest occupational safety and health injury rates primarily due to the transient nature of the business. In the past, owners left occupational safety and health issues to the general contractor, but owners cannot avoid becoming involved due to increasing third party legal cases and insurance issues. Aggressive use of past safety performance (e.g., total recordable injury rates, lost time injury rates, etc.) and other contract clauses, improves the pool of eligible general contractors. This chapter addresses some of those issues.

Construction operations have somewhat different safety and health considerations than industrial operations, primarily since the project is transient. However, more injuries and deaths occur on a construction site than in general industry due to accidents from slips, falls, ergonomic, electrical, etc. Responsibility for job safety on a construction site lies with the general contractor, not the owner or the designer. The owner must identify unusual safety concerns (e.g., flammability, toxicity, etc.) in the contract and review the general contractor's

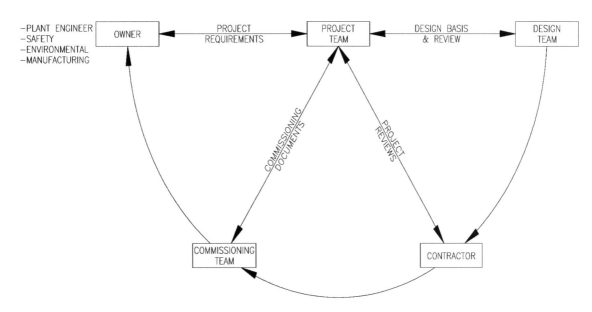

FIGURE 1-1. Project team as central part of installation

safety plan. The owner's on-site representative and construction inspector may observe the safety operations but should not stop the work. Unless there is imminent danger such as unstable shoring, the owner's representatives should negotiate the correction with the general contractor/builder as soon as possible. For insurance and legal purposes, the owner should not direct workers to change their work practices. However, the owner can direct the contractor to conform to specific safety requirements.

The owner's representative should review the general contractor's safety plan as part of the initial contract review and periodically ensure that the contractor is conforming to the safety plan. Appendix A1 contains a partial review of the major components in a safety plan.

1.2.5 Deliver Project on Time. A primary goal in construction is on-time project delivery. Well-defined initial project documentation is the least likely to generate problems, such as change orders and work stoppages, later in the project.

Many contracts contain clauses encouraging early or on-time completion by providing a bonus for early delivery. Favorable post-project evaluations and public relations are also of value to a contractor. Conversely, some contracts even levy penalties by withholding payment for excess time beyond the contract period. It is in the owner's interest to complete the contract on time in order to occupy the facility, and it is usually in the contractor's interest to complete the project on time to move the workforce forward to the next project.

1.2.6 Contain Costs. Within the US, *construction management costs* for typical projects are typically 6-8% of the project costs. A complex industrial ventilation project may be more expensive due to regulatory and safety issues. While not all of the cost is incurred on site, the economy of scale permits a lower percent as the project grows larger. An additional 4-8% should be added for international projects.

Value engineering is a total quality management concept that attempts to give the owner lower cost options for specific project items and systems. Value Engineering must consider the full life cycle costs of the project (See Chapter 12 of *Industrial Ventilation: A Manual of Recommended Practice for Design*). The value engineer is sometimes enlisted to identify savings when project costs begin to escalate above the project budget bid. The best procedure is to identify key cost considerations during the design process. Choices made to save costs after the completion of the design may impact operability of the system. For example, removing blast gates used for system balancing may save costs but render the system useless or make it impossible to balance.

After a design is proposed and accepted, the value engineer goes through the design and identifies items and systems that may be unnecessary, or identifies which specifications can be less stringent than called out in the specification. Sometimes these suggestions can save the owner considerable costs. However, the owner must be aware that some industrial ventilation design decisions are not negotiable without considerable performance or later operations and maintenance consequences. For example:

1) In a balance by design system, each duct run is specifically sized to meet the minimum transport velocity and balance with the rest of the system. This frequently means several sizes of duct are needed. However, it is usually less expensive to order more of the same sized duct. Should the same sized duct be ordered, the system would not be balanced when installed.

2) Duct for particulate material requires a heavier gauge

material and sometimes extra reinforcement at elbows. Reducing the gauge in the elbow will reduce first costs but the elbow will need to be replaced sooner.

3) Testing, Adjusting and Balancing is eliminated from the contract late in the project because it is expensive and the owner believes the funds can be obtained elsewhere.

4) Selection of a fan to optimize fan efficiency may compromise the stability of the system, especially if it operates over a wide pressure range.

5) Some electrical provisions, (heavier wire gauge, larger motor horsepower) may add desirable contingency to the system.

The Value Engineer can be important to the final design, especially with respect to ongoing operating costs. Industrial ventilation systems use large volumes of air to move relatively small quantities of dust. Consider a 20,000 scfm exhaust system with a dust loading of 0.1 grains per cubic foot. The system requires about 45 tons of air to remove 17 pounds of dust in an hour from the workroom. The efficiency and reliability of the industrial ventilation system are extremely important to plant safety; however, the systems can have significant operating costs.

1.3   PROJECT TEAM ORGANIZATION AND RESPONSIBILITIES

1.3.1 Owner's Responsibility. The owner of a large facility usually also has a representative who is responsible for construction management at the building site. That individual would be a key part of the Project Team. The owner may be his/her own representative for smaller projects. There is a temptation to release the Project Team, especially the system designer, once the construction phase of the project begins; however, this practice is not recommended. This is especially the case when building complex industrial ventilation systems where design changes may significantly impact contaminant control and the process. In addition, if the system has been designed using the "Balance by Design" Method (see *Industrial Ventilation: A Manual of Recommended Practice for Design*, Chapter 5) any changes in the construction phase could have a serious effect on the operation of the system.

1.3.2 Key Project Team Members. During the construction phase, key project positions or functions answerable to the owner and the general contractor may include some or all of the following:

- *Owner* – Individual or firm with a need for or benefiting from the industrial ventilation system.

- *Project Planner* – Individual responsible for purchasing equipment and supplies and scheduling work activities.

- *Project Manager* – Individual responsible for construction for the owner and usually also

responsible for the design. May work for the owner directly or be part of the designer's and/or general contractor's staff and may be located off site.

- *Designer* – Individual of the architectural and/or engineering firm hired to create a system design using owner requirements, code considerations and design standards.

- *Contracting Office* – In a large organization this group is responsible for announcing and awarding contracts. The Contracts Office may also manage invoices and make payments.

- *On-site Construction Manager* – Ideally should be a third party independent of the designer and the general contractor who coordinates contractor and subcontractor contracts, monitors project phases, adjusts work to accommodate changes, determines that work and material conform to project documents, arranges for field tests, prepares change orders and change proposals, and reviews progress payments. Typically is part of the general contractor's or designer's team.

- *Resident Project Representative* (also called resident engineer, resident inspector, resident manager) – member of the owner's technical staff who is permanently or intermittently on-site representing the owner's interest.

- *Quality Control Inspector* – Works for the Resident Project Representative to insure that the owner's interests are attained by examining material and workmanship to confirm that they meet the specifications and drawings.

- *Prime Contractor* – Lead building contractor hired by the owner to install the local exhaust ventilation system, the total process or plant. This firm can take the form of a general contractor, design/build firm or specialized contractor such as a sheet metal or industrial piping firm. These firms typically specialize in constructing buildings.

- *Subcontractor(s)* – Building trades specialists who specialize in one aspect of the building, e.g., mechanical (HVAC and/or plumbing), electrical (lighting, direct digital controls), fire protection, etc. Subcontractors normally perform contracted work directly for the prime contractor. Ideally, the Testing, Adjusting and Balancing (TAB) subcontractor should be hired by the owner and be independent from the prime contractor. However, to simplify contract administration and funding, the prime contractor often hires the TAB contractor.

- *Trades People* – Individuals trained to perform the contractor's and subcontractor's tasks (see Appendix B1).

- *Commissioning Agent* – Individual responsible for commissioning a system for the owner (see Chapter 2 for a description of the commissioning process).

Other individuals are likely to be involved during the construction phase (or startup), especially for large, complex, or unusual projects:

- *Original Ventilation Equipment Manufacturers* – Vendors who supply complete integrated systems (such as building automation systems) or larger pieces of equipment (fans, motors, air pollution control equipment). These representatives are usually on site when large systems start up to confirm that their equipment is tested properly and it is installed as recommended.

- *Suppliers* – Vendors who supply commodity items such as duct, wiring, piping, etc. Ducts are typically shipped to the site intact. However, it is sometimes less expensive to assemble the duct on-site for some large projects. This is particularly true of spiral wound duct frequently used in supply air systems.

- *Code Reviewing Officials* – Typically work with the drawings and specifications to determine that the ventilation systems comply with appropriate regulations.

- *Code Enforcement Officials* – Government officials (or owner's and contractor's safety representatives) responsible for compliance with environmental, building safety and other regulations. Environmental, Occupational Health and Safety (EOHS) inspectors may be on-site to determine that there is minimal harm during construction. Other EOHS inspectors determine that there are no negative effects from operating the facility. This may or may not be the same person.

- *Testing, Adjusting and Balancing (TAB) Contractor* – Individual or firm that adjusts ventilation system components to achieve the desired airflow. Ideally, the TAB subcontractor should be hired by the owner and be independent from the prime contractor. However, for contract administration and funding purposes, the prime contractor frequently hires the TAB contractor.

1.3.3 Field Office. The resident engineer and or inspector will usually have an on-site office to store plans, make phone calls, conduct informal meetings and discuss the project. This person may also fill the role as Project Manager. In some cases, **Field Office** fees, included in the contract for larger projects, can include furnishings, utilities, janitorial, sanitary and telephone services. Large construction projects may require that installers have their own field office in a trailer. In these cases, overhead and the utility services for the trailer are included in the contract fees and bid. Sometimes these offices

are shared with the owner's representative. This can be convenient when the project goes smoothly, but there is no privacy if there is a potential for disputes.

Generally the owner's representative and the contractor are the only two parties who can determine if a change to the original design is required. The design firm or design engineer passes their comments through the Project Manager to the Owner's representative. The trades' people (who may be the first who are aware of a potential conflict or issue) pass their comments through the general contractor via their own foreman and contract's representative. Required reports, submittals, shop drawings, etc., follow the same pattern. This communication must also be documented especially when cost revisions are necessary or there is a possible impact on items such as access for maintenance, etc.

Larger projects make use of on-site personnel to handle paperwork and document distribution, freeing the resident engineer and inspector from administrative work such as payroll, distributing documents, recording change requests, maintaining owner's manuals, etc. Suggested total staffing is shown in Table 1-1.

1.3.4 The Role of the Designer in the Project Team. There is a temptation to dismiss the system designer once the construction phase of the project begins. Instead, it is recommended that the designer be involved in the construction phase, especially when constructing complex industrial ventilation systems where field changes may significantly impact contaminant control or the functioning of the industrial process. In addition, if the system has been designed using the Balance by Design Method (see Chapter 5 of *Industrial Ventilation: A Manual of Recommended Practice, 25th Edition*) any changes in the construction phase could have serious consequences on the system's operation.

The designer should have a presence during the construction of all but the simplest projects. This individual is best equipped to note when the installation does not conform to the design and is in the best position to guide any needed adjustments caused by field conditions. During construction, the design engineer is often responsible to ensure that the general contractor complies with the drawings and specifications in concept but is not the full-time quality control/quality assurance inspector. The main communication path will be between the owner and the contractor but the designer may have input, particularly on technical issues.

TABLE 1-1. Suggested Field Office Staffing[1.1]

Project Size (1997 base)	Inspection Person-year/year
< $1 Million per year	1.0
$1-5 Million per year	2.5
> $5 Million per year	2.5 + 2/each add $5M

1.3.5 *Skilled Construction Trades.* Skilled trade workers are affiliated through trade unions and hired by installing contractors. Union workers are usually closely connected to their union rather than to the individual construction company since most construction jobs are transient. Some states and projects permit the use of non-union installers who are direct hires of the contractors. Management and selection of the type of contractor (union vs. non-union) is based on plant and owner preferences and agreements. The trades' people either work under a union contract or open shop. Regional differences can affect the prevalence of union shops, with unions more common in larger cities. Mechanical contractors may or may not have agreements to hire union trade persons. Appendix B1 discusses unions in more detail.

1.4   CONSTRUCTION DOCUMENTS

The ultimate goal of the project is the successful installation of the ventilation system or systems that meets all of the Owner's requirements for regulatory, safety and process issues. Ultimately the system will be commissioned and turned over from the General Contractor to the Owner and documents, even in the Construction Phase, must be tailored for the transfer of the system ownership. Construction Documents are typically split into two main areas, drawings and specifications Some projects only provide the drawings with the specification information embedded in the drawings. Drawings show the project form and specifications establish the quality of the system.

1.4.1 *Specifications.* Specifications are the legal written documents in the construction contract. If a dispute occurs, specifications usually take precedence over the drawings. While conflicts sometimes occur between the drawings and specifications, the parties should attempt to work out any differences hopefully before equipment is ordered or delivered. Disputes of this nature can be arbitrated at the site but there may be issues of back charges or extra charges to the contract depending on the resolution. It is during these cases that proper organization, documentation and document control are especially important. All verbal communications should be kept at a minimum even on small projects. Confirmation of verbal communications should be backed up with written or e-mail communications in most cases and always when any potential changes are anticipated.

Specifications typically include: instructions to the bidder, general and supplemental conditions, forms (e.g., bonds), certifications, affidavits, representation requirements and technical specifications. Specifications also contain the qualitative requirements for materials and workmanship.[1.2] Example specifications are:

- ***Functional Specification*** – most open in terms of competition, allows the contractor to be innovative and creative, but provides minimal quality assurance for the owner. Owner must accurately describe the function in terms that can be measured during competition and at project completion. For a functional or performance specification, it is critical for the design firm and project team to review the contractor submittals to confirm the likelihood that the proposed system will perform as designed.

  - Not usually used for complex industrial ventilation systems because the owner must maintain a certain amount of control during the design process.

  - Example – Design an electroplating shop that exceeds the environmental and occupational safety and health requirements of the state, city and federal regulations.

- ***Performance Specification*** – allows some innovation. The contractor must meet a certain requirement but allows flexibility in the means and methods. The owner may have difficulty defining the level of performance required.

  - This method is frequently used for simple industrial ventilation systems such as single paint or abrasive blasting booths.

  - Example – Design an electroplating shop that controls workroom exposures to below the Federal OSHA standard, 29 CFR 1910.1000, with adequate air emissions controls to meet the requirements of the installation permit. In addition, the contractor shall use the most current BOCA, ASHRAE, AWMA and ACGIH® guidelines.

- ***Design Specification*** – the most restrictive in terms of competition. Specifications can contain precise and detailed definitions to assure the use of correct material and assembly.

  - Due to complex nature of many industrial ventilation systems this method is usually used, although the trend is to move to functional or performance standards for less complicated systems and bidding by Design-Build contractors.

  - Specifications follow an organizational format, as defined by the Construction Specification Institute. Although there is a proposal to change the current numbering system, the following sections are of most interest in an industrial ventilation project:

    - Div 11 – Equipment including incinerators, fume hoods, air pollution control devices.

    - Div 13 – Special construction including fire alarms, carbon monoxide detectors, energy monitoring and control systems, radon, mitigation, lead, asbestos and polychlorinated biphenyl control, removal and demolition.

- Div 15 – Mechanical, including HVAC and plumbing, direct digital controls. For industrial ventilation systems this can be the most critical section to review.

- Div 16 – Electrical includes information on motors, power and electrical controls.

- Other sections, such as building materials and demolition requirements, may be required for the complete installation of the ventilation system.

Specifications are typically divided into three parts:

1) **Part 1 – General** gives information on submittals, delivery, storage and handling, material or product quality assurance, job conditions, guarantees, etc.

2) **Part 2 – Products** defines the materials, mixes, fabrication and possibly manufacturers. Note: "Or approved equal" clauses permit the contractor to substitute an item or process of equal quality. This is usually done with the owner's approval. It frequently provides a cost savings to the contractor and the Owner.

3) **Part 3 – Execution** defines the inspections preparation, installation, application, performance field quality control, testing, adjustment, cleanup and schedules.

1.4.2 Use of "Shall" and "Should". When the term "shall" is used, there is usually no room for alternatives. "Shall" typically means a mandatory requirement, where "should" is taken as advisory and open to judgment. Disagreements sometime occur between the contractor and Owner when they have differing interpretations for the requirements listed as "should." One method of eliminating the "should/shall" issue is to use active voice in the command mode, for example "Use flat-backed elbows with ceramic wear plates. Replaceable rubber lined elbows are not acceptable."

Note: The above statement is only an example and should not be taken as a recommended practice for most cases.

1.4.3 Drawings. Drawings include plans that show the horizontal relationships and elevations show the main vertical structural features. Sections can show larger horizontal or vertical relationships for more clarity. Details show the more complex content that cannot be shown in other drawings. Schedule drawings are a listing of required equipment with selection information provided. A system flow diagram is a pictorial representation of the operating systems. Flow diagrams are frequently provided for balancing, fire protection and controls systems. Appendix C1 contains information on drawings and level of detail required for different projects.

1.4.4 Areas of Potential Dispute. There are many potential opportunities for dispute when information is passed among the Designer, Owner and General Contractor. These include (but are not limited to):

1. The owner did not adequately communicate the design needs to the designer.

2. The designer did not completely understand the process and the design needs for the systems.

3. The owner did not fully understand the drawings and specifications information.

4. There is a disparity between the design basis (see Chapter 2 of *Industrial Ventilation: A Manual of Recommended Practice for Design*) and design package.

5. Different information is shown on the drawings and in the specifications.

6. The information in the drawings or the specifications can be interpreted in more than one way.

7. Information is incorrectly interpreted by the designer or contractor.

8. Information on system requirements is not communicated by the Owner.

9. There are changes to the system requirements after drawings and specifications are issued and approved.

1.4.5 Submittals. Submittals are drawings, catalogue cuts, samples and other types of information used to identify the proposed equipment or system components for installation by the contractor. The submittal may also include operational and maintenance information for future use by the system owner. The submittals are typically reviewed for compliance with the contract documents. If they are acceptable, the Owner's representative and/or the project manager approve the submittals based on the project organization. The contractor, or subcontractors, will have frequent submittals throughout the project. A procedure must be set up to allow rapid review of the submittals to ensure that the project maintains its schedule.

1.4.6 Warranties. Typical construction related warranties consist of at least three separate and distinct categories of warranties:[1.3]

1. A **construction (or project) warranty** may be provided by the construction contractor and covers the project as a whole. A construction warranty is usually defined for a period of one year from occupancy, which allows the building or system to be exercised through a full cycle of seasons.

2. Various **commercial warranties** associated with the various components of the project, such as fans, motors, air pollution control equipment, HVAC condensers, water heaters, air compressors, etc.

3. Specific **system warranties** (also called implied warranties), typically associated with installed systems that are made up of multiple components and installed on the job site, such as a ventilation system.

The subject of warranty responsibilities should be an agenda item at the pre-construction and partnering conferences on all projects. The general contractor should be informed that warranty performance is a factor in all performance evaluations, and evaluations will be adjusted appropriately to reflect exceptionally good or bad performance.

Depending on the contract, all of these warranties may not be available for the particular project. Under the contract warranty clauses, the general contractor warrants that the work conforms to the specifications and is free of defects. This warranty usually runs one year from acceptance, or from possession, if earlier than acceptance. The general contractor fixes any defect including consequential damage, and restores any other work damaged during warranty work. In some cases, any corrected work is warranted for one year after correction. The general contractor also obtains and enforces subcontractors' and suppliers' warranties.

1.4.7 Warranty Requirements. Provide a list of components covered by commercial warranties, the warranty start date, the warranty period, local manufacturer or supplier point of contact, and specification section in which the items are included. The purpose of this list is to provide maintenance personnel with a ready reference to the warranties for a particular project, making it more likely that the warranties will actually be used.

Tag each component with a "warranty tag": The tag provides the basic information regarding the warranty of that particular item. There may be some components that cannot be practically tagged in this fashion; however, they still have a warranty. A warranty tag should be placed in a location that does not interfere with the performance or appearance of the item, but is easily found by field maintenance personnel.

The warranty start date for these components should be the same as the project acceptance date, unless the component is in regular use prior to the acceptance date. In this case, the warranty start date should be the date the component is placed in regular use. If the start date policy conflicts with the manufacturer's normal commercial practice, the general contractor must meet the requirements stated in the contract documents. Some manufacturers warrant their products from date of purchase. Equipment can sit at a building site for a couple of months before installation, especially if delays or disputes occur.

In addition to the project warranty and the "commercial" warranties included under the warranty clause, the contract should include specific system warranties for those items where performance risk is high or where normal industry practice would require or provide such a warranty. Some specific items to consider are direct digital control systems, air pollution control devices, and roof-top make-up air units.

Cost reimbursement contracts are significantly different from fixed-price contracts in regards to warranty. Since the general contractor is reimbursed the cost of performing the work, including rework, there is no practical use for a construction project warranty. Therefore, the "normal" practice of a one-year warranty of construction is not part of the cost-reimbursement contract.

1.4.8 Substantial Completion. "Substantial Completion" is a term used to indicate that the system or building is available for use by the Owner and any remaining general contractor activity will not interfere with the use. During or prior to this time there may still be a list of minor items still to be completed called a *Punch List*.

There are times when the owner may want to occupy the facility, in whole or part, before construction work is complete. The contract must define the parameters for *beneficial occupancy*. This is particularly true in phased construction projects. Frequently the warranty period begins when the first occupants or processes move into the building. Sometimes this practice can mask problems with the industrial ventilation system since it is not operating at full capacity.[1.5]

1.4.9 Drawings of Record (As-Built Drawings) and Shop Drawings. Many contracts require that the contractor keep a running record of changes on a set of drawings. During the construction project, some change may be required. The reasons for the changes can be highly variable. These records become a critical record of the project.

Changes are usually documented informally with a colored pencil. Often the contractor must modify a formal set of the designer's drawings when the project is complete. On smaller projects with only a few hoods, informal drawings may be sufficient. However, changes that are hidden (behind a wall, under a concrete pad, etc.) should be documented on a set of drawings even with small jobs. All change orders, modifications and deviations from the original design should be reflected on the *drawings of record*. The original designer, the contractor or a third party completes the drawings as required by the terms of the contract. Note: This information must be communicated to the designer, especially if it can impact system operation by increasing or decreasing system pressure requirements.

These drawings are also referred to as "*as-built drawings*." This term has fallen from popularity since the designer cannot, in many cases, truly certify that the drawing reflects actual construction (e.g., buried pipe, the depth and material of the mist eliminator pads, the gauge of the installed duct, etc.).

Shop drawings are prepared by a contractor "in the shop" to allow proper layout of materials. They are different from as-built drawings. Suppliers and equipment manufacturers also furnish shop drawings. Shop drawings can include approval drawings of floor equipment such as fans or dust collectors and can also include fabrication sketches of items such as hoods or special duct fittings. These drawings may have a requirement for certification to ensure that dimensions required for installation are met. For example, certified drawings of a fan for a ventilation system are necessary so that concrete foundations can be installed before the fan arrives at the jobsite.

Appendix C1 includes a training session on reading Drawing

1.4.10 Owner's Manuals and Manufacturer's Literature. A car manufacturer provides the new car buyer with an owner's/operator's manual. In addition to the owner/operator manual, the auto repair shop has more detailed technical repair (shop) manuals for the specific model and make of each car. The industrial ventilation system owner needs the equivalent of the shop manuals to maintain the industrial ventilation system after the contractor turns over the project to the Owner.

The general contractor provides the Owner with one or several sets of operating manuals for each piece of equipment requiring maintenance. In addition, the contractor arranges for the Owner's personnel to be trained in the usage and maintenance of the equipment and systems. Industrial ventilation equipment includes: fans, fan motors, variable frequency drive controllers, air cleaning equipment, boilers, chillers, pumps, dampers, direct digital controls (DDC), compressors, air dryers, sound attenuators, duct, stacks, hoods, and other auxiliary equipment.

The Owner's operators and maintenance employees usually need training on the controls and electrical systems. Control systems training includes all possible operating conditions and various seasonal differences. Workers using industrial ventilation systems with multi-stage processes and special safety considerations, such as fire and explosion hazards, may also require further specialized training.

1.5 PROJECT SCHEDULING

Along with the budget, *project schedule* is a tool used to monitor the project progress by breaking up the individual elements. Project schedules are used to confirm that the project is meeting deadlines, to evaluate the progress of team members and to monitor individual commitments. There are several types of schedules used in conjunction with construction projects. They differ in complexity, level of detail, and degree of information related to relationships. Choosing the best type of schedule for a project depends on the length of the project, interferences with existing plant operations, the number of organizations working on the project, the complexity of the work and the ability of the project leadership.

There are numerous computer programs available for schedule management. Many programs are tailored specifically for construction projects.

Characteristics of successful schedule management:

1. All parties understand and commit to meeting the schedule.

2. Schedule contains enough flexibility to handle changes in priorities and task completion dates and weather.

3. Schedule provides for revisions after completion of a task.

4. Schedule requires early but reasonable deadlines to keep everyone working efficiently.

5. Schedule uses the calendar to exhibit time duration (not working days).

1.5.1 Milestone Chart. The simplest type of schedule is a listing of *milestones*. Such a schedule is easy to prepare and provides focus on deadline of the tasks involved in the project. A milestone schedule does not convey when it is best to start a task; nor are there any correlations between project tasks. A sample milestone chart is provided in Table 1-2.

1.5.2 Bar or Gantt Chart. The bar chart, also known as a *Gantt Chart*, provides a more graphic representation of the schedule. It communicates the start date and duration for a task as well as its desired end date. The advantage of the bar chart is its ability to effectively communicate all elements of a schedule. An example of a bar chart is provided in Figure 1-2.

1.5.3 Critical Path (Network) Planning Chart. Project planning can also be shown on a *critical path* or network chart.

TABLE 1-2. Sample Milestone Chart

Task	Responsibility Party	Due Date	Completion Date
1. Airflow Measurements and Exposure Monitoring	Manufacturing Plant	March 20	March 20
2. Identify Exhaust and Supply System Deficiencies	Ventilation Engineer	April 5	April 7
3. Present Concept Design for the Modifications of the Ventilation Systems	Ventilation Engineer	April 21	April 22
4. Complete Detailed Design of Ventilation System Modifications	Ventilation Engineer	May 18	
5. Finalize Contract with the General Contractor to Install Ventilation Modifications	Manufacturing Plant	June 10	
6. Approve Shop Drawings and Submittals for the Ventilation Modifications	Ventilation Engineer	As submitted	
7. Install Modifications	Contractor	July 27	
8. Install Process Equipment	Manufacturing Plant	July 16	
9. Replace Fan Motor	Contractor	July 29	
10. Commission Equipment and Rebalance Airflow	Commissioner and TAB Contractor	August 2	
11. Take New Airflow Measurements and Air Samples	Manufacturing Plant	August 8	

Gantt Chart - Project Schedule

Task Name	ID	January
		1 2 3 4 5 6 7 8 9 10 11 12 13 14 15 16 17 18 19
Do Initial Design	1	◇━━━◇
Price Design	2	⬇━━━⬆
Order Materials	3	▽━━━△

FIGURE 1-2. Example Gantt Chart excerpt for a simple industrial ventilation project

In this schedule, the relationship between tasks is shown along with the task duration, start and desired end times. This chart identifies those tasks that require completion before other tasks can begin. If, in order to meet the schedule's milestones, a new task must begin as soon as the previous task is completed, these tasks are on the project's critical path. If a later task can start a few weeks after an initial task and still meet the project's deadline, then there is float in the timing of the later task. If the later task must start immediately after the previous task, there is no float between the two tasks and the two tasks can be considered on the project's critical path. To begin a critical path chart the relationships between tasks must be established. There are three types of relationships between tasks:

1. The initial task must be completed before a second task can begin.

2. The second task can be started before the initial task is completed.

3. The initial task must be completed before the second task can be completed.

Critical path items in a typical industrial ventilation system are:

- Preliminary design
- Air pollution control permit
- Site preparation, process determinations (air volume, heat, moisture for processes to be controlled)
- Site authorization or permit to build
- Design drawings and specifications
- Purchase of long lead-time items such as the pollution control equipment (fabric filter, scrubber, oxidizer, etc.), fan, supply air unit, etc.
- Confirmation that there are sufficient utilities (power, water, waste disposal, etc.)
- Impact on the manufacturing process especially when the manufacturing process will continue during the construction project

Once the relationship between tasks is established, the duration of the each task must be identified. This information is typically estimated in days or weeks and entered on a listing of the tasks. The relationship information can be combined with the duration to form a bar chart type presentation. This bar type chart becomes a critical path chart when the task dates are assembled providing the shortest time to complete the project. For large and complex projects, the selection of the tasks that form the critical path can be a time consuming effort. However, several computer programs are available that reduce the effort involved in creating this type of schedule. Figure 1-3 is an example of a critical path type schedule.

1.5.4 Progress Reports. Depending on the contractual agreement, the general contractor submits reports (sometimes with photographs or other proof of performance, each week or month based on the project requirements. ***Progress reports*** summarize work performed to date, project changes, milestones met and concerns. Reports are submitted to the project manager or directly to the Owner. Depending on the terms of the contract, payments may be made to the general contractor for work completed to date based on the progress reports. Progress reports are another way to monitor progress and anticipate changes.

1.6   MANAGING CHANGE AND AVOIDING DELAYS

1.6.1 Change Order Requests. Change Orders do not benefit any party and are disruptive. Sometimes a scope change costs more than the original work. Change orders occur for a myriad of reasons including:

- The owner discovers there are insufficient funds to complete the project as envisioned and cannot meet the obligations of the contract.
- Unusual weather delays the project.
- There are conflicts between the drawings and specifications not identified before construction.
- A change in building codes, governmental regulations or best practice guidelines occurs while the project is in the design-bid-build process. In industrial ventilation systems, the change could occur in the air pollution control requirements or even a change in the OSHA Permissible Exposure Limit, ACGIH® Threshold Limit Value, or general information in the toxicity or handling of the material being controlled by the industrial ventilation system.
- Equipment is unavailable, e.g., cranes or helicopters to move equipment onto the roof during scheduled downtimes.
- Unexpected findings such as lead or asbestos or historical artifacts or buried utilities discovered during construction demolition.
- A process change requires a modification to the industrial ventilation system design.

Change orders in one discipline frequently affect other dis-

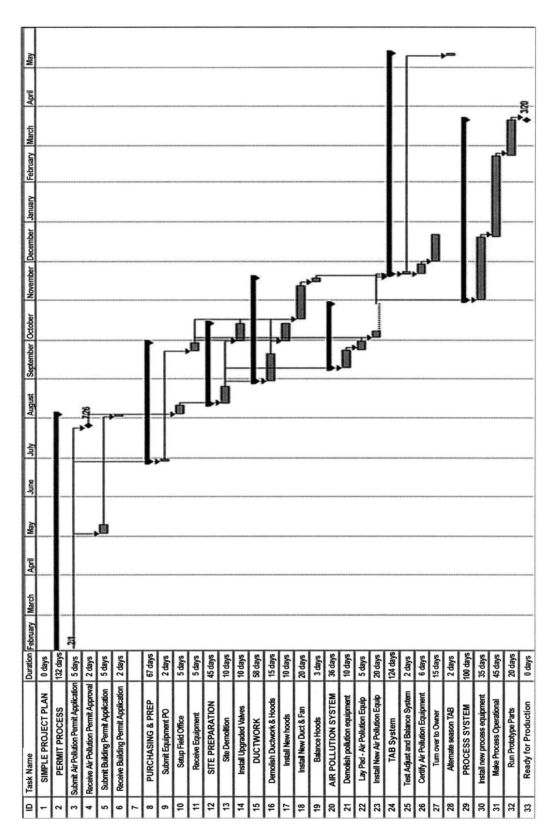

FIGURE 1-3. Critical Path Analysis Chart for an industrial ventilation project with intermediate complexity

ciplines. For instance, increasing the volumetric flow of a ventilation system may require a larger fan and motor. This could also require a more substantial reinforced roof and heavier gauge power wiring and starters. In retrofits and extreme cases, larger motors may require the installation of new transformers to gain additional power to the site. Change orders are expensive because some trades may not be able to do their work while the change order is being prepared and ongoing labor costs are incurred.

Since the project work is a contract, neither the owner nor the general contractor has the right to arbitrarily or unilaterally change the contract conditions. However, during the conduction of the project, many conditions may cause the significant project modifications (see the discussion in Section 1.1). In these cases, the contract may need to be modified based on changing conditions. There are legal and contractual procedures, beyond the scope of this manual, used to resolve conflicts over change orders, contract modifications, errors and omissions, etc. Consult construction contract administration publications for further information. In most projects, both the Owner and the General Contractor agree to the need for the modifications. See Figure 1-4 for a sample Estimate of Adjustment in Contract Amount worksheet and Figure 1-5 for a sample Change Order Request Form.

Contingency funds are usually added to a contract during the budget process. These funds cover unexpected difficulties. Contingency funds range from 2-3% for well-defined projects to 5-10% if the drawings and specifications are incomplete. Consider higher contingencies for retrofit projects especially if the building conditions (e.g., inside walls, underground piping, etc.) are uncertain.

1.6.2 Field Orders. Field orders include minor changes submitted without major changes in the contract price or time. Field changes must not affect the design. A field order may change the fan speed or directions on how to run the duct to avoid an obstacle. Although these design changes appear to be small, they could have a significant effect on the ultimate performance of the system and the designer should be involved in the decisions. Filed orders should be documented and recorded.

1.6.3 Design Errors and Omissions. Unforeseen field condition differences in equipment specified, changing design requirements coupled with short schedules, partial agreement between the Owner and the Designer, and competitive fees can lead to ***design errors and omissions***. Since every design is unique and has differences from previous designs some degree of extra construction cost due to errors and omissions can be experienced. Contingencies (extra funds) for this occurrence should have a goal of 2-3% of the project cost.

When an architect or designer fails to identify some aspect in the design or makes an error in the design, the legal community frequently becomes involved to assign fault. Examples of errors could include: using incorrect versions of a standard,

failure to oversee junior employee's calculations, or failure to hire specialized consultants to perform advanced analyses.

If the Designer makes an error or omission, the designer will normally correct the design at no cost. This situation is often covered in the contract between the Owner and the designer. In other special cases, the Designer can compensate the General Contractor for small oversights. Alternatively, the Owner compensates the General Contractor for higher cost design errors. The Owner may also be asked to help pay for system rework or equipment that cannot be used in the new design. The Owner should pay for additions to a system that increase the value of the system. Sometimes the Owner, General Contractor and Designer engage in negotiated settlements and/or arbitration to settle their differences. Most design firms carry insurance to cover the costs incurred during a major error or omission dispute.

1.6.4 Performance Documents. The Owner or the project manager should keep records of poor or excellent performance for future work. This practice is easier for large companies. Consider photographing and/or videotaping work progress. This may also assist in resolving disputes and provide material for the public relations department.

1.7   CONSTRUCTION REVIEWS

Construction Team Reviews reduce the possibility of unexpected project delays. An experienced General Contractor will formally or informally perform these reviews after the Designer completes the project and before bidding on the project. The General Contractor will go back to the contracting agent or purchasing agent or Designer with their concerns. In some cases, the contract may have to be re-advertised or re-bid to reflect unrecognized issues. It is essential to anticipate problems and work through them before the project scope and compensation are agreed upon in the contract. Consider the following issues.[1.3, 1.4]

1.7.1 Bidability Review. Prior to the issuance of a request for bid, the drawings and specifications are reviewed to ensure that the contractors can bid the project. Specific areas of review include:

1. Drawings and specifications are clear and unambiguous.

2. No conflicts exist between the drawings and the specifications.

3. Specifications or detailed descriptions are provided for all items shown on the drawings.

4. Referenced standards and criteria are current.

5. No "prohibited" specifications – some owners use their own internally developed specifications. Others only permit the use of commercial specifications such as those developed by the Construction Specification Institute. See http://www.csinet.org/s_csi/index.asp for more information.

Sample Form
Estimate of Adjustment in Contract Amount

Work Categories	Estimate Time in Work Hours					
	Super-visor	Designer	Drafts-person	Other		
Drawings						
Design Calculations:						
Structural						
Electrical						
Mechanical						
Equipment Selection						
Equipment Revision						
Specifications Sections:						
Architectural						
Structural						
Mechanical						
Electrical						
Construction Time Duties						
Cost Estimating						
Total Hours						

Position	Hours	Hourly Rate	Total
Supervisor			
Designer			
Draftsperson			
Other 1.			
Other 2.			
Other 3.			
Total Design Costs			
Overhead & Profit _____		% of Design Costs	
Printing Costs (computer time, reproduction & binding)			
TOTAL			

Note: Each design firm has its own estimate sheet that is usually computerized.

FIGURE 1-4. Sample Form – Estimate of Adjustment in Contract Amount[1.5]

Sample Form
Change Order Request Form

Project Title:_____

Owner: _____

Project Number: _____ Contract Number: _____ Contract Date: _____

Contractor:_____

Proposed by: _____ Date: _____

Submitted by: _____ Date: _____

_____ Owner   _____ A&E   _____ Construction Firm

Describe existing conditions in area of proposed changes

Contractor authorized to proceed with changes ☐ yes ☐ no

Other Contracts Affected

Contract Number	Drawing Required	Sheet #	Specifications Paragraphs

Description of Work to be Performed:

Current Contract Amount _____

Amount of this Order _____

(Decrease) (Increase)

Revised Contract Amount _____

Estimated Design Cost: _____

Inspection: _____

Changes Approved

Owner: _____ Signed by: _____ Date: _____

Contractor: _____ Signed by: _____ Date: _____

A/E Firm: _____ Signed by: _____ Date: _____

FIGURE 1-5. Sample Form – Change Order Request Form[1.5]

6. Referenced specifications are actually included in contract package.

7. No unnecessary specifications are included in the contract package.

8. No or limited "sole source" requirements unless justified.

9. No references to specific brand and model of product unless justified.

10. No products specified that violate company policy, e.g., "Buy American," union work, etc.

1.7.2 Constructability Review. A second review addresses potential obstacles to construction. The review is especially important when several design departments or firms collaborate on the design. Specific areas of concern include:

- No physical conflicts shown on drawings, for example:
  - No water pipes pass above electrical panels.
  - Specified materials and equipment appear to be reasonable for intended use.
  - The air pollution control equipment can fit in the mechanical room, on a new concrete pad or on the roof or be transported through the building to its intended installation site.
  - Structure inadequate to support the equipment.
  - Design does not conform to building code.
  - Maintenance access properly positioned.

- Construction scheduling and phasing (if applicable) makes sense and appears to be workable.

- Commissioning procedures appear to be reasonable and complete.

- Testing and Balancing procedures appear to be reasonable and complete.

- Craftsman qualifications are adequate and are appropriate for the job requirements. Qualifications are not so burdensome that qualified craftsmen will be unavailable or unnecessarily costly or a significant administrative burden for project office to monitor.

- Submittal requirements are limited to those necessary for a quality project. Avoid requirement for "Project manager approval" of submittals as much as possible.

- Limits the amount of rework needed in the contract.

- Using prefabrication, modular sectionals and pre-assembly reduces the need for onsite construction. This also reduces the number of trades at the building site. Industrial duct may be an exception.

- Are sufficient utility resources provided to construct the building?

- In hot processes, is there sufficient room between ducts and hangars to allow expansion and proper roof penetrations provided to protect the building?

- Are elbows sufficiently robust (e.g., 2 gauges thicker) for ducts carrying abrasive material?

- Is there any conflict with "hot work" areas or limits on welding in sites intended for installation?

See Figure 1-6 for a sample of Constructability Check List.

1.7.3 Operability Review.

- Sufficient space around mechanical and electrical equipment for operations and maintenance work.
  - Sufficient space to remove filters, mist eliminators, etc.
  - Sufficient airflow in mechanical room to protect maintenance personnel and dissipate heat from the equipment.
  - Maintenance access at hoods, fans, air cleaning devices, replacement air units, etc., including OSHA approved platforms, ladders and/or stairs.

- Shutoff valves provided on both sides of strainers, pumps, and other items requiring maintenance or possible replacement, including pipe unions.

- Equipment requiring maintenance located in an accessible location.

- Stairs rather than ladders to the basement, roof or mezzanine eliminate the need for fall protection for the maintenance personnel while accessing the equipment.

- Safe platforms and mezzanines for testing and maintenance personnel reducing the fall protection program complexity.

- Adequate training specified for system operators.

- Instructions sufficiently displayed and provided in mechanical systems.

- Adequate sets of operation and maintenance manuals to be provided.

- Bleed valves, access valves, balancing valves and dampers, access doors, test ports, etc., provided where needed to successfully operate and maintain the system.

- Sufficient utility resources provided to *operate* the building.

- Is there easy access to duct and hood plenum clean-out doors?

- Are the duct construction classes (see SMACNA manuals) appropriate for the material?

- Do the supply air, exhaust air and equipment interlocks work appropriately for all conditions?

Sample Form
Constructability Review Checklist

BIDDING INFORMATION — Some larger organizations use the same template for contract announcements. When multiple contracts are released from different offices of the same organization take care to ensure that the bid information is correct. Consider using the following checklist.

Bidding Information Item	Yes	No
	Initials	
1. Bid Item wording is correct and is correctly shown on the drawings.		
2. Multiple bid items correct.		
3. Bidding place address correct.		
4. Plan Issue Office address and telephone number correct.		
5. Correct telephone number for bid inquiries.		
6. Pre-bid site visitation date, time, and phone number correct.		

The following tables are useful in checking the bid package. Although mechanical plans and specifications fall under Division 3, other divisions are included since they can impact the mechanical design.

Division 1 Item	Yes	No
	Initials	
1. Adequacy of General Intentions & General Description sections.		
2. Adequate time for completion and commissioning.		
3. Contract completion dates compatible with phasing & sequencing schedule.		
4. Provision of liquidated damages including those for multiple completion dates.		
5. Correct drawing numbers & titles in both specifications and drawings.		
6. Construction Cost Categories specified.		
7. Salvage material/equipment requirements clearly specified.		
8. Quality Control Office requirements correctly specified.		
9. Lay down area clearly indicated.		
10. Level of scheduling requirements appropriate for size/complexity of project.		
11. Contingency Planning Management specification correct (verify requirement to have schedule approved prior to start of work).		
12. Utility Outage requirements properly specified.		
13. Ground Fault Equipment Monitoring requirements clearly specified.		
14. Working space adequate.		
15. Security requirements properly specified.		
16. Special permits (Building Permit, local jurisdiction's codes, environmental etc.) in hand.		
17. Environmental Protection requirements properly specified.		
18. Availability of utilities properly specified; location, cost, etc.		
19. Quality control staffing is adequate including specialty inspectors and submittal reviewers.		
20. Level of quality control required is appropriate for size and complexity of contract.		
21. Check wording on "Work after Normal Work Hours" clause to make sure it is consistent with operational requirements such as facility security, nearby housing, etc.		
22. Adequate description of potential hazards and unusual safety concerns.		

FIGURE 1-6. Sample Form – Constructability Review Checklist[1.3, 1.6]

SPECIFICATION CHECK	Yes	No
		Initials
1. Compare architectural finish schedule to specification index. Ensure all finish materials are specified.		
2. Check major items of equipment and verify they are coordinated with contract drawings. Pay particular attention to horsepower ratings and voltage requirements.		
3. Verify that items specified "as indicated" or "where indicated" are in fact indicated on drawings.		
4. Verify that cross-referenced specification sections exist.		
5. Ensure that owner provided equipment is noted.		

PLAN CHECK MECHANICAL AND PLUMBING	Yes	No
		Initials
1. Verify all new electrical, gas, water, sewer, etc. lines connect to existing.		
2. Verify all plumbing fixture locations against architectural drawings and specifications. Verify all plumbing fixtures against fixture schedule and/or specifications.		
3. Verify storm drain system against architectural roof plan. Verify that pipes are sized and that all drains are connected and do not interfere with foundations. Verify wall chases are provided on architectural drawings to conceal vertical piping.		
4. Verify sanitary drain system pipes are sized and all fixtures are connected.		
5. Verify HVAC floor plans against architectural drawings and specifications.		
6. Verify all sections are identical to architectural/structural drawings and specifications.		
7. Verify that adequate ceiling height exists at worst case duct intersection.		
8. Verify all structural supports required for mechanical equipment are indicated on structural drawings.		
9. Verify required dampers are indicated at smoke and fire walls.		
10. Verify diffusers against architectural reflected ceiling plan.		
11. Verify all roof penetrations (ducts, fans, etc.) are indicated on roof plans.		
12. Verify all duct is sized.		
13. Verify all notes.		
14. Verify all air conditioning units, heaters, and exhaust fans against architectural roof plans or mechanical room plans, and mechanical schedules.		

FIGURE 1-6 (Cont.). Sample Form – Constructability Review Checklist[1.3, 1.6]

PLAN CHECK ELECTRICAL	Yes	No
		Initials
1. Verify all plans are consistent with architectural drawings.		
2. Verify all light fixtures against architectural reflected ceiling plan.		
3. Verify all major pieces of equipment have electrical connections.		
4. Verify location of all panel boards and that they are indicated on the electrical riser diagram.		
5. Verify all notes.		
6. Verify there is sufficient space for all electrical panels to fit.		
7. Verify electrical panels are not recessed in firewalls.		
8. Verify electrical equipment locations are coordinated with site paving and grading.		

SPECIALTY ITEMS	Yes	No
		Initials
1. Asbestos abatement properly specified.		
2. Raised floor systems and pits properly specified and drawn.		
3. Cranes properly specified.		
4. Loading Dock properly specified.		
5. Uninterrupted Power Source system properly specified.		
6. Energy Management Control Systems and Direct Digital Control systems properly specified, proprietary specifications included, if required.		
7. Adequate requirements for operations and maintenance manuals and training of activity personnel.		
8. Service elevator properly specified.		
9. Adequate requirements for start-up, testing, and turnover of mechanical and electrical equipment.		
10. Verify keying and access requirements.		
11. For all plans ensure that Legends, Abbreviations and Notes are complete and accurate.		
12. Ensure handicapped access is provided unless facility does not require it.		

FIGURE 1-6 (Cont.). Sample Form – Constructability Review Checklist[1.3, 1.6]

- Does the supply air work for all outdoor air conditions? For example systems close dampers in freezing winter or humid summer condition permitting no or minimal outside air.

1.7.4 Environmental and Occupational Safety and Health Reviews.

- No lead-based paints specified.
- Demolition includes provisions for proper removal and disposal if on site.
- Prohibit lead based paints in the new installation.

- No asbestos containing materials specified and demolition includes provisions for proper removal and disposal if on site.
- No ozone-depleting materials specified.
- Proper handling and disposal of hazardous construction waste and debris specified.
- Backflow preventers provided where necessary to avoid cross-connection of potable and non-potable water systems.
- Air emissions and hazardous material/waste permit

ADMINISTRATIVE ITEMS CHECKLIST						
CONTRACT: *[Insert Contract Number and Title]*						
ITEM	SPEC	PARA	N/A	Date Complete	Initials	Comment
1. Record Drawings (As-built drawings)						
2. Submittals						
3. Equip. Warranty Tags						
4. Special Warranties						
5. O&M Manuals						
6. Special Inspections						
7. Spare Parts/Extra Stock						
8. As-Built Record of Material						
9. Tabulation of Tests						
10. Keys						
11. Non-Compliance Log						
12. Training						
13. Operating Tests						
14. Salvaged Equipment						
15. Operating Instructions						
16. Air Pollution Permits						
17. Industrial Hygiene Acceptance						
18. Safety Acceptance						

FIGURE 1-6 (Cont.). Sample Form – Constructability Review Checklist[1.3, 1.6]

requests submitted and approved and acceptance testing arranged.

- Compliance with OSHA 1926, the Construction Standard.

1.8 PREPARATION FOR SYSTEM COMMISSIONING

Testing, Adjusting and Balancing provides for systematic, sequential quality control processes that, *when followed*, minimize shortcomings and failures in accepting the contractor's work. TAB is the final part of the total commissioning process, as discussed in Chapter 2. The testing, adjusting and balancing and automatic controls system specification sections of the construction contract address complete procedures for submittal of test plans and documentation, and provide procedures for testing and acceptance. Prior to any testing, the contractor should complete the punch list discussed in Chapter 2. In the rush to complete a project, testing and balancing is frequently overlooked or even waived. This practice puts the Owner at a disadvantage since 1) the Owner has no assurance that the system performs as designed and 2) there is no record of the baseline system performance.

Ideally, the Owner should reserve project funds to hire a Testing, Adjusting and Balancing firm that is totally independent of the designer and the general contractor. However, typical projects add these tests into the prime contract, since it is easier to write one large contract. This contracting practice can lead to a conflict of interest when actual system operation does not meet specified performance. To maintain leverage, final payment on the construction contract is sometimes not made until the commissioning and/or balancing work is certified. For warranty purposes it is important for the Owner not to unduly delay the testing and balancing process so that equipment is in the "delivered and as-built" condition.

Industrial ventilation system testing requires an additional level of knowledge beyond the typical HVAC system. It is important to note that HVAC and industrial ventilation testing firms only test to confirm that they system performs *as designed*. They do not test to determine that the system protects the worker. In-house or contracted occupational safety and health personnel must perform exposure assessments. The testing may be written in the contract, especially in the functional or performance type specification. Since some contaminants are so harmful, a system may perform as designed and not fully protect the worker. Therefore, use caution in restricting payment solely based on the results of air sampling.

1.9   CLOSEOUT PROCEDURES AND RESPONSIBILITIES

The process by which the project is completed, accepted, and turned over to the Owner for operation and maintenance is the *Project Closeout* process. Both the Owner and the General Contractor have important roles to play in this phase of the project. A highly successful project can become an unsuccessful project just by being poorly handled during closeout.

In some cases, the Owner may hold 10% or more of the full payment as a *retainage fee* to ensure the General Contractor completed the project to the design specifications. This practice can cause cash flow problems for the general contractor and subcontractors. In recent years, the retainage fee has been negotiated lower and other arrangements made, such as escrow accounts, to ensure the project is complete. While the General Contractor's performance and payment bonds assist the Owner in obtaining a completed project, these bonds are only invoked when a breach of contract occurs. Damages from late completion and incomplete punch lists are also negotiated at this point.

1.9.1 Owner. The Owner is ultimately responsible for acceptance of the work. In addition, the Owner may "handoff" the completed facility to the end user who will occupy and operate it and the facilities engineering organization that will maintain it. For small projects, the same person can take on all roles. In others, the Owner could be headquarters and the end user could be the plant facility. The turnover should include the commissioning issues discussed earlier, but regardless of whether a formal commissioning process has been established, certain items must be completed. Figure 1-7 includes a checklist of items to review for each project during closeout. Not every item is applicable to every project, but it provides a baseline from which to start.

1.9.2 General Contractor. To be paid in full the General Contractor ties up the project and hands it over to the Owner. Sometimes a General Contractor will forgo the final payment and decline to perform the final acceptance commissioning tests. This practice is detrimental in industrial ventilation systems since almost all systems require some adjustment. The General Contractor should provide the following items:

- Equipment/Product Warranty List
- Commissioning reports, as appropriate
- Record Drawings (As-built drawings) – reproducible and some require these to be stamped by a registered engineer
- Record of Materials – e.g., heat exchanger fluids, Item, specification, manufacturer, where used and Material
- Utility Usage Records
- Utility Record Drawings, if utility changes were incurred
- Equipment/product warranty tags
- Other, as required by the contract, e.g., monthly hazardous material used/waste generated
- Demolition and recovered materials report for items like Freon, asbestos, lead paint, etc.
- Operations and Maintenance Manual

Good general contractors will clean the site before leaving the facility. Ensure that system is free from debris and construction materials. The contract will specify the level of cleanup. Additional information is available in *Duct Cleanliness for New Construction Guidelines* published by SMACNA.[1.7]

REFERENCES

1.1   Fisk, E.R.: Constriction Project Administration, Fifth Edition. Prentice-Hall Inc., Upper Saddle, NJ (1997).

1.2   Construction Technology for Non-Engineers, Navy Civil Engineering Corps Officer School, Port Hueneme, CA (March 2003).

1.3   NAVFAC Construction Quality Program, P-445 (NAVFAC 0525-LP-037-7202), Naval Facilities Engineering Command, Washington, DC, https://portal.navfac.navy.mil/portal/page (June 2000).

1.4   Miller, J.: US Army Corps of Engineers, personal communications (Spring, 2003).

1.5   Naval Facilities Engineering Command: Resident Officer in Charge of Construction Handbook, https://portal.navfac.navy.mil/portal/page (July 6, 2004).

1.6   Industrial Ventilation Guide for Resident Officers in Charge of Construction, NEESA 70.2-013, Naval Energy & Environmental Support Activity (now Naval Facilities Engineering Service Center), Port Hueneme, CA (Sept, 1993).

Sample Form
Contract Completion Checklist

Project Manager Responsibilities			
A. Before Final Acceptance			
Item	Initials	Date	Comment
1. Pre-Final Inspection Held			
2. Local Inspections Held (Fire, Elevators, TABs, etc.)			
3. Final Inspection with Customer and facilities			
4. Establish Usable Completion Date			
5. Turn Over Letter to Owner			
6. Acceptance Letter to Contractor			
7. Document Environmental Permit Compliance for Construction Certification (if applicable)			
8. Inform Owner/Client of requirements for operating permits, Certificates of Occupancy, or Terminations of Construction Permits, if required			
B. Before Final Payment			
Item	Initials	Date	Comment
1. Punch List Complete			
2. List of Warranty Agents to Owner/Customer			
3. As-Built Drawings Submitted and Reviewed (2 sets or as required) and As-Built Record of Materials			
4. Operations and Maintenance Manuals Reviewed/Submitted to Facilities Manager			
5. Submittals to Facilities Manager			
6. Keys to Facilities Manager or Owner			
7. Spare parts, special tools and extra stock to Facilities Manager			

FIGURE 1-7. Sample Form – Contract Completion Checklist[1.3]

8. Account for all owner provided and salvage material			
9. Determine status of contractor utility bill			
10. All changes/equitable adjustments finalized			
11. All general contractor claims resolved			
12. Final release from General Contractor received			
13. Property Record Forms sent to Owner/headquarters			
14. Final progress photos taken			
15. General Contractor Evaluation, if required by Headquarters (HQ)			
16. Designer Evaluation, if required by HQ			
17. Quality Control Manager Evaluation, if required by HQ			
Quality Assurance Representative's Responsibilities			
A. Before Final Acceptance			
1. Schedule Pre-Final inspection and develop Punch List			
2. Verify Resolution of all Non-Compliance Notices			
3. Verify Completion of all Modification Work			
4. Review Requirements for Submittals and Training and Operations Manuals due at Turnover			
5. Inspections Scheduled and are Satisfactory			
6. Electrical/Mechanical System Tests Complete			
7. Tag Warranty Equipment			
8. Framed Instructions/ Warranties Mounted			
9. Schedule Final Inspection, Develop Punch List			

FIGURE 1-7 (Cont.). Sample Form – Contract Completion Checklist[1.3]

10. All Test Results and Certifications Received			
11. Facilities Manager/ User/Owner Training Completed			
B. Before Final Payment			
1. Punch List complete			
2. Final review of As-Built drawings for completeness			
3. Final review of Operations and Maintenance Manuals for completeness			
4. Final demobilization & clean-up completed			
5. Contractor site passes returned			
C. Before Closing Out File			
1. Final Progress Photos Taken			
2. Provide Inspector's copy of submittals to Facilities Manager			
Contract Specialist Responsibilities			
A. Before Final Payment			
1. Liquidated damages assessment, if required			
2. Payrolls complete, including Statement of Compliance			
3. All modifications accepted & completed			
4. Final release received from project manager			
5. All bonds returned			

FIGURE 1-7 (Cont.). Sample Form – Contract Completion Checklist[1.3]

1.7   Sheet Metal and Air Conditioning Contractors'
       National Association: Technical Paper on Duct
       Cleanliness for New Construction Guidelines.
       SMACNA, Chantilly, VA
       http://www.smacna.org/technical/index.cfm (2000).

A1.1   Naval Facilities Engineering Command, Safety &
       Health Department: Public Works Officer Safety and
       Health Resource Guide. Norfolk, VA (10/20/2000).

Additional Resources

Clough, R. H.; Sears, G.A.: Construction Contracting, sixth
edition. John Wiley & Sons, Inc., New York, NY (1994).

Garvey, D.: Construction Safety & Health, The Synergist, pp.
37-39. AIHA Publications, (February 2004).

O'Leary, A.: A Guide to Successful Construction, Effective
Contract Administration. BNI Building News, Anaheim, CA
(1997).

Mossman, Jr., M.J.: RS Means Mechanical Cost Data 1998,
21st Edition. RS Means Company, Kingston, MA (1997).

APPENDIX A1

**SAFETY CONSIDERATIONS FOR CONSTRUCTION
PROJECTS[A1.1]**

In 2001, 23% of all occupational fatalities were related to
the construction industry, even though only 8% of the workforce is in construction. Using 1991–2001 data, OSHA lists the
top 10 reasons for construction related fatalities:

- Fell from/through roof
- Fell from structure other than roof
- Run over/crushed – non-operator
- Electric shock by equipment contacting power source
- Fell/crushed/hit during lifting operations
- Run over/crushed – operator
- Crushed/suffocated from trench collapse
- Electric shock from equipment installation
- Crushed from collapse of structure
- Shock by touching exposed wire

The Owner's representative should review the general contractor's safety plan as part of the initial contract review. In
addition, all workers, especially new arrivals should be trained
to report all mishaps and near misses. Reporting near misses is
the only opportunity to prevent accidents. Emergency procedures should be predetermined. Depending on the work crew,
the OSHA general industry (29 CFR 1910), or construction
(29 CFR 1926) or maritime (29 CFR 1915) standards may
apply. The Owner's organization may have its own additional

requirements. Large sites will require most of these programs
and smaller sites may only require a few. The following are
construction site safety issues that should be considered in the
general contractor's safety plan:

- Accident prevention signs and tags – red – danger,
  yellow – caution, green – safety instruction, directions,
  traffic signs, accident/defective tags and lock out/tag
  out energy control tags. See OSHA regulations 29
  CFR 126.200 & 29 CFR 1910.145
- Asbestos control – Asbestos must be identified to the
  general contractor BEFORE the contract is released.
  Unidentified asbestos found on the job will stop the
  project until demolition occurs. Unexpected
  asbestos may be found on underground pipes, in
  boiler rooms (insulation and gaskets), in
  fireproofing, and in some coatings. When found,
  work should be stopped and an abatement project initiated by the prime contractor or another contractor
  should be hired. See 29 CFR 1910.1001
- Bloodborne Pathogens – Since cuts, slips and falls
  can occur at construction sites, the safety plan should
  provide provisions to protect all workers from bloodborne pathogens. See 29 CFR 1910.1030
- Confined Space Entry Program – These spaces 1)
  are not designed for routine entry, 2) are large
  enough and/or configured so a worker can enter 3)
  are poorly ventilated and/or 4) have a limited/
  restricted means of entry/exit and 5) contain
  potential and/or known hazards. The definitions and
  requirements are found in 29 CFR 1910.146 and 29
  CFR 1915, Subpart V. The general contractor, not
  the Owner, must provide the competent person to test
  the spaces.
- Construction Equipment – Operator duties and
  licenses are listed in 29 CFR 1936, Subparts O and
  W. This equipment includes asphalt/water
  distributors, core drills, earth augers, crawler cranes,
  ditching machines, excavators, graders, loaders,
  rollers, scrapers, off-highway trucks, trailers and
  tractors, crawlers, wheel tractors, sweepers, snow
  plows, refuse trucks, railroad cars and locomotives,
  truck mounted cranes, crash cranes, hydraulic cranes
  and railway cranes.
- Weight Handling Equipment – Cranes are used to lift
  large fans and pre-designed supply air systems into
  place on a roof or in a tight industrial area. Rigging
  operations and crane operations are listed in 29 CFR
  1910.179 -182 and 184 and 29 CFR 1926, Subpart N
  – Cranes, Derricks, and Hoists. Before entering the
  work site, the general contractor must provide the
  Owner with the following, a certificate of
  compliance, crane inspection records, and operator
  qualification documents.

- Electrical Safety – Lock out/tag out programs are imperative on a construction site. The site must also have assured equipment grounding conductor program or be protected with ground fault circuit interrupters per 29 CFR 1926.404. Larger projects and even some small projects become involved with high voltage distribution. See 29 CFR 1910.269 for more information on Electric Power Generation, Transmission and Generation. See 29 CFR 1910.147 for Control of Hazardous Entry (Lock Out/Tag Out). See the National Electric Code, NFPA 70, ASTM Volume 10.02 and 29 CFR 1910.331 to 333 for more information on electrical safety and electrical protective equipment.

- Emergency Action and Fire Protection – Provide the workers with sufficient well-marked exits in case of fire. Fire/emergency/reporting, escape routes, rescue, medical and evacuation duties, and employee accounting procedures should be identified before anyone enters the job site. Some large production facilities have their own fire/emergency crews. The general contractor should coordinate with the emergency team with jurisdictional authority. See 29 CFR 1910.38 and 165 for more information.

- Ergonomics – While there is currently no federal program many companies recognize that nearly 50% of their worker compensation costs are due to ergonomic injuries. Providing equipment that permits the worker to comfortably do the job is one way to reduce ergonomic injuries.

- Fall Protection – Because construction sites are transient extra caution must be employed in designing handrails and guardrails especially on roofs and in mezzanines and upper floors of a construction site. Any work conducted more than 6 feet above the walking/working level requires fall protection. Some conditions require a fall arresting system. See 1910.1926 Subpart M and 1910.1910.23 and 1910.66 for more information.

- Vermin, Vectors, Poisonous Plants and other Hazards – Workers should be cautioned to watch for possible sources of diseases. Hantavirus, Histoplasmosis and other diseases are found in areas where rodents and birds congregate such as crawl spaces, attics, electrical vaults, storage sheds, etc. Histoplasmosis spores can be aerosolized during construction. Spiders of concern are the black widow and brown recluse spiders. Both nest/hide in undisturbed places. Poison oak, poison ivy and poison sumac are found in different locations. Bees, wasps, hornets and yellow jackets are frequently found in construction sites especially before construction begins. Therefore, dust control measures, area disinfecting and/or eradication may be required to protect workers.

Workers may be required to wear personal protective equipment.

- Hazardous Material – Many job sites require hazardous materials, such as sealants, cleaning fluids, gas cylinders, etc. The general contractor must have a written hazardous communication and training program, and must provide workers with the Material Safety Data Sheets for the material. The Communication plan must include hazardous material disposal procedures, emergency spill response, hazardous material labeling system, and hazardous materials inventory. Construction equipment may require absorbent material to contain hydraulic and oil system leaks. Refer to 29 CFR 1910. 1200 and 29 CFR 1925.59 Hazard Communication for more information.

- Hazardous Waste – Usually these do not apply to building operations unless the site itself is a hazardous waste site. Requirements are similar to the hazardous materials procedures with additional precautions due to the nature of the hazard. Refer to 29 CFR 1910.120

- Lasers – Lasers are frequently found on work sites for surveying, to measure distances, drilling and welding. Refer to 29 CFR 1926.54 for more information.

- Lead – Lead based paint on older buildings is the most frequent source of lead in construction but it is also found in soldering flux in piping. As with asbestos, unless it is identified in the contract and provisions for removal or encapsulation are made, a project may halt until it is corrected. See 29 CFR 1926.62 and 1910.1025 for more information.

- Lockout/tagout – Lockout/tagout not only refers to electrical systems but also mechanical systems. Especially susceptible mechanical systems are fan blades rotating when the building pressure changes. Lockout is the preferred method of energy control. Tagout is best used when an energy-isolating device cannot be used for the system. Both devices should identify the employee, employer and a phone number, date applied, and equipment, machine or system component deenergized. Lockout/tagout systems are critical when multiple employers are on the construction site. Testing the deenergized equipment machine or component is critical before beginning work. In electrical systems be aware that inadvertently induced voltage and unregulated back feed can occur. See 29 CFR 1910.147, Control of Hazardous Energy and ANSI Z44.1-2003, Control of Hazardous Energy Lockout/Tagout and Alternative Methods.

- Medical and First Aid – Because the injury rate for construction sites is so high, the general contractor should have personnel trained in first aid and cardio-pulmonary resuscitation (CPR) on-site. In cases of suffocation, severe bleeding and other life threatening injuries, a three to four minute response window is all the available time between an injury and the application of first aid. The first aid kit should be in a weatherproof container. Sample first aid kits are discussed in ASNI Z 308.1-2003, American National Standard for Workplace First Aid Kits. Phone numbers, addresses and directions to the local hospital or urgent care center should also be posted. Refer to 29 126.50 for more information.

- Motor vehicles traffic injuries are a common injury among organizations whether it's a truck fleet or a single vehicle. The conventional wisdom about seat belts, riding in the rear of a truck, wearing head phones and earphones should be evaluated. Commercial driver's licenses may be required for drivers carrying the fans, HVAC units, etc. onto the job site.

- Personal Protective Equipment (PPE) – Typical PPE for a construction site is a hardhat, steel-toed shoes and safety glasses. Specific jobs and those located nearby may also require more specific hearing and eye protection. When working with electrical systems, rubber lined leather gloves may be necessary to protect against unexpected shock. Lockout/tagout is the first line of defense for electrical work. High voltage electricians also use electrical grade hard hats, gloves with leather protected sleeves, shoes and sometimes NOMEX covered shirts or coveralls. Use of all the PPE requires specialized training, recertification and occasionally medical examinations. Refer to 29 CFR 1910 Subpart I, Personal Protective Equipment for more information. The following standards address specific types of PPE:

  - ANSI Z87.1 – 2003, Practice For Occupational and Educational Eye and Face Protection
  - ANSI Z89.1 – 2003, Requirements for Industrial Head Protection
  - ANSI Z 41 – 1999, Personal Protection, Protective Footwear
  - Z 88. 2 – 1992 (revision expected in 2005) Respiratory Protection

- Portable Ladders – Newer buildings and larger facilities usually have an internal stairwell to access the roof or mezzanine. For smaller jobs, ladders are frequently used to access the roof and outdoor mounted equipment supports. Ladders are used to access duct, cleanout doors and the fan especially during testing. Aluminum ladders should not be used to perform work near electrically energized parts. Refer to 20 CFR 1910.25 and 26 for information on Portable Wood Ladders and Portable Metal Ladders, respectively.

- Power Elevated Mobile Work Platforms – This equipment, frequently called cherry pickers, is used when installing duct and fans. They are also occasionally used to test the fans located in hard to reach locations (not a good design practice). Personal fall arrest systems are required while working on these systems. The operator is usually licensed for the lift equipment. Refer to ANSI/SIA A92.2-2002 American National Standard for Vehicle-Mounted Elevating and Rotating Aerial Devices and ANSI/SIA 92.6-1999, Self Propelled Elevating Work Platforms.

- Powered Industrial Trucks – Forklifts and other powered trucks are frequently on a construction site, primarily to move supplies closer to the job site. Operators must be trained and authorized to use the truck. The following standards apply:

  - 29 CFR 1926.602, Lifting and Hauling Equipment
  - 29 CFR 1910.178, Powered Industrial Trucks
  - NFPA 505 – Fire Safety Standards for Powered Industrial Trucks
  - ANSI B56.5 – 2003, Safety Standard for Rough Terrain Forklift Trucks
  - ANSI B56.1 – 2004, Safety Standard for Low Lift and High Lift Trucks

- Roofing – Whenever workers are working on a roof, fall protection must be used. Fall protection, especially guardrails with toe kick boards and safety nets, help prevent equipment from falling on people below the roofline. Roofing tar can contain cancer-causing materials. Workers installing industrial ventilation systems should not be nearby until the volatile emissions have abated to a safe level. Shingles and roofing material containing asbestos may require PPE and special abatement should be practiced during site preparation and demolition.

- Scaffolding – Workers sometimes stand on scaffolding to install duct and fan, or to move equipment up to the fan location. Sometimes permanent "scaffolding" is used to mount air pollution control equipment or fans. A competent person is required to supervise the erection, dismantling and movement of any scaffolding. Refer to 29 CFR 1926.451, Scaffolds.

- Tree Maintenance – Tree maintenance may be required when performing renovations or upgrading a system. Information listed in the following sections may apply: roofing, scaffolding, powered industrial trucks, hand tools, etc.

- Trenching and Excavation – Trenching and excavation occur during demolition and on new projects and related accidents usually have severe consequences. Cave-ins, flooding, asphyxiation, fire, explosion and collapse are concerns during trenching and excavation. Electrical, natural gas and water lines should be marked prior to excavation. A competent person must supervise all excavations. See 29 CFR 1926.650 through 1926.652.

- Welding and Cutting – Welding and cutting, also called "hot work," are a primary construction activity where portable ventilation may be required to install a permanent industrial ventilation system. Duct is frequently cut and welded on-site. Even precut duct lengths must be connected frequently by welding. Exhaust ventilation may be required to prevent the accumulation of toxic material (e.g., galvanized aluminum, stainless steel, etc.) and supply ventilation may be required to prevent oxygen deficiency. Fire extinguishing equipment and a trained fire watch are required at the weld site. Special precautions regarding rescue and escape are required when welding occurs in confined spaces such as basements and chases. Other safety equipment includes weld helmets with the correct eye filters protection and protective gloves and aprons. For more information see 29 CFR 1910 Subpart Q, Welding Cutting and Brazing and American Welding Society Z49.1-1999, "Safety in Welding and Cutting and Allied Processes." Other 29 CFR 1910 standards address specific types of welding including 1910.253, 1910.254 and 1910.255, which address oxygen fuel gas for welding and cutting, arc welding and cutting, and resistance welding, respectively.

- Weight Handling Equipment – Crane and rigging accidents occur in high proportion to other construction accidents. Cranes are used to move packaged supply air systems, air pollution control units, exhaust fans, and stacks into place on roofs, mezzanines and basements. Crane operators and riggers undergo training and certification. Refer to 29 CFR 1926 Subpart N and 29 CFR 1910, Subpart N for more information. General contractors must comply with ASME B30.5- 2002, Mobile and Locomotive Cranes and ASME B30.22-2000, Articulating Boom Cranes.

The issues listed here are not all encompassing nor are all the standards and codes related to the issues covered. They are meant to give the reader a starting place to examine the myriad of safety issues occurring at a construction site.

APPENDIX B1

TRADE UNIONS IN VENTILATION PROJECTS

Workers are typically recognized at three competence levels:

1) *Apprenticeship* requires a high school or General Education Diploma. Some areas may require written exams and/or personal interviews to enter the apprenticeship. Apprenticeship usually lasts a few years.

2) *Journeyman* requires the completion of the apprentice program and satisfactory completion of tests developed by the union and contractors.

3) *Master Craftsman* has special requirements at higher skill levels.

Other positions are based on the contract arrangements of the local contractors and unions.

Trade unions

To protect workers wages, benefits and rights, unions have developed bargaining agreements, job assignments and hiring procedures. At times when workloads in certain areas are stretched due to heavy construction requirements, some unions have the ability to transfer workers from other areas to meet the workforce needs.

The contract negotiated between the employer and the union spells out not only wage rates, but other conditions of employment, such as work hours, vacations, time off for family emergencies, how work assignments are made, and the employer's role in safety issues. Because they are negotiated regularly, contracts may be modified to account for changing conditions in the workplace. Union contracts always include a formal grievance procedure for the worker who feels the company is not living up to its end of the bargain. These agreements are in force when operating on plant premises.

Open shop

Contractors who hire non-union and union trades people without the union labor agreement are called merit-shop or *open shop* contractors. Recruiting workers is more informal than through union halls although some trades have registries and referral services. During difficult economic times union trades people may also work for these companies. There are limits on their pool of workers for extremely large projects but many are of sufficient size to handle most common sized local exhaust ventilation systems.

APPENDIX C1

CONSTRUCTION DRAWINGS

This Appendix provides basic training on how to read engineering drawings and relate them to a Local Exhaust Ventilation system. All the illustrations in this training Appendix are based on the scale model of an exhaust system.

TABLE A1-1. Typical Unions and Trades Involved with Industrial Ventilation Systems

Trade	Typical tasks
Sheet Metal Workers (also called tinsmiths)	• Fabricate (incl. welding), install and maintain HVAC and ventilation systems • Also work on gutters, roofing, siding and food service equipment • Different jurisdictions have different rules but typically handle duct and breechings of ¼" or less • Fine tune, test, balance and maintain ventilation systems
International Brotherhood of Boilermakers, Iron Ship Builders, Blacksmiths, Forgers and Helpers	• Fabricate, install and maintain heavy equipment used for energy generation and distribution • Typical trades are blacksmiths, forgers, ship builders, cement workers, stove workers, metal polishers • For local exhaust systems, Boilermakers are normally employed on heavy gauge plate duct and breechings (> ¼" thick)
United Association of Journeyman and Apprentice of the Plumbing and Pipe Fitters Industry of the United States and Canada	• For ventilation systems, can install fire protection, compressed air (for baghouses) and other auxiliary systems such as water and drain piping for scrubbers • Typical trades are plumbers, pipe fitters, sprinkler fitters, refrigeration fitters, and service technicians • In some cases, they may also be involved in the installation of heavy pipe used for local exhaust ventilation systems with extreme erosion potential or high vacuum systems used for pneumatic conveying and central vacuuming systems
Other unions such as the United Auto Workers (UAW) have mixed trades people dedicated to building a certain product line	• Air conditioning and refrigeration mechanics can change filters and make coil and compressor changes • Boilermakers fabricate and install metal products greater than ¼" • Electricians run wiring, engage power distribution systems and install control systems • Millwrights install collector bags, set, align and balance fans • Pipe fitters, plumbers, steam fitters all work on the pneumatic dust conveyors; also install hydronic components of the supply air systems • Stationery engineers operate the boilers and conduct supply air filter changes

TABLE A1-1 (Cont.). Typical Unions and Trades Involved with Industrial Ventilation Systems

Other trades people are found within the above mentioned unions or they belong to other unions	<ul><li>Ironworkers install structural bases for large industrial ventilation systems</li><li>Masons install footings for fan bases</li><li>Riggers prepare heavy equipment for movement to the rooftop and basements</li><li>Laborers and assistants to all the trades may or may not be skilled in the trade</li><li>Mechanics install smaller equipment and maintain larger ventilation systems</li><li>Welders join duct segments together or join system components</li></ul>

The system is of a dust control system serving a carton filling machine and its feed systems, as shown in Figure C1-1. Photographs and several drawings illustrate the information contained in engineering drawings. Ventilation system operators and maintenance personnel will find the ability to interpret the information on engineering drawings is important to the successful long term operation of ventilation systems.

Process and Dust Control Description

In Figure C1-1, a belt conveyor on the third floor of the building delivers powdered material to a chute feeding an oscillating sifter on the second floor. A laboratory hood on the third floor provides a dust controlled location to perform process quality checks. The sifter removes lumps and passes the powder to the head of the carton filling machine on the first floor. Cartons are filled to weight in the filling head. Cartons are checked at the reject cabinet for correct volume and weight; off specification cartons are kicked out of the line before sealing and tumbled into the hopper of the reject cabinet. Operators dump the contents of the carton into a feed hopper which pneumatically conveys the powder to the dust control filter which discharges its files onto the belt conveyor.

The dust control system filter and fan are on the fourth floor and are connected to the process with a duct system of several branches connected to:

- The belt conveyor (provides face velocity when one access door is open)

- The laboratory hood (provides face velocity at the opening)

- The top of the filter fines bulk container for whenever the filter is not discharging fines to the belt conveyor

- The carton filler head dust ring and spillage removal slot

- The carton reject cabinet combined dust control and

pneumatic conveying branch.

Three different types of engineering drawings are needed to fully describe the system and are shown on later pages of this Appendix:

1. **Plan and Elevation Drawings** are to scale representations of the physical system. Process equipment, duct, fabric filter, and the exhaust fan show the local exhaust ventilation system from top (plan) and side (elevation) perspectives. It takes three drawings to show the model system. First look at Figures C1-2 and C1-4 which are side (or elevation) photographs of the model, positioned opposite the elevation view, which shows the same information in Figures C1-3 and C1-5. Figure C1-6 is a top (or plan) view of the four floors of the building with the process equipment and duct visible.

2. **Piping & Instrument Diagrams** (P&IDs) show the process equipment, piping or duct, and control instrumentation as can be seen in Figure C1-7. This schematic format shows how all the parts of the system are connected and controlled. Process Safety Engineers use this information to ensure that the system is safe from overpressure and dust explosion hazards.

3. **Flow and Pressure Schematics** provide an isometric view (three dimensional representations) of the local exhaust system, with nodes and test points marked. See Figure C1-8. They also list the Baseline Static Pressures and Flows measured at the test points as well as balancing device information (blast gate positions or orifice plate diameters and locations in this case). Equipment specification information is listed for the fan, its motor and drive belts, the filter, and its dust removal rotary airlock valve and motor.

Closely compare the photographs to the drawings and you will see how the engineering drawing provides useful information.

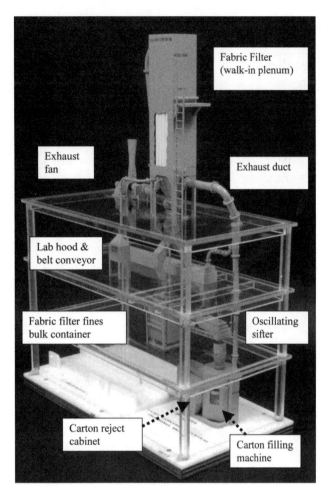

FIGURE C1-1. Perspective view of ventilation system model (Reprinted with permission from Procter & Gamble)

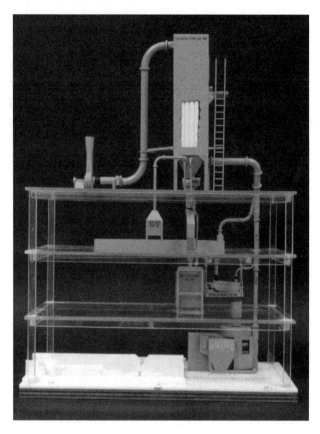

FIGURE C1-2. Elevation photo of side of dust control System Model (Reprinted with permission from Procter & Gamble)

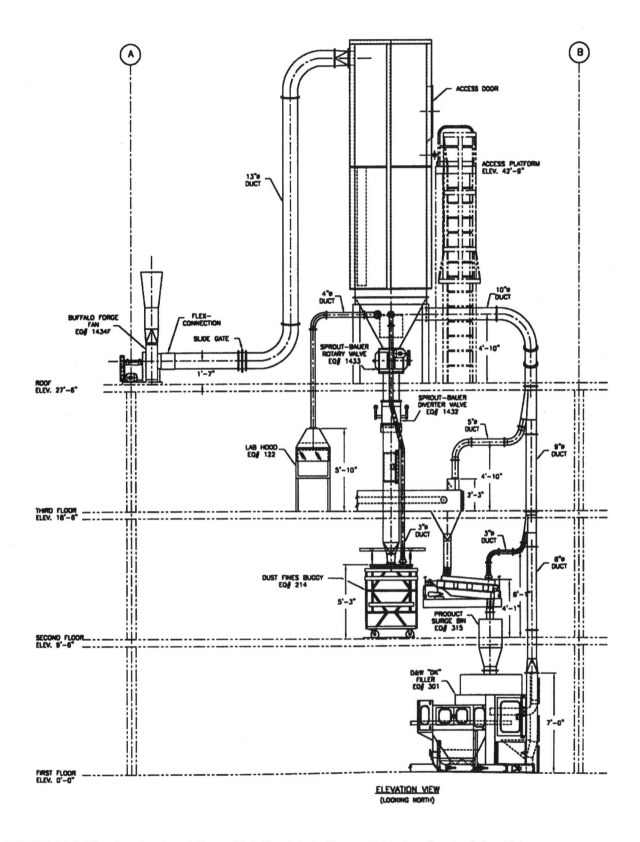

FIGURE C1-3. Elevation drawing of Figure C1-2 (Reprinted with permission from Procter & Gamble)

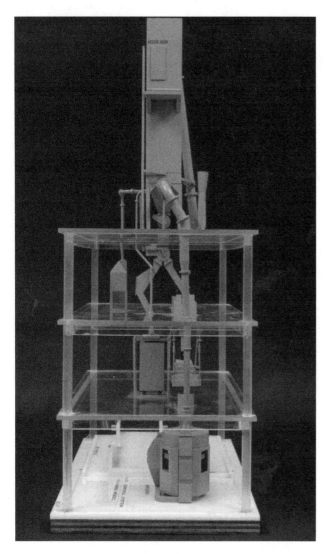

FIGURE C1-4. Elevation photo of narrow end of model
(Reprinted with permission from Procter & Gamble)

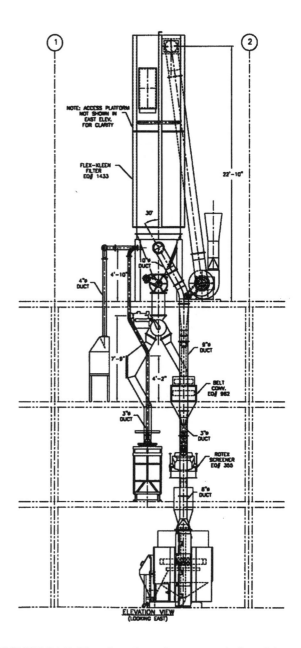

FIGURE C1-5. Elevation view of narrow end of model
(Reprinted with permission from Procter & Gamble)

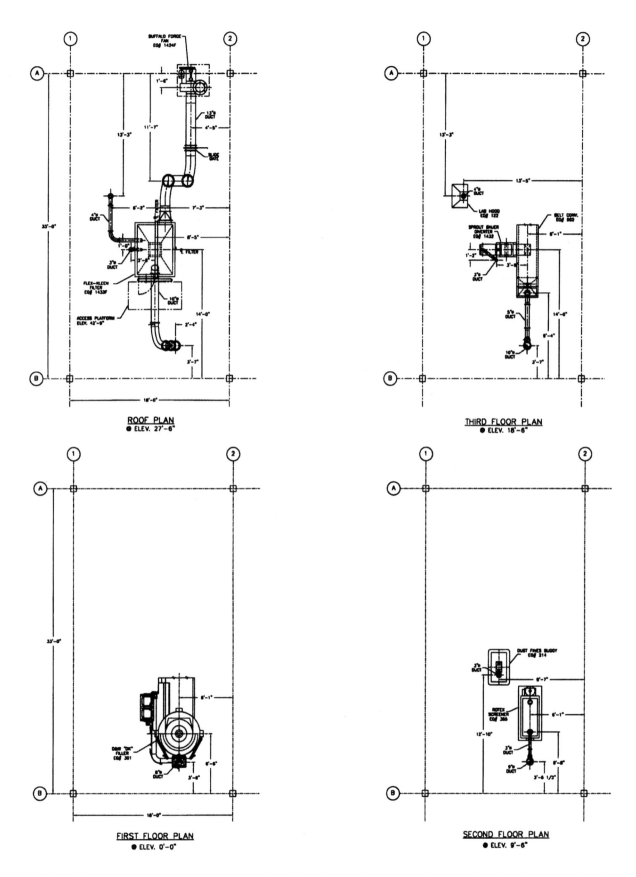

FIGURE C1-6. Plan or top views of dust control model, all four floors (Reprinted with permission from Procter & Gamble)

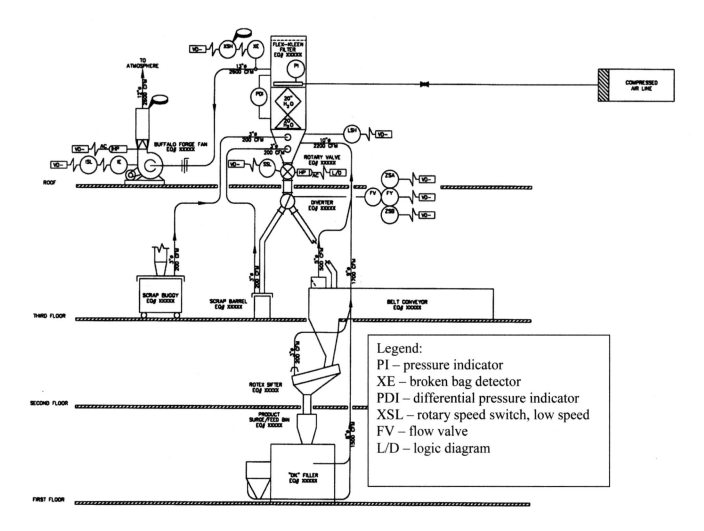

FIGURE C1-7. Piping & Instrument Diagram of dust control system (Reprinted with permission from Procter & Gamble)

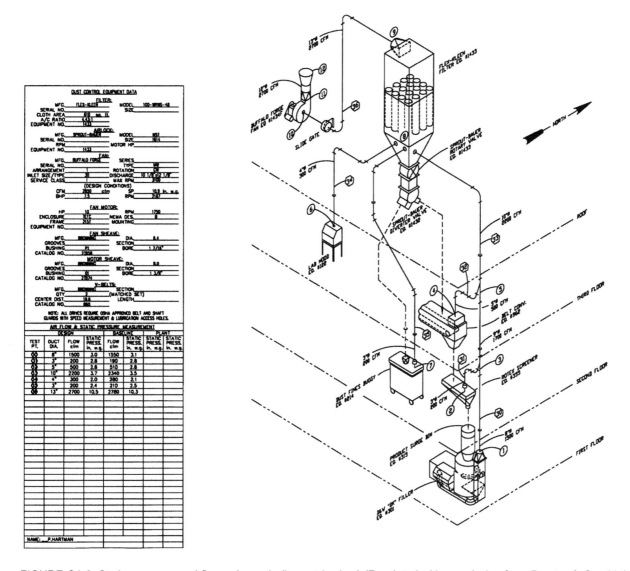

FIGURE C1-8. Static pressure and flow schematic (isometric view) (Reprinted with permission from Procter & Gamble)

Chapter 2
COMMISSIONING AND PROOF OF PERFORMANCE

2.1   INTRODUCTION

After the construction of the ventilation system is complete, there is a transfer of the system ownership from the installer or builder to the Owner. This normally includes a formal or informal step of proof of performance at the completion of the installation. Commissioning is a program of quality assurance and documentation that provides the verification of proper and specified operation of the ventilation system. In addition to testing to assure compliance with regulatory requirements, there may also be requirements to review the more detailed terms of the specifications. For example, if there is a requirement for high-efficiency motors on all fans or special grease fittings on all bearings, there will need to be verification that these were installed throughout the system.

During the installation of a ventilation system, there are final steps necessary to verify the performance of work so all terms of the contract can be fulfilled and ownership can be given to the plant. The final steps of this Proof of Performance include:

1) Review of punch-lists

2) Test to assure regulatory compliance

3) Review of steps taken to meet detailed specifications ("commissioning").

These steps are performed formally or informally based on the size of the project. A smaller project may require only verbal approval and verification that all equipment and the system meet the requirements of the contract or work order. For larger projects, depending on the complexity or size of the project, a more formal procedure may be required, normally using a punch-list. A punch-list is a list of ongoing concerns, items that need to be completed, construction mistakes that need to be corrected, or other construction items that need attention as the project draws near completion. This punch-list represents an agreement between the Owner and the contractor or architect/engineer, and is a tabulation of all items still to be installed or altered to meet all of the specification requirements.

In addition to the punch-list, there may be a requirement for in-plant industrial hygiene testing or exhaust stack testing to ensure that the installer is meeting all contractual obligations for equipment and system performance.

2.1.1 *Purpose of Commissioning.* The purpose of Commissioning is to demonstrate to the Owner of the ventilation system that all contractual requirements have been met. Commissioning is intended to enhance the quality of the start-up and ensure that the Owner has received a satisfactorily operating ventilation system that can be maintained with reasonable effort.

In addition, there may be Proofs of Performance requirements that could include warranties on the life of system components, control efficiencies or outlet loadings from control equipment. Such proofs of performance may also include

industrial hygiene assessments (operator exposure or stationary air samples) in the plant or at workstations. Other requirements could include correct building air balance and pressure or the furnishing of supply air systems to match exhaust from the new ventilation system.

A person can be designated to provide the logistics for the commissioning process. This person would normally be called the Commissioning Administrator or Commissioning Agent. As with other discussions of team and project organization, the assumption and details are shown for large projects but can also be adapted for smaller installations. In some cases, the same person may fill the role of Project Manager and Commissioning Administrator or Commissioning Agent. In cases of smaller ventilation installations, the communications and documentation for commissioning may be provided by a simple inspection after completion of the installation. The information below lists the likely issues that should be resolved and verified, whether formally or informally (verbally), as required.

2.1.2 *When to Start the Commissioning Process.* The commissioning process should begin in the design phase of the project. As the requirements are defined during the development of the project, a Design Basis is developed. The Design Basis includes the instructions and expectations of the Owner and is communicated to the Design Team. At this early stage, the designer should consider the eventual verification of the design. It is important that commissioning documents be incorporated into the project documents. Certain parameters may be built into the design specifications. For example, the designer may be required to specify a fabric filter with a minimum bag life of one year and not exceed a pressure drop of 6.0 "wg. Such a requirement would definitely influence the choice of collection media and air/cloth ratio for the design. Therefore, specifications and the requirements for verification of fabric filter performance should be developed at the same time. The intent is to ensure that the Owner and all suppliers have a clear understanding of the system requirements and how the requirements will be verified while still in the bidding and design process.

The Commissioning Agent should draft the system checklists and commissioning plan as the system is specified and designed. Figure 2-1 shows a sample test plan outline for the commissioning. It includes a description of the project, identification of responsible parties, and lists specific requirements. As the design develops, the design team expands on the specific requirements. This expansion includes the requirements, the responsible party, and the method of measurement. If done early enough in the design process, it is very likely that there will be agreement among the Owner's needs, system design specification requirements, guarantees and purchase orders and contracts for any equipment. This plan should also include the training of the Owner's personnel in the operation of the ventilation system. Chapter 9, Training for Ventilation System Users, provides some guidance for the required training.

COMMISSIONING PLAN

Company Name   _____

Project   _____

General Contractor   _____

Commissioning Agent   _____

1) Description: The following plan includes all of the responsible parties and scope of work to be included in the Commissioning of the Project.

2) Responsibilities:

   a. Commissioning Agent: Coordinate all requirements, control and distribute Commissioning documents; provide communications between Owner and all contractors; designate and approve all test methods; coordinate and manage the efforts of all independent test companies not included in construction contracts; coordinate and communicate all safety requirements of the project to all parties during Commissioning.

   b. Owner: Approve and review all Commissioning information and results; provide final sign-off for receipt of approved equipment and systems.

   c. General Contractor: Manage the efforts of all vendors, sub-contractors and testing companies in their contract; provide labor and equipment for support of Commissioning effort by sub-contractors including access to equipment and cleanup. Complete alterations to equipment to meet contract requirements.

   d. Controls Engineer: Provide all information for proper sequence of operation and safety issues for system operation.

   e. Testing, Adjusting and Balancing (TAB) Contractor: Provide initial data and preliminary air balance of all hoods; verify flows and pressures at key locations; proportionally balance all branch lines and make recommendations for changes to system if volume or pressure not obtained; provide final balance and certified report to Commissioning Agent of results after all alterations.

3) Related Work

   a. Plant Safety Issues

   b. Schedule

   c. Test Methods

      i. Static Test Checklists

      ii. Dynamic Test Checklists

      iii. Proof of Performance

   d. Report Transmittal

   e. Retesting

   f. Operation and Maintenance Manuals

   g. Training of Owner Personnel

   h. Deferred Testing

   i. Deferred Proof of Performance

FIGURE 2-1. Sample test plan outline

2.1.3 Proof of Performance. The term "Proof of Performance" can be used in two ways in the completion of projects. The more prevalent usage is in the context of performance of a contract where the equipment supplier provides the successful delivery of the good or service. In ventilation system design the same term has included verification of the system operation to meet regulations. Normally this would be accomplished by some certified testing of the inside air or the exhaust gas quality from air cleaning devices. Because the expanded definition is normally used in the ventilation design field, it will also be used in this Manual.

2.2   COMMISSIONING TEAM ORGANIZATION

As the design team is organized in the early stages of the project, the commissioning team can also be organized. The size and make-up of the team should depend on:

1) The complexity of the project
2) The project cost
3) The value of the Owner's investment
4) The method of design (e.g., in-house vs. design/build vs. design-construct).

Ideally, the Commissioning Agent will verify compliance for the Owner, and should be selected before the installation begins. For small companies, the Commissioning Agent could be the Owner or plant engineer. The Commissioning Agent may or may not be a part of the design team.

Besides monitoring and managing the installation, the Commissioning Agent is delegated as the holder of all commissioning records for the project. The Project Manager is responsible for communicating all contract requirements to all parties on a continuous basis so there are no surprises during the commissioning and closure of the project. It is easier to resolve any conflicts arising in the project while the contractor is still on site than to wait until there is a dispute after the contractor is off of the site.

If the project is large or complicated, it may be advisable for the Owner also to designate a Test Engineer to oversee all testing for the project. That person would be a representative of the Owner and report to the Commissioning Agent. As the Owner's representative, the Commissioning Agent would also provide information to the Project Manager. The Commissioning Agent position has responsibilities throughout the design and construction phase. Table 2-1 outlines many of these responsibilities.

Note that the commissioning of the ventilation systems may be a part of a larger project (plant expansion or new plant). In those cases, the Commissioning Agent for the ventilation system may be part of the larger team for the commissioning of the total project.

TABLE 2-1. Duties of the Commissioning Agent in Each Phase of Construction

Design Phase

- Review all Contractor's and/or Engineer's start-up plans
- Review Contractor's Test Procedures and Requirements*
- Review Engineer's Specification for Testing, Adjusting and Balancing (TAB)*
- Prepare or supervise the preparation of all Static, Dynamic and Proof of Performance checklists

Construction Phase

- Review the Contractor's installation and inter-system checking if required for electrical controls
- Verify and approve the completion of all Static Checks on equipment including proper receipt on site, proper installation and nameplate data
- Verify and approve the Dynamic Checks on all required components as performed by the Contractor
- Review and approve the proper Testing, Adjustment and Balancing work, whether performed by the Contractor or an independent certified agency*

Commissioning Phase

- Develop all testing schedules and coordinate with Environmental Representative to ensure all regulatory forms have been submitted*
- Arrange for tradesmen or other individuals to have access to the ventilation system for testing
- Review all safety requirements for off-site testing personnel*
- Manage all cross-system testing as required (fire alarms, safety controls, etc.)
- Oversee and approve the results of all Proof of Performance testing (or the efforts of the designated Test Engineer) as required to complete the terms of the contract*
- Arrange for or coordinate with Design Team for engineering expertise to provide for correction of deficiencies if they occur
- Obtain all documentation of tests and submit to Owner and Project Manager
- Update the Design Basis, if necessary, to reflect actual conditions as tested
- Ensure that a baseline for all ventilation systems is developed
- Ensure that all training of Owner's personnel is completed per specification and terms of the Purchase Order
- Receive and verify that all training and operations manuals are in place and that training has been accomplished

*Can also be provided by a designated Testing Engineer.

2.2.1 Coordination During the Design Phase. During the Preliminary Design phase, the primary responsibility for the Commissioning Agent will be to determine the list of systems and equipment that will require commissioning. This list may be revised as the systems are revised during detailed design. This information will be incorporated into the Design Basis before issue and review. The Design Basis is a set of instructions from the Owner to the Design Team describing the requirements of the system. With small projects, this may be more informal but should always be documented.

The first document in the process is a Commissioning Plan, which is included with the Design Basis. This can be in any format as provided with the Design Basis (see Figure 2-1); however, at a minimum the Commissioning Plan should accomplish the following:

1) Display an Organization Chart showing the relationships among the Owner, Design Team, Engineer, Contractor, and Commissioning Agent with identification of key personnel.

2) Identify who will be responsible for producing the test procedures, documentation and document control for testing and commissioning.

3) Show either a commissioning schedule incorporated in the Project Schedule or as a separate document with references to key dates in the main schedule; this would include all requirements before start-up.

4) Describe minimum acceptable methods and recommended Testing, Adjusting and Balancing (TAB) procedures with instrumentation (e.g., Pitot tubes and manometers vs. anemometers for airflow measurement).

5) If measurements are used, describe the range of acceptability.

6) Describe who will pay for testing and any retesting required for correction of deficiencies.

7) Describe the format for reports and any requirement for certified TAB work or specified testing contractors.

8) Provide for the documentation of baseline data for use in future system evaluation and troubleshooting.

During the Detailed Design Phase, the list will be refined to match actual design conditions. At the same time, a scope document will be developed and possibly inserted into the Project Specifications. This would include the requirements for the completion of the project and the responsibilities of all parties involved. If a formal specification package is submitted, it may be included under Mechanical Systems Commissioning Section and Commissioning Requirements. During this period, the checklists and formats for review and verification will be provided to contractors with the bid documents.

2.2.2 Using a Certified Firm. Because of the complexity of industrial ventilation designs and more stringent regulations, larger projects may also include the services of a Professional Commissioning Manager. This person would have credentials that include a detailed knowledge of mechanical systems and organizational skills tailored to commissioning. Care must be taken in selecting this person because many certified firms often only have expertise in the commissioning of building mechanical systems (heating ventilating and air-conditioning

or HVAC) and may not be qualified for industrial ventilation systems. As with consultants, testing and balancing firms and contractors, the Owner should check qualifications and references before using a particular service. Balancing firms and some commissioning firms normally carry accreditation from NEBB (National Environmental Balancing Bureau) or ABC (American Balancing Council). If industrial hygiene or emission testing is included, additional credentials and experiences are likely required.

2.2.3 Process of Project Completion. When considering the end of a project, the Owner and Commissioning Agent must begin with all contractual documents. Final payment to the contractor is not made until all of the requirements are completed and verified. With a small project (e.g., modification to an existing ventilation system or installation of a small air cleaning device), the requirements may include only a simple list, and all that may be required for project completion is a joint visual inspection by the Owner and installer.

Larger projects obviously can be more complex. There may be a number of mid-project changes in design or scope with extra payment by the Owner ("change orders"), charges by the Owner against the contractor or engineer due to errors in the design or installation ("back charges"), and other modifications to the original contract that must be rectified. All of these changes and records are normally controlled and communicated by the Project Manager. Assuming all project management activities are timely and there are no questions about the performance of the installation itself, verification of the operation and Proof of Performance to complete the terms of the contract will still be required.

2.3   COMPONENTS OF THE COMMISSIONING PROCESS

The examples below are for typical types of equipment found in ventilation systems. They are separated by the three commissioning components (Static Checks, Dynamic Checks and Proof of Performance). The detail of the reports and documentation will vary by project. Information that is more detailed is used for large systems with many engineering disciplines, complicated equipment parameters, and/or very stringent environmental regulations.

Three primary requirements must be met for the contract to be verified and completed. Each component of the commissioning process will be verified and documented with sign-off by the Commissioning Agent. The simplest method is the use of checklists with appropriate requirements and signatures. Sample checklists are shown in Figure 2-2 for a fabric filter, Figure 2-3 for a centrifugal fan static checklist, and Figure 2-4 for a centrifugal fan dynamic checklist. The forms should be flexible enough so that a small system, possibly not requiring stack tests, may forego the Proof of Performance checks as they are accomplished during the Dynamic Checks phase.

2.3.1 Static Checks. Static checks (also called pre-startup inspections) are inspection checks of the equipment before it is operated. These can be accomplished while the installation is in progress. These should not be confused with static pressure checks. Static Checks could include review of nameplate data while on the receiving dock and before installation. They could also be used to ensure that installation was done to equipment supplier's and engineer's requirements. Discrepancies found during these checks would be brought to the attention of the Project Manager, engineer and equipment supplier to determine how to proceed. Figures 2-2 and 2-3 are examples of static check forms.

2.3.2 Dynamic Checks. Dynamic checks (also called functional performance tests) are equipment checks made while the equipment is operating. These checks involve the mechanical operation of the equipment itself, and are normally completed and signed off before any balancing of the system volumes and pressures takes place. Discrepancies found at this stage may be more difficult to rectify, particularly if equipment is installed and connected. Figure 2-4 is an example of a dynamic check form.

During this phase, a fan, for example, must be checked to ensure that it rotates in the correct direction, operates vibration free, has operating dampers that respond to electrical or pneumatic signal, etc. Final flow verification would be accomplished during Proof of Performance.

All checklists should include data such as equipment model number, manufacturer's serial number, Owner's equipment number, purchase order number, nameplate ratings and other limits as specified by equipment supplier.

2.3.3 Checklists for Ventilation Equipment. Because the numbers and types of equipment in an industrial ventilation system can be varied, not all possible checklists have been included. Tables 2-2 through Table 2-18 include information for sample ventilation equipment. The tables include normal considerations for verification of Static Checks, Dynamic Checks and Proof of Performance for these types of equipment. Documents such as those shown in Figures 2-2, 2-3 and 2-4 can be constructed using any or all of the information in the tables.

2.3.4 Steps in Project Completion and Closeout Process. In many cases, there may be a lag time between the final installation and the verification of performance by stack tests or industrial hygiene tests. However, it is in the best interest of all parties to monitor the timing so the project can be officially closed as soon as possible. This issue can be clouded if there are long-t-erm requirements. For example, long-term filter media replacement guarantees for fabric filters may go beyond normal testing periods. These terms (payment and expectations) must be written into project contracts and reconciled during the bidding process.

The documents required for project closure are as varied as the size and complexity of the project. The simplest projects would show completion by sending an invoice for the last payment on the contract. Larger and more complicated projects

TABLE 2-2. Sample Checklist for Ducts

Static Checks:

Materials of construction

Duct size

SMACNA class (metal thickness)

Elbow radius

Entry angles (fittings)

Balancing devices located correctly (orifice plates or blast gates)

Proper support spacing and methods

Design and suitability of roof and wall penetrations

Pressure or leak tests

Painting

Methods of duct connection (angle rings, welded)

Safe access to test ports

Dynamic Checks:

Operation of any dampers for temperature or flow control

Proper sequence from central controller

Proof of Performance:

Air balance including all operational variances in system

Summer operation

Winter operation

By-pass damper operation

Verification of minimum transport velocities in all ducts at all times

TABLE 2-3. Sample Checklist for Hoods

Static Checks:

Materials of construction

Metal gauge thickness

Transition to duct system

Balancing devices located correctly (orifice plates or blast gates)

Conform to engineering drawings

Attachment of machine guards integral to hood

Signage or painting to meet plant safety standards

Location of personal cooling fans or other equipment affecting hood performance

Painting

Dynamic Checks:

Operation of any dampers for temperature or flow control

Proper sequence from central controller

Proof of Performance:

After testing and balancing is complete,

   Verification of minimum face velocities at hood faces

   Comparison of ambient to hood face exposures

PRE-STARTUP STATIC CHECKLIST
FABRIC FILTER

SYSTEM IDENTIFICATION	
EQUIPMENT NUMBER:	
MANUFACTURER:	
MODEL NUMBER:	
SERIAL NUMBER:	

ACTION ITEM LIST	SEE REMARKS	OK
1. Verify that fabric filter physical characteristics comply with specifications and vendor information.		ENTER DATE ABOVE
2. Inspect for shipping or installation damage.		ENTER DATE ABOVE
3. Verify that doors, door hardware, and gaskets are properly installed and in good working order.		ENTER DATE ABOVE
4. Verify that filter media is in compliance with specifications and installed properly (type of bag material, finish, grounding, etc.).		ENTER DATE ABOVE
5. Verify static pressure sensors or test ports are properly located and installed to measure pressure drop across filter media.		ENTER DATE ABOVE

FIGURE 2-2. Sample static checklist for fabric filter

ACTION ITEM LIST (cont'd.)	SEE REMARKS	OK

6.   Verify that filter cleaning mechanism (pulse-jet, shaker, reverse air) is provided and properly installed. If possible, operate cleaning system prior to startup. Verify compressed air pressure and quality.

ENTER DATE ABOVE

_____
_____
_____

7.   Verify that dust removal system complies with specifications and is installed properly. Check belt or chain tension and gearbox oil levels. Verify rotary valve and/or screw conveyor rotation.

ENTER DATE ABOVE

_____
_____
_____

NOTES:

FIGURE 2-2 (Cont.). Sample static checklist for fabric filter

PRE-STARTUP STATIC CHECKLIST
Centrifugal FAN

EQUIPMENT IDENTIFICATION	
EQUIPMENT NUMBER:	
MANUFACTURER:	
MODEL NUMBER:	
SERIAL NUMBER:	

RECEIVING INSPECTION	SEE REMARKS	OK
1. Check all parts against shipping list and purchase order. Note missing or damaged parts below. _____ _____ _____		ENTER DATE ABOVE
2. Verify nameplate data with specifications and vendor information. _____ _____ _____		ENTER DATE ABOVE
3. Verify physical characteristics agree with specifications and vendor drawings. (rotation, discharge, materials of construction, etc.) _____ _____ _____		ENTER DATE ABOVE
4. Verify correct type and size fan wheel is installed per vendor's data sheets. Make certain the wheel is of correct rotation and not installed backwards. _____ _____ _____		ENTER DATE ABOVE
5. Check for physical damage, fan casing and wheel cracks, defects and welding quality. Check interior for debris. _____ _____ _____		ENTER DATE ABOVE

FIGURE 2-3. Sample centrifugal fan static checklist

RECEIVING INSPECTION (cont'd.)	SEE REMARKS	OK
6. Verify that drain(s), access door(s), heat slingers, shaft/bearing guards, belt guard(s) are provided per specifications.		
	ENTER DATE ABOVE	
7. Verify that shaft turns freely, fan wheel does not rub or wobble, belts do not contact guard. Rotate by hand not less than 5 full revolutions.		
	ENTER DATE ABOVE	
8. Verify that all grease fittings are extended external to guarding. Fittings must be easily accessible.		
	ENTER DATE ABOVE	
9. Verify that there is a tachometer access hole in belt guard. Hole diameter must be not less than 3/4" diameter.		
	ENTER DATE ABOVE	
10. Verify that fan wheel hub key is in place and set screws are tight. Verify that drive sheave key is in place and set screws are tight.		
	ENTER DATE ABOVE	
11. Check fan wheel-to-inlet clearance against manufacturer's specs.		
	ENTER DATE ABOVE	

INSTALLATION INSPECTION	SEE REMARKS	OK
12. Verify that all fan and motor bearings are correctly lubricated.		
	ENTER DATE ABOVE	

FIGURE 2-3 (Cont.). Sample centrifugal fan static checklist

INSTALLATION INSPECTION (cont'd.)	SEE REMARKS	OK

13. Verify that fan base is secured per specifications and that unit is level.

ENTER DATE ABOVE

14. If vibration isolators are specified, check that they are installed for uniform deflection and per design.

ENTER DATE ABOVE

15. Belt drive: check for proper components; check all fan shaft bearing mounts are secure.

ENTER DATE ABOVE

16. Direct drive: verify mounting and alignment per coupling manufacturer's instructions.

ENTER DATE ABOVE

17. Belt drive: check sheave alignment. Axial alignment shall not exceed 1/32" per foot of motor / shaft center-to-center distance.

ENTER DATE ABOVE

18. Verify that belt, shaft and coupling guards are installed and secure.

ENTER DATE ABOVE

19. Verify that all duct connections are not binding duct to fan. Verify that flexible connections are built and installed to specifications. Verify alignment of fan and duct.

ENTER DATE ABOVE

FIGURE 2-3 (Cont.). Sample centrifugal fan static checklist

INSTALLATION INSPECTION (cont'd.)	SEE REMARKS	OK

20. Check any inlet and outlet dampers for correct installation. Dampers <u>must be</u> free to operate over the desired range.

ENTER DATE ABOVE

21. Verify that variable inlet vane damper is installed with blades in proper alignment. As blades close they must cause air to spin in the same direction as fan wheel.

ENTER DATE ABOVE

22. Verify that motor rotation will provide proper fan rotation. "Bump" start fan to determine proper rotation after all electrical wiring is permanently connected.

ENTER DATE ABOVE

23. Verify the location of local disconnect and motor controls are per specifications and are weatherproof where required.

ENTER DATE ABOVE

24. Verify that fan is properly grounded.

ENTER DATE ABOVE

25. Verify that all painting is per specifications.

ENTER DATE ABOVE

26. Verify that insulation (if required) is provided and installed per specifications.

ENTER DATE ABOVE

FIGURE 2-3 (Cont.). Sample centrifugal fan static checklist

DYNAMIC CHECKLIST
Centrifugal FANS

EQUIPMENT IDENTIFICATION
EQUIPMENT NUMBER:
MANUFACTURER:
MODEL NUMBER:
SERIAL NUMBER:

ACTION ITEM LIST	SEE REMARKS	OK
1. Verify that all FANS & BLOWERS STATIC CHECKLIST items are complete		
	ENTER DATE ABOVE	
2. Verify that all ELECTRICAL STATIC CHECKLIST items are complete.		
	ENTER DATE ABOVE	
3. Verify that all DUCT STATIC CHECKLIST items are complete.		
	ENTER DATE ABOVE	
4. Close all system airflow control dampers 50%		
	ENTER DATE ABOVE	
5. Energize fan motor.		
	ENTER DATE ABOVE	

FIGURE 2-4. Sample centrifugal fan dynamic checklist

ACTION ITEM LIST (cont'd.)	SEE REMARKS	OK

6. Record (below) time, in seconds, it takes for blower to reach full speed.

ENTER DATE ABOVE

_____
_____
_____

7. Record starting amperage.
    T1 _____ T-2 _____ T-3 _____

ENTER DATE ABOVE

_____
_____
_____

8. Record motor nameplate data:
    FLA _____ at _____ volts

ENTER DATE ABOVE

_____
_____
_____

9. Record full speed fan shaft RPM.

ENTER DATE ABOVE

_____
_____
_____

10. Record full speed motor shaft RPM.

ENTER DATE ABOVE

_____
_____
_____

11. Record running amperage.
    T1 _____ T-2 _____ T-3 _____

ENTER DATE ABOVE

_____
_____
_____

12. After one hour operation at full speed, observe drive belt(s) for excessive stretching. Shut down and have trades adjusted as required.

ENTER DATE ABOVE

_____
_____
_____

FIGURE 2-4 (Cont.). Sample centrifugal fan dynamic checklist

ACTION ITEM LIST (cont'd.)	SEE REMARKS	OK

13. Set dampers to actual operating positions.
    Record total air volume _____ (ACFM)
    Record fan inlet air temp. _____degrees F
    Record fan static pressure: _____ "wg
    Fan static pressure = $SP_o - SP_i - VP_i$

ENTER DATE ABOVE

NOTES:

FIGURE 2-4 (Cont.). Sample centrifugal fan dynamic checklist

TABLE 2-4. Sample Checklist for Dampers

Static Checks:

Materials of construction

Transition to duct system

Location to prevent duct wear and provide reliable operation

Proper installation of operator and connection to control system

Bearings and shaft seals

Locking methods for position control

Painting

Proper blade design (opposed vs. parallel blades, etc.)

Location of tab or other method to identify blade position when connected to duct

Safe access for maintenance

Dynamic Checks:

Operation of any dampers free and without binding under duct flow and temperature at design point

Proof of Performance:

Pressure drop vs. damper position

Pressure drop in full open position

Pressure maintained at full closed position

TABLE 2-5. Sample Checklist for Fire and Smoke Dampers

Static Checks:

Manufacturer's rating

Transition to duct system

Location to prevent duct wear and provide reliable operation

Proper installation of operator and connection to control system

Bearings and shaft seals

Painting

Proper blade design

Installation to conform with all NFPA, local and plant codes

Safe access for maintenance and reset

Dynamic Checks:

Operation of any dampers free and without binding under duct flow and temperature at design point

Response to fire, smoke or other required testing

Output signal from limit switch, etc. with deployment

Proof of Performance:

None

TABLE 2-6. Sample Checklist for Centrifugal Fans

Static Checks:

Materials of construction

Housing rotation

Manufacturer's rating

Proper inlet or outlet damper and operator

Proper wheel type

Vibration isolation

Location and type of access doors

Location and type of housing drain with proper trap

Location of inlet cone

Bearings and lubrication per specifications

Size of sheaves and belts

Installation of shaft and drive guards

Proper mounting of sheaves and belts or coupling

Proper installation of inertia base

Proper connection to inlet and outlet duct include secure flexible connections

Painting

Safe access for maintenance

Inlet and outlet duct free of System Effect conditions

Dynamic Checks:

Proper rotation (bump test)

Operation with vibration below manufacturer's and plant standards

Proof of Performance:

Air volume (acfm and scfm)

Static Pressure (inlet and outlet)

Horsepower (amperage)

Fan Speed (rpm)

Temperature

Noise

Vibration

This procedure can start as early as a month or two before completion of the installation and can be built into project schedules. The Punch-List would be updated daily and copies circulated to all parties as changes are made. The Project Manager is responsible for preparation and updating of this document. A sample form for a Punch-List is shown in Figure 2-5. The complexity can be more or less based on project needs.

Step 2. Start pre-closing of the project by completion of Static Checks (*see* section 2.3.1)

This is the visual inspection and verification of all of the components of the project. Again, complexity can vary but

will require more written verification of the procedure including the following steps:

Step 1. Preparation and Management of the Project Punch-List

Local Exhaust Ventilation System Punch-List

Date: _____   System: _____

ID Number	Task Description	Group	Vendor	Comments/Observations	Date Posted	Originator	Date Completed	Date Verified	Status

Status Key
U - Underway
V - Ready to Verify
PS - Prior to Shipment
C - Complete
A - Action Item

Group Key
PM - Project Management
P - Process Engineer
C - Controls Engineer
EE - Electrical Engineer
I - Installing Contractor/Sub

ME - Mechanical Engineer
O - Owner
T - Testing Firm
TAB - Air Balance Firm
S - Software Engineer

FIGURE 2-5. Sample Punch-List form

TABLE 2-7. Sample Checklist for Vaneaxial and Duct Fans

Static Checks:

Materials of construction

Rotation direction

Manufacturer's rating

Proper wheel type

Motor mounting and support

Location and type of access door

Bearings and lubrication per specifications

Proper mounting and size of sheaves and belts

Proper connection to inlet and outlet duct including secure flexible connections

Painting

Safe access for maintenance

Inlet and outlet duct free of System Effect conditions

Dynamic Checks:

Proper rotation (bump test)

Operation with vibration and noise levels below manufacturer's and plant standards

Proof of Performance:

Air volume (acfm and scfm)

Static Pressure (inlet and outlet)

Speed of rotation (rpm)

Horsepower (amperage)

Temperature

Noise

Vibration

TABLE 2-8. Sample Checklist for Roof Curbs

Static Checks:

Materials of construction

Proper mounting to roof surface

Roof bonding issues

Temperature rating

Insulation and heat shields as required

Painting

Safe access for maintenance

Dynamic Checks:

None

Proof of Performance:

None

TABLE 2-9. Sample Checklist for Air Handlers and Replacement Air Units

Static Checks:

Materials of construction

Fan (see Fan section)

Motor (see Motor section)

Gas train or steam coil condition

Reheat coils

Type of filters

Filters installed

Location and type of housing drain with proper trap

Proper connection to inlet and outlet duct including secure flexible connections

Painting

Safe access for maintenance

Inlet and outlet duct free of System Effect conditions

Door seals

Condensate pan drainage

Bird screen installed

Security and signage for access doors

Proper mounting of thermostat and other external controls

Lighting installed

Smoke detection

Dynamic Checks:

Proper rotation (bump check)

Operation with vibration below manufacturer's and plant standards

Noise levels

Valve and damper operation

Safety checks for gas train

Water or other liquid flow to coils

Operation of dirty filter switches

Proof of Performance:

Air volume

Static Pressure

Delivery temperature

Turndown capability

Horsepower (amperage)

Temperature rise

Face and by-pass damper operation

Confirm operation with building automation system

Test economizer during all conditions

Operating design points as required including relative humidity, enthalpy or dew point control

TABLE 2-10. Sample Checklist for Electric Motors

Static Checks:

Frame size

Horsepower

Correct base and proper securing to concrete or steel

Manufacturer's rating

Voltage

Correct starter type

Local disconnect requirements

Efficiency type

Temperature rating

Explosion or atmosphere rating

Bearings and lubrication per specifications

Painting

Safe access for maintenance

Amperage rating

Correct wire and starter size

Breakers or fuses correct

Dynamic Checks:

Proper rotation

Operation with vibration below manufacturer's and plant standards

Proof of Performance:

Amperage

Motor temperature

Overload protection

TABLE 2-11. Sample Checklist for Liquid Pumps

Static Checks:

Pump type

Materials of construction

Rotation

Manufacturer's rating

Proper inlet or outlet valves and controls

Proper impeller type

Vibration isolation

Bearings and lubrication per specifications

Proper mounting of sheaves and belts or coupling

Proper mounting of inertia base

Proper connection to inlet and outlet pipe including secure flexible connections

Painting

Safe access for maintenance

Backflow prevention

Dynamic Checks:

Proper direction and speed of rotation

Operation with vibration below manufacturer's and plant standards

Proof of Performance:

Liquid flow

Operating pressure

Horsepower (amperage)

Temperature

there may need to be proof of such items as (but not limited to):

1) Proper metal thickness and materials in duct and hood installation

2) Proper fabric filter components including filter media, filter media size and shape, cage and housing materials of construction, proper installation of filter media cleaning mechanisms (or any set of requirements for different types of control devices)

3) Proper radius of elbows and angles of entry, supports for duct, location of blast gates or orifices, test ports

4) Proper insulation (thickness, type, weather protection, etc.)

5) Proper fan construction including materials of construction, bearings, wheel type, dampers and operators, grease fittings, vibration isolator plus removal of all stays or other restrictions during packing

6) Proper motor design to meet specifications (high efficiency, etc.)

7) Location and design of any safety devices including fire protection, explosion relief and access platforms and ladders

8) Location and design of inspection, cleanout and maintenance access doors

9) Proper installation of burners and piping for replacement air or other similar devices and inclusion of all safety controls and calibration of pressure switches, testing for zero leakage of fuel safety shut-off valves and other requirements of Insurer, NFPA and local and plant codes, etc.

10) Verification of power and control wiring including proper connection to correct terminal block, calibration and testing of all pneumatic controls, properly sized fuses and breakers and any inspection required for insurance and local codes.

Many of these inspections can be done during the receipt of materials on site before installation. It is often simpler to verify proper design while items are on the receiving dock than when installed. In some cases, the contract may actually call for inspection and verification in the equipment supplier's plant before shipping. Timely determination and correction of a deficiency before installation can reduce the adverse effect

TABLE 2-12. Sample Checklist for Steam Train

Static Checks:

Materials of construction

Manufacturer's rating

Location and type of access doors

Location and type of housing drain with proper trap

Verification of sizes of Pressure Reducing Valve

Modulating Control Valve

Steam Trap

Strainer

Steam Siphon

Painting

Safe access for maintenance

Inlet and outlet duct free of System Effect conditions

Dynamic Checks:

Steam flow under control conditions

Proof of Performance:

Steam flow

Operational temperature for supply air

TABLE 2-13. Sample Checklist for Gas Burner and Fuel Train

Static Checks:

Materials of construction

Manufacturer's rating

Connection to fuel source with proper regulator

Safe access for maintenance

Safety check per insurance company or other regulator

Inclusion of all gas controls and safety controls including

　Safety Shutoff Valve

　Blocking Valve

　High Gas pressure switch

　Low Gas pressure switch

　Pilot Fuel Regulator

　Pilot Solenoid Valve

　Vent Valve

　Fuel Control Valve

　Main Burner Solenoid Valves

Dynamic Checks:

High fire switch operation set

Low fire switch operation set

Pilot and main gas pressure

Combustion chamber pressure (design and operating range)

Burner gas orifice differential pressure

High fire fuel pressure

Low fire fuel pressure

High temperature limit set points

Proof of Performance:

Gas flow

Operational temperature for supply air

on cost and schedule.

Step 3. Complete the Dynamic Checks to continue Commissioning process (see Section 2.3.2).

This is intended to demonstrate and verify that equipment is in working order. As with static checks, some of these may be accomplished during the installation. Dynamic checks may come in two stages. For example, fans may be "bumped" to verify correct rotation and condition of the drive during motor and drive installation, but a second stage of dynamic checks for vibration and flow measurement may occur during a later stage of commissioning.

2.3.5 Baseline Data for Future Use. During the process of providing the commissioning of the duct system (and all ancillary equipment), it is important to provide baseline data on the operation of the system (airflows, pressures, etc.) during the start-up and commissioning phases. This data will be extremely important during future management of the ventilation systems.

1) Balancing Ventilation Systems (Chapter 4)

2) Monitoring and Maintaining Ventilation Systems (Chapter 5)

3) Monitoring and Maintaining Air Cleaning Devices (Chapter 6)

4) Troubleshooting Ventilation Systems (Chapter 7)

5) Managing Changes in Ventilation Systems (Chapter 8)

2.4   FORMS AND DOCUMENTS

There are numerous sources of detailed forms and procedures for commissioning. Some are listed as references at the end of this chapter.[2.1, 2.2, 2.3, 2.4] Some of these are in the public domain and can be downloaded and copied for use. They can also be modified for equipment designed specifically for ventilation systems. Most of the information published pertains to heating, ventilating and air-conditioning (HVAC) systems and building mechanical systems, so some revision will be required. The detail of documentation is dependent on the size and type of system installed.

2.5   PROOF OF PERFORMANCE

These tests and verifications will actually define the completion of the project. Until all contractual obligations are made by the presence and reliable working order of all deliverables (including training), final contract completion should

TABLE 2-14. Sample Checklist for Pulse Jet Fabric Filter

Static Checks:

Materials of construction – hopper/housing/cages

Manufacturer's rating

Metal thickness – housing/hopper/tube sheet

Flange construction – inlet/outlet/hopper

Bag diameter

Bag length

Bag fabric

Location and type of access doors – hopper/housing

Solenoid valves

Pilot valves

Connection to compressed air system

Compressed air filter/dryer

Proper connection to inlet and outlet duct

Painting

Safe access for maintenance – ladders/cages/railing

Hopper cleaning – rappers/air cannons

Hopper or housing heaters

Insulation

Bag/cage installation and seals

Pre-treat system

Leakage – housing/doors

Installation of blow tubes and alignment with bags

Installation of gauges and tubing

Dynamic Checks:

Compressed air quality – pressure/dew point

Bag cleaning (pulsing on all rows)

Proper application of seeding or pre-coat on bags

Pulse cleaning set points (sequence, pulse duration, time between pulses)

Operation of off-line cleaning dampers

Hopper heaters

Hopper cleaning devices

Temperature set points (by-pass, auxiliary heat, air-bleeds)

Startup and shutdown sequence

Proof of Performance:

Pressure drop

Efficiency (outlet vs. inlet loading)

Outlet loading

Temperature

Moisture or Dew Point

Bag life

TABLE 2-15. Sample Checklist for Cartridge Fabric Filter

Static Checks:

Materials of construction – hopper/housing/cages

Manufacturer's rating

Metal thickness – housing/hopper/tube sheet

Flange construction – inlet/outlet/hopper

Cartridge size

Cartridge media

Location and type of access doors – hopper/housing

Solenoid valves

Pilot valves

Connection to compressed air system

Compressed air filter/dryer

Proper connection to inlet and outlet duct

Painting

Safe access for maintenance – ladders/cages/railing

Hopper cleaning – rappers/air cannons

Hopper and/or housing heaters

Insulation

Bag/cage installation and seals

Pre-treat system

Leakage – housing/doors

Installation of blow tubes and alignment with cartridges

Installation of gauges and tubing

Dynamic Checks:

Compressed air quality – pressure/dew point

Cartridge cleaning (pulsing on all rows)

Pulse cleaning set points (sequence, pulse duration, time between pulses)

Proper application of pre-coat or seeding on cartridges

Operation of off-line cleaning dampers

Hopper heaters

Hopper cleaning devices

Temperature set points (by-pass, auxiliary heat, air-bleeds)

Startup and shutdown sequence

Proof of Performance:

Pressure drop

Efficiency (outlet vs. inlet loading)

Outlet loading

Temperature

Moisture or Dew Point

Cartridge life

TABLE 2-16. Sample Checklist for Reverse Air/Shaker Fabric Filters

Static Checks:

Materials of construction – hopper/housing

Manufacturer's rating

Metal thickness – housing/hopper

Flange construction – inlet/outlet/hopper

Bag diameter

Bag length

Bag fabric

Location and type of access doors – hopper/housing

Shaker motors

Shaker mechanism (shafts, bearings, connectors)

Proper connection to inlet and outlet duct

Painting

Safe access for maintenance – ladders/cages/railing

Hopper cleaning – rappers/air cannons

Hopper or housing heaters

Insulation

Bag installation and seals

Pre-treat system

Leakage – housing/doors

Installation of gauges and tubing

Reverse air fan (see Fan section)

Guards on shaker motors

Dynamic Checks:

Bag cleaning (shaking mechanisms operating on all rows)

Cleaning set-points (sequence and duration of shaking and reverse air fans)

Operation of off-line cleaning dampers

Proper application of seeding or pre-coat on bags

Hopper heaters

Hopper cleaning devices

Temperature set points (by-pass, auxiliary heat, air-bleeds)

Startup and shutdown sequence

Proof of Performance:

Pressure drop

Efficiency (outlet vs. inlet loading)

Outlet loading

Temperature

Moisture or Dew Point

Bag life

TABLE 2-17. Sample Checklist for Scrubber

Static Checks:

Materials of construction – housing

Manufacturer's rating

Metal thickness – housing

Flange construction – inlet/outlet/liquid feed/drain

Location and type of access doors

Pump design

Pump motor

Proper connection to inlet and outlet duct

Painting

Safe access for maintenance – ladders/cages/railing

Housing heaters

Insulation

Leakage – housing/doors

Installation of gauges and tubing

Guards on motors

Installation of Venturi(s) to correct dimensions

Installation of trays and impingement media

Installation of water treatment system

Installation of sludge removal and treatment system

Dynamic Checks:

Cleaning set-points – liquid flow/pressure drop

Operation of off-line cleaning dampers

Heaters

Temperature set points (by-pass, auxiliary heat, air-bleeds)

Startup and shutdown sequence

Proof of Performance:

Pressure drop

Efficiency (outlet vs. inlet loading)

Outlet loading

Temperature

not occur.

The examples in Tables 2-2 through 2-18 include a variety of proofs required based on the type of equipment being commissioned. For example, a Proof of Performance of a hood may include a minimum face velocity at the hood face. A total system (hoods, duct, fan, collector and stack) may be required to meet minimum exposure levels in a plant, either area samples or operator breathing zone samples. Similarly, the Proof of Performance of a fabric filter would be its ability to meet all regulatory requirements for emission levels; however, it also may include filter media life, maximum operating pressure drop or some other requirement.

Since the cost of verification is ultimately borne by the project, the selection of these criteria should be evaluated and a

TABLE 2-18. Sample Checklist for Screw Conveyor/Rotary Valve

Static Checks:

Materials of construction

Size

Housing thickness

Screw Rotation

Seals

Bearings and lubrication

Number of hangers and location

Motor (see Motor section)

Proper connection to equipment flanges

Gasket material

Painting

Safe access for maintenance

Security and signage for access doors

Guards

Heaters

Dynamic Checks:

Proper rotation (bump check)

Operation with vibration below manufacturer's and plant standards

Noise levels

Rotation speed

Interlocks with equipment

Startup and shutdown sequence

Proof of Performance:

Operating at design points as required (material flow rate)

realistic list presented in the bid documents. For example, it could be difficult and expensive to test efficiency on each hood in a system of 40 hoods and drop points. If worker exposure is the main purpose of the installation, then area samples and samples at key locations in the system can be chosen ahead of time to keep the approval process more manageable. Generally, outlet testing for the operation of the dust collector is defined by regulators and permit information. In some cases, extra requirements may also be placed on the equipment (maximum pressure drop, etc.).

Whenever verification of Proof of Performance is considered, the application and air balance provided by the supply air in the area must be considered. Systems can under-perform as much as 10 to 30% because of a shortage of supply air in the area. In addition, poorly designed supply air systems can create room air currents that can disrupt the performance of local exhaust hoods. Any requirement for new exhaust systems should consider supply air issues at the design stage as well as during commissioning. In some cases, new exhaust ventilation systems are required to furnish or modify supply air systems with capacity to match new exhaust volumes. This should be

specified and engineered during the definition of scope by the Owner and communicated in the Design Basis and bid documents. If proper air supply is not provided, the exhaust system may never perform to its design specifications.

2.5.1 Hood/Duct System Proof of Performance. After the system has been installed and balanced, the operation can be tested for the effectiveness of the hood/duct system. The goals and measurable quantities for this part of the system usually focus on the ability to clean the air around the dust emission points. This is done by enclosure of these points as well as providing enough exhaust flow to keep contaminants inside the hood and transported to the air cleaning device. Hood airflows and pressures may be one way to specify proof of performance of a system. However, hood performance can be affected by outside factors. These would include cross drafts from open doors and windows as well as personnel cooling fans or other disturbances. Hood performance can also be affected if there is not enough supply air furnished to the area to allow proper hood and system operation.

There are some methods for proof of hood performance. These include USEPA Method 204 to test the performance of Total Enclosures. These standards are primarily used for the capture of Volatile Organic Compounds (VOCs) and designate a minimum in-draft velocity of 200 fpm at all hood openings. In addition, there are restrictions on the distance that any emission point can be located from the hood face. These may or may not be suitable for dust-laden air. It should be noted that most VS-plates shown in the Design Manual do not address the minimum in-draft velocity for a total enclosure. The VS-plates are based on other field data and results. In some cases, 200 fpm can be too high for proper control around processes that are vulnerable to high velocities.

It is possible to show Proof of Performance for duct systems based on the TAB report. The primary function of the duct system is to deliver the collected air and emissions to the control device. This is usually accomplished as long as minimum transport velocities are maintained. In some cases, the balance procedure may yield velocities in certain ducts that are so high that premature wear can occur, so meeting minimum transport velocities may not be the only requirement.

Overall Proof of Performance may be centered on the system's ability to lower operator exposures for particular chemicals or particulate. Since the intent of the system is to reduce that exposure, the Proof of Performance of the system may include a requirement to meet specified exposure levels. The Owner will be responsible for meeting these values; however, the ability to capture and control all contaminants by the new ventilation system will be dependent on many factors including:

1) Other ventilation systems in operation in the plant that may influence the outcome of tests of the new system

2) Cross-drafts and personal cooling fans that may overpower the ventilation system

3) Material handling techniques (forklift traffic, leaking conveyors, fugitive dust from storage areas)

4) Housekeeping and operator work habits

5) Replacement air shortage (negative pressure conditions in the plant)

When determining Proofs of Performance for the system, it will be necessary to recognize the limits of the new ventilation system and define acceptable test methods during the design phase.

2.5.2 Fan/Motor/Drive Proof of Performance. The fan is the heart of the system and must meet the design intent to ensure proper exhaust. If duct or other resistance in the system is substantially higher than estimated, a fan may not be able to meet its airflow Proof of Performance. In those cases, the discrepancies may be focused back to the duct and hoods so that flow can be restored. Otherwise, the documentation and methods to measure flow, pressure and horsepower are straightforward and field data can be compared to published tables or curves to determine proof of performance. Care must be taken to consider System Effects that may cause the fan to operate differently from its predicted values (see the Chapter on fans in the Design Manual). Measurements must also consider changes in air density due to temperature, moisture, elevation, duct pressure and gas constituents.

There may be cases where measurements taken during Commissioning vary from those taken at other times. This is especially the case when comparing data between stack tests using USEPA methods, airflow measurements taken according to Chapter 3 of this Manual, and other accepted methods. Calculations methods and equipment used may vary, and there may be differences when tests were not taken on the same date and under the same plant conditions. Any discrepancy in readings will have to be reviewed so that there is agreement between the Owner and Contractor or Vendor on the actual conditions.

2.5.3 Air Cleaning Device Proof of Performance. Air cleaning devices normally convey the final exhaust air either to the atmosphere or back into the plant. In either case, a test should determine the actual operation. Stack tests are the normal method of determining the actual operation for fabric filters, scrubbers, thermal or catalytic oxidizers and other air cleaning devices. Also referred to as emissions testing and source testing, this is the empirical means of determining the concentration and/or emission rate of a particular pollutant or group of compounds. Generally, stack testing methods collect a sample from the stack and analyze it by some means to determine the levels of contaminants present in the gas. The Commissioning Agent uses these tests to determine Proof of Performance. In addition, stack tests, early in the development stage of the project can determine emission levels from existing stacks or process exhaust streams.

This information, coupled with the carrier gas measurements and/or volumetric flow rates, allows calculation of the emission rates or efficiencies. The Commissioning Agent compares the results to applicable standards as published by regulators or the operating permit. The Design Team must know these requirements, or other restrictions, before selecting equipment for the ventilation system. Consequently, it is important to list applicable regulations in the Design Basis document and make it available for all suppliers of the ventilation equipment and system.

There are many stack testing methods based on the chemicals used in the process and, sometimes, on the process equipment. Most are specified by the USEPA and contained in the Federal Register under 40CFR60-Appendix A, 40CFR61-Appendix B, 40CFR51-Appendix M and 40CFR63-Appendix A. The Office of Solid Waste publishes reference and guidance documents related to the handling of contaminants captured by ventilation systems. In addition, some states have developed and published test methods for particular emissions, while others have been developed by organizations such as American Society of Testing Material (ASTM), National Council for Air and Stream Improvement (NCASI), International Organization for Standardization (ISO), and others.

Other methods of emission testing can include a combination of testing and calculations such as mass balances. As with all test procedures, the Owner must be selective on the choice of testing agency. At this writing, there is no certification process for stack testing and bad information can easily give false readings indicating passing or failure. Similarly, care must be taken to duplicate the process conditions when testing to mimic as close as possible the actual emissions, temperature, moisture and other conditions that the equipment will see on a continuous basis.

The reporting for this section of the Commissioning process is normally specified by local and state agencies. Stack testing reports can be as few as 10 pages, but very complicated projects can have reports of several volumes each over 100 pages. At a minimum, the report should contain:

1) Executive Summary – normally one page to give a quick review of the emissions measured

2) Introduction – including a description of the methods used, contacts at the plant, testing managers, local regulators at site, etc.

3) Process Description – short description of the system and type of process being tested and any special process requirements for the tests

4) Sampling and Analytical procedures – a summary and description of the methods used (USEPA or other type), sketches of the process, sampling port locations and sampling trains, methods for determining process rates, etc.

5) Test Results – in Table or other format that gives the actual results normally considered in Proof of Performance

6) Appendices – various sections including the compilation of field data, lab reports for any analysis, calculations, quality assurance procedures and results, chain of custody documents for handling of samples, etc.

Note that this does not include the requirements of the project for Proof of Performance. The independent testing company under contract would furnish the data in the above report to the Owner, engineer or contractor. That data would then be compared with the guarantee requirements and operating permit regulations. These requirements may include the need to meet all of the appropriate emission regulations (included in the Design Basis) or some other added requirements of the project as specified. For example, the regulations may include only a required outlet emission level but no requirement for opacity. The project, in the Design Basis, would list this requirement as an added proof of performance.

2.6   TRAINING

Another requirement for Proof of Performance normally includes a training component. Depending on the level of complication of the ventilation system, there may be a need for training of plant personnel for its continued reliable operation. Chapter 9 of this Manual contains information regarding the training of plant personnel for operation of systems that includes the basics for operation and simple troubleshooting techniques; however, more intense training may be needed for the operation of fans, electric controls (especially if connected to building management systems), and complicated control devices. These sessions could be taught by the engineer, contractor or specialized staff from the vendors of the equipment in the system, and may be videotaped for future employees and operators. The requirements for training should also be included in the Design Basis.

2.7   SUMMARY

As the project draws to a close, there must be verification that all of the contractual requirements have been met. The commissioning process should begin in the design phase of the project. The Design Basis and Purchase Order documents are reviewed and the system is inspected for the preparation of a punch–list of items that must be completed.

In addition, there may be a requirement for a more detailed inspection of all equipment to ensure that specifications and performance levels have been met. This starts with a series of Static Checks and Dynamic Checks and continues with a final Proof of Performance process that could include testing of in-plant exposure levels, outlet emissions and training of operators.

The purpose of commissioning is to ensure the Owner of the ventilation system that all contractual requirements have been met. Commissioning is intended to enhance the quality of the start-up and ensure that the Owner has received beneficial transfer of an operating and maintainable ventilation system. The administrator of the commissioning process may be the Project Manager on small ventilation systems but may have a designated Commissioning Agent on larger projects. The Commissioning Agent would be responsible to draft the system checklists and Commissioning Plan almost simultaneous with the design.

REFERENCES

2.1   USDOE/PECI. Model Commissioning Plan and Guide Commissioning Specifications, NTIS: #DE 97004564, (1997).

2.2   American Society of Heating, Refrigerating and Air-Conditioning Engineers. The HVAC Commissioning Process, ASHRAE Guideline 1-1996, ASHRAE Publications Dept., Atlanta, GA.

2.3   U.S. Army Const. Engineering Research Laboratories. Standard HVAC Control Systems Commissioning and Quality Verification User Guide, Facilities Engineering Applications Program, U.S. Army Engineering and Housing Support Center, Ft. Belvair, VA, FEAP-UG-GE-94/20, 1994.

2.4   National Environmental Balancing Bureau (NEBB). Procedural Standards for Building Systems Commissioning, Rockville, MD (1993).

Chapter 3
TESTING AND MEASUREMENT OF VENTILATION SYSTEMS

3.1   INTRODUCTION

Proper design, installation, operation, and maintenance of ventilation systems can assure effectiveness in controlling contaminant exposures. Measurement of the system performance is an important tool in assessing the effectiveness of a system and the adequacy of maintenance.

3.1.1 Reasons for Monitoring Ventilation Systems.
Airflow and static pressure measurements of a ventilation system are often required to determine the performance of the ventilation system. Some of the reasons include:

1. *Commissioning:* Recording the initial performance of the ventilation system and determining if it is functioning in accordance with specifications and meets the design basis (see Chapter 2)

2. *Proof of Performance:* Determining the degree of compliance with applicable codes (e.g., OSHA, EPA) or trade association standards (see Chapter 2)

3. *Balancing Ventilation Systems:* Adjusting airflows to match the desired distribution. Balancing may be done during commissioning, after alterations are made, or to re-adjust systems where blast gates may have been tampered with (see Chapter 4)

4. *Baseline Maintenance:* Obtaining data through periodic checks and comparing to baseline or reference values to determine when maintenance or repairs are necessary (see Chapter 5)

5. *Troubleshooting Ventilation Systems:* Determining whether, where and why system components have changed in ways that change flows in undesirable ways, such as partial blocking by obstructions or coatings, inadvertently disconnecting hoods, and addition or removal of branch ducts (see Chapter 7)

6. *Change Management:* Obtaining data to assist in the design of future systems or alterations such as adding or removing branches (see Chapter 8)

3.1.2 Why Airflow and Static Pressure Measurements Are Necessary.
It is important that the airflow through each hood remains at the level needed for that hood. For that reason, one must verify periodically that the airflow through each hood is adequate (e.g., meets or slightly exceeds design specifications). Too little airflow may mean inadequate control by the hood. Airflows above target levels often will not make the hood much more effective, so excessive flow typically represents wasted energy. More importantly, excess airflow in one hood often results in reduced airflow through another hood. Therefore, finding higher than normal airflow through a hood is not necessarily a good thing.

It is important to measure airflow directly to determine if hoods are getting enough airflow, but airflow measurements are time-consuming. Measuring static pressures typically is much quicker and easier. Pressure measurements do not elim-inate the need for airflow determinations, but pressure measurements can be even more informative. Since changes in pressure will occur with any change in airflow, one can use measured pressures to detect changes in airflow. In addition, it is often easier to determine why airflows have changed and where they have changed by measured changes in pressure than by using changes in airflow.

3.1.3 Measurements Necessary for Routine Monitoring.
Unless hood effectiveness is evaluated routinely in the field using tracer gases or other direct measures of performance, practitioners must rely on indirect measures of hood (and thus system) effectiveness. An important indicator of effectiveness is volumetric flow. Although little is known about the sensitivity of hood effectiveness to changes in airflow volumes, it is prudent to insure that hood airflows do not fall below recommended values. In addition, a decline in hood airflow produces a corresponding decline in downstream duct velocities, increasing the risk of settling and plugging in particulate control systems. For those reasons, a decline from specified (or previous) airflow quantities should be considered a cause for concern. Once the decline has been observed, it should initiate corrective action.

Airflows and pressures vary from day to day (or from hour to hour). In addition to random measurement errors, both may vary due to reasons requiring intervention and due to reasons that do not require intervention. Examples of the former include disconnected hoods or ducts, plugging of ducts with settled materials, unplanned changes to damper settings, and development of major leaks. The changes due to such events may persist over time. Other changes may not be permanent and, therefore, produce seemingly random changes in airflows and pressures. These include the effects of manual or automatic damper adjustments done as a strategy to minimize airflow requirements, cyclic changes in resistance to flow at some air-cleaning devices, the effects of moving hoods connected to flexible ducts, and many other causes. In those cases, the accompanying changes in airflow and pressure would not persist over long periods, but they would introduce variability.

Because of variability, it is often difficult to tell from a change in a single parameter whether a deleterious event has occurred. If the current measurement falls within the range of many previous measurements, the system may be functioning normally and no action is needed. However, if repeated readings over time show a trend in the average reading – upward or downward – the system is likely changing and investigation of the cause is warranted.

The most important indirect indicators of system functioning are hood static pressure (SP_h) and volumetric flow (Q) for each branch duct and the static pressure (SP_{end}) at the terminus of each run of duct – e.g., branch, submain, or main (see Figure 3-1).

3.1.4 Frequency of Monitoring.
The recommended minimal schedule for measuring pressures and flow shown in Table

3-1 may be adequate for typical systems. The recommendations may be insufficiently protective for systems that frequently have problems or systems controlling highly hazardous materials. One should monitor frequently enough to avoid significant health or process problems. In considering that issue, one should plan for both system-wide measurements and evaluations and for monitoring of specific hood flows.

System-wide Monitoring: The volumetric flow should be determined for each branch duct at least annually, and whenever there has been a major alteration to the system (e.g., adding or removing a branch duct). In addition, the hood static pressure and the static pressure at the end of the branch should be measured at the same time. More frequent system-wide monitoring should be considered if:

1. The system frequently has problems with plugging or leaks

2. The contaminant is highly toxic and has poor warning properties (e.g., can't smell unless at dangerous levels)

3. The process must be shut down if the system fails

4. Regulations, for example OSHA or EPA, require specific monitoring frequency

Ventilation monitoring is pointless unless it is used to make decisions and take action. When a problem or deviation from the norm is observed, take steps to rectify conditions that produce unacceptable airflows. Rectification should take place soon after discovering such problems.

Monitoring Specific Hoods: Few facilities conduct system-wide measurements on a monthly basis, much less daily; however, it is often important to know in days (or sometimes hours or minutes) if a hood is getting insufficient airflow. Hence, in addition to annual system-wide monitoring, more frequent monitoring of specific parts of the system should be considered. The areas that typically should be monitored frequently are:

1. Pressure drop across the air-cleaner

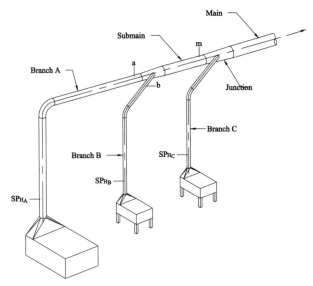

FIGURE 3-1. Useful locations for measurements

2. Static pressure at the hoods

3. Static pressure at or across sites of frequent plugging or other problems

For hoods that prevent high exposures to hazardous airborne contaminants, the hood static pressure should be measured at least monthly. Continuous monitoring of pressures for all areas where failure could quickly produce unacceptable exposures should be considered.

It is particularly useful to permanently install an inexpensive pressure gauge to measure static pressure for each hood that is needed to prevent unacceptable exposures. A reasonable procedure is to:

1. Install the gauge when the hood airflow is known to be close to desired levels

2. Mark the level shown on the display with a green permanent marker

3. Mark in red ranges unacceptably higher and lower than

TABLE 3-1. Recommended Maximum Monitoring Intervals[1]

Maximum interval, months[2]	SP_h	Temp.[3]	SP_{end}	Fan inlet	Across air-cleaning device	Pitot Traverse
1	X				X	
12	X		X	X	X	
24	X	X	X	X	X	X

Notes:

1. Frequency based on systems with moderate hazards and moderate frequency of problems.

2. For the same level of protection, "clean" systems can be monitored less frequently and "problem" systems (e.g., plagued by plugging or abrasive) should be monitored more frequently.

3. Air temperature measured in a branch duct. In many cases, the duct temperature is about the same as the room temperature.

the green line (for example plus and minus 10 percent of the design or benchmark value)

4. Provide signage on or near the gauge to instruct the operator on required actions. This may include specific operator-level maintenance, reporting requirements, or, in severe cases, termination of operations until performance is restored

5. Instruct the supervisor to monitor operator compliance

6. Inspect, clean and check calibration at least annually and more frequently under conditions likely to produce blockage at the probe

7. In critical cases, connect the monitor to an automatic alarm (e.g., flashing lights and a mild audible alarm). It is also reasonable to have sensors report to a remote location where values are continuously monitored by a combination of computers and human operators (ideally with automatic alarms)

Any significant change should prompt an immediate investigation. Higher hood static pressures are sometimes associated with reduced flows at the hood, so one should investigate both increased and decreased hood static pressures.

3.1.5 Limitations of Monitoring. The monitoring described in this chapter pertains to measurement of airflow, temperatures, and pressures. These tests are useful indicators of consistent behavior by systems moving air through hoods, but they do not directly predict hood effectiveness in controlling exposures. Environmental and exposure sampling should be conducted prior to and after installation to verify system performance in reducing exposures and ambient contamination. The services of a qualified industrial hygienist may be required for sampling contaminant exposures.

3.2 COMPUTING AIR VELOCITY AND AIRFLOW RATES

No instrument measures volumetric flow directly in typical contaminant control systems. However, many instruments have sensors whose output can be used to measure air velocity at a point. Once the velocity is measured, it can be used to compute the airflow. The following sections describe how to determine the average velocity and the airflow from these measurements.

3.2.1 Computing Average Velocity. One velocity measurement is seldom enough to determine the average velocity, because the velocities at a hood face or duct cross-section are seldom uniform. It is important to measure the velocities at several locations chosen to be representative then compute the average of those values. For the measured velocity to be a good estimate of the true value, measurements must be taken correctly, in the right locations, and there must be enough measurements to include most to the variability (both spatial and temporal).

As an example of computing the average velocity in a duct, consider the traverse values shown in Figure 3-2. The average

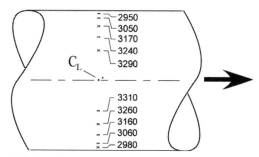

FIGURE 3-2. Values measured in a duct cross-section

velocity in that duct would be computed as the simple average:

$$V = \frac{2950+3050+3170+3240+3290+3310+3260+3160+3060+2980}{10} = 3150 \text{ fpm}$$

3.2.2 Computing Airflow from Average Velocity. The estimated airflow can be computed from the average velocity multiplied by the cross-sectional area normal to the flow:

$$Q = V * A \qquad [3.1]$$

Where: Q = volumetric flow rate, actual cubic feet per minute (acfm)

V = average velocity normal to the cross-section, actual feet per minute (fpm)

A = cross-sectional area of duct or hood at the

measurement location, ft^2

EXAMPLE

If the average velocity at the face of a 3 ft by 4 ft enclosing hood is 100 fpm, the estimated airflow into the hood can be determined as follows:

$$Q = (100 \text{ fpm})*(3 \text{ ft})*(4 \text{ ft}) = 1200 \text{ acfm}$$

EXAMPLE

If the average velocity in a 6-inch diameter duct (area = $0.1964 \ ft^2$) were 3000 fpm, the estimated airflow would be:

$$Q = (3000 \text{ fpm})*(0.1964 \ ft^2) = 588 \text{ acfm}$$

Most calculations are made on a calculator or computer. The readout of the device often implies greater accuracy than is warranted for ventilation calculations. In the above problem, the velocity was given as 3000 fpm. The accuracy of the 3000 fpm may be ± 100 fpm. The answer should imply no greater accuracy. A scientifically correct answer to the above problem would be 590 acfm. For simplicity, this manual will assume three places of accuracy. The calculations will be made without rounding until the final answer.

Ventilation practitioners sometimes convert the actual airflow to "standard" airflow by multiplying the true value by the density factor (df), the ratio of the actual density to standard density:

$$Q_{std} = df * Q_{act} \qquad [3.2]$$

Where: Q_{std} = airflow rate that would exist at normal temperature and pressure for dry air, scfm

Q_{act} = actual airflow rate, cfm or acfm

df = density factor

In most ventilation systems, the actual airflow is more important than standard airflow. The hoods, ducts, air cleaning device, and fan design are based on actual airflow.

3.2.3 Computing Average Velocity from Velocity Pressure Readings.
Velocity can be computed from observed velocity pressures if the air density is known or can be determined. For the velocity at a single point:

$$V = 4005\sqrt{VP/df} \qquad [3.3]$$

Where: VP = Velocity pressure, "wg

df = Ratio of actual density to standard density

EXAMPLE

If the velocity pressure is 0.5 "wg and the density factor is 0.95, the velocity would be computed as:

$$V = 4005\sqrt{0.5/0.95} = 2910\,fpm$$

Although a velocity can be computed from a velocity pressure, the average velocity cannot be computed from the average velocity pressure. Instead, when determining the average velocity from velocity pressure measurements, compute the individual velocities from individual velocity pressures, then the average velocity can be computed from the mean of those velocities.

EXAMPLE

Compute the average velocity for the 10 velocity pressure measurements in Figure 3-3 when the gas stream has a density factor of 0.88.

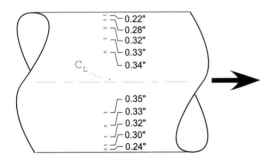

FIGURE 3-3. Measured VP traverse values

First 5 VP Values			Second 5 VP Values		
Point	VP "wg	V fpm	Point	VP "wg	V fpm
1	0.22	2003	6	0.35	2526
2	0.28	2259	7	0.33	2453
3	0.32	2415	8	0.32	2415
4	0.33	2453	9	0.30	2338
5	0.34	2489	10	0.24	2092
Average velocity = 2340 fpm					

3.2.4 Computing Density Factors.
Equations 3.2 and 3.3 require computation of the density factor. Many conditions affect the density factor, including elevation, duct pressure, air temperature, and air water content. Using the ideal gas laws, the value of df can be computed as:

$$df = (df_e)*(df_P)*(df_T)*(df_m) \qquad [3.4]$$

Where: df_e = elevation density factor

= $[1-(6.73*10^{-6})(z)]^{5.258} \qquad [3.4a]$

where z = elevation, ft

df_P = duct pressure density factor

= $(407 + SP)/407 \qquad [3.4b]$

where SP = system static pressure, "wg

df_T = Temperature density factor

= $(530)/(T + 460) \qquad [3.4c]$

where T = temperature, F

df_m = moisture density factor

= $(1 + \omega)/(1 + 1.607\,\omega) \qquad [3.4d]$

where ω = absolute moisture, lbm water/lbm dry air

Values of the pressure at an elevation, P_e, can be read from Table 3-2, which is based on Equation 3.4a. The table assumes the temperature of the air is 70 F.

EXAMPLE

Consider a system with a velocity pressure reading of 1.0 "wg taken with a Pitot tube in a duct where the dry-bulb temperature is 300 F, the moisture content is 0.1 lbm water/lbm dry air and the static pressure is -23.5 "wg. The system is installed at an elevation of 5,000 ft. What would the density factor and actual velocity be at that point?

df = $(df_e)(df_P)(df_T)(df_m)$

df_e = $[1-(6.73*10^{-6})(5000)]^{5.258} = 0.835$

df_P = $(407 - 23.5)/407 = 0.942$

df_T = $530/(300+460) = 0.697$

df_m = $(1 + 0.1)/(1 + 1.607*0.1) = 0.948$

TABLE 3-2. Altitude, Barometric Pressures and Density Factors

Altitude	P_e	df_e		Altitude	P_e	df_e
ft	"wg			ft	"wg	
-5000	484	1.19		3000	366	0.898
-4500	476	1.17		3500	359	0.882
-4000	468	1.15		4000	353	0.866
-3500	460	1.13		4500	346	0.851
-3000	452	1.11		5000	340	0.835
-2500	444	1.09		5500	334	0.820
-2000	437	1.07		6000	328	0.805
-1500	429	1.05		6500	322	0.790
-1000	422	1.04		7000	316	0.776
-500	414	1.02		7500	310	0.762
0	407	1.00		8000	304	0.748
500	400	0.982		8500	299	0.733
1000	393	0.965		9000	293	0.720
1500	386	0.948		9500	288	0.707
2000	379	0.931		10000	282	0.693
2500	372	0.915		10500	277	0.680

$$df = (df_e)*(df_P)*(df_T)*(df_m)$$
$$= (0.835)*(0.942)*(0.697)*(0.948)$$

$$V = 4005\sqrt{1.0/0.520} = 5550 \text{ fpm}$$

Note that the value of velocity would have been 4005 fpm — an error of 39% — if density effects had been ignored.

Measurement of air velocity at non-standard conditions requires calculation of the true air velocity, accounting for difference in air density due to air temperature, humidity, elevation and static pressure. The following example illustrates the method of calculation and the effect of varying air density.

EXAMPLE

Two 10-Point traverse readings are shown in the following tables:

Conditions: SP = +2 "wg;

Dry-Bulb temperature = 79 F

Wet-Bulb Temperature = 50 F

Elevation 1,000 feet

Duct diameter = 24"

From the psychrometric charts (with dry-bulb = 79 F and wet-bulb = 50 F), the water content ω is given by

$$\omega = 0.0011 \text{ lbm water/lbm dry air}$$

$$df = (df_e)(df_P)(df_T)(df_m)$$
$$df_e = [1-(6.73*10^{-6})(1000)]^{5.258} = 0.965$$
$$df_P = (407 + 2.0)/407 = 1.005$$

$$df_T = 530/(460+79) = 0.983$$
$$dfm = (1 + 0.0011)/(1 + 1.607*0.0011) = 0.9993$$

$$df = (df_e)*(df_P)*(df_T)*(df_m)$$
$$= (0.965)*(1.005)*(0.983)*(0.9993)$$
$$= 0.953$$

The conversion from velocity pressure to velocity is given by:

$$V = 4005\sqrt{VP/0.953}$$

EXAMPLE

The table below shows the results of a 10-point traverse in the horizontal and vertical axis of a 12-inch duct. The following environmental conditions prevailed:

Conditions: SP = – 2 "wg;

Dry-Bulb temperature = 150 F

Wet-Bulb Temperature = 100 F

Elevation 1,500 feet

Duct diameter = 12"

Vertical Traverse Pts				Horizontal Traverse Pts		
Traverse Pt	VP, "wg	V, fpm		Traverse Pt	VP, "wg	V, fpm
1	0.22	1924		1	0.23	1968
2	0.28	2171		2	0.27	2132
3	0.32	2321		3	0.33	2357
4	0.33	2357		4	0.34	2392
5	0.34	2392		5	0.34	2392
6	0.35	2427		6	0.35	2427
7	0.33	2357		7	0.34	2392
8	0.32	2321		8	0.32	2321
9	0.30	2247		9	0.32	2321
10	0.24	2010		10	0.25	2051
Average	2253			Average	2275	
Average Velocity = 2264 fpm						
Volumetric flow = VA = (3.1416)*(2264) = 7110 acfm						

From psychrometric charts ω = 0.031 lbs of moisture/lb of dry air

$$df = (df_e) (df_P) (df_T) (df_m)$$
$$df_e = [1-(6.73*10^{-6})(1500)]^{5.258} = 0.948$$
$$df_P = (407 - 2.0)/407 = 0.995$$
$$df_T = 530/(460+150) = 0.869$$
$$df_m = (1 + 0.031)/(1 + 1.607*0.031) = 0.982$$

$$df = (df_e)*(df_P)*(df_T)*(df_m)$$
$$= (0.948)*(0.995)*(0.869)*(0.982)$$
$$= 0.805$$

The conversion from velocity pressure to velocity is given by:

$$V = 4005\sqrt{VP/0.805}$$

	Vertical Traverse Pts			**Horizontal Traverse Pts**	
Traverse Pt	VP, "wg	V, fpm	Traverse Pt	VP, "wg	V, fpm
1	0.22	2093	1	0.23	2141
2	0.28	2362	2	0.27	2319
3	0.32	2525	3	0.33	2564
4	0.33	2564	4	0.34	2603
5	0.34	2603	5	0.34	2603
6	0.35	2641	6	0.35	2641
7	0.33	2564	7	0.34	2603
8	0.32	2525	8	0.32	2525
9	0.30	2445	9	0.32	2525
10	0.24	2187	10	0.25	2232
	Average	2451		Average	2476
	Average Velocity = 2263 fpm				
	Volumetric flow = VA = (0.7854)*(2463) = 1930 acfm				

3.2.5 Correcting Instruments for Density. As stated earlier, no field device actually measures velocity directly. All instruments measure other parameters related to velocity by calibration. The scales for nearly all velocity meters are calibrated for standard density of air. If air density is non-standard, then that scale reading will be incorrect, sometimes by a significant amount. To determine the actual velocity from the meter's velocity scale, one must correct its reading for density. The correction depends on the type of device. (See Section 3.5 for a discussion in ventilation measuring instruments.)

Pressure Devices: Pressure devices include digital manometers, inclined and vertical manometers, velometers, aneroid gauges, and most other gauges that respond directly to pressure changes. They sense static pressure and velocity pressure directly, so the scales for velocity pressure and static pressure require no correction for density.

The problem develops when the instrument reads velocity. The instrument scale calibration is based on "standard" air (df =1) and is incorrect for any other density. The instrument velocity (V_{meter}) reading should be corrected as shown below:

$$V = \frac{V_{meter}}{\sqrt{df}} \qquad [3.5]$$

Where: V = Actual velocity
V_{meter} = Velocity reading of instrument
df = Density factor

Thermal anemometers: Thermal anemometers sense loss of heat from a heated element to the passing air but are calibrated to display that heat transfer as a velocity reading. Heat transfer is proportional to air density, so the instrument readings are correct only for standard density air. To compute the correct velocities from meter readings use:

$$V = \frac{V_{meter}}{df} \qquad [3.6]$$

Since thermal anemometers always measure temperature as part of their functioning, it would be possible for them to correct automatically for temperature's effect on density (but not for any other effect on density). For such instruments, the correct velocity would be computed from the instrument reading as:

$$V = \frac{V_{meter}}{df/df_T} \qquad [3.7]$$

Thermal anemometers sometimes have an attachment to "measure" pressure. They measure the velocity through a small opening, which can be calibrated to produce an estimate of pressure. Since the instrument is sensing the effects of air velocity, the readout is correct only for standard density and must be corrected for any other condition using the equation below.

$$SP = df * SP_{meter} \qquad [3.8]$$

EXAMPLE

An electronic rotating vane anemometer is used to determine the velocity in a very large duct at sea level where the dry-bulb temperature is 250 F, the static pressure is -10 "wg, moisture is negligible and elevation is 800 ft. What is the actual duct velocity if the anemometer reading is 3150 fpm?

$$df = (df_e)(df_P)(df_T)(df_m)$$
$$df_e = [1-(6.73*10^{-6})(800)]^{5.258} = 0.972$$
$$df_P = (407 - 10.0)/407 = 0.975$$
$$df_T = 530/(460+250) = 0.746$$
$$df_m = (1 + 0.00)/(1 + 1.607*0.000) = 1.000$$

$$df = (df_e)*(df_P)*(df_T)*(df_m)$$
$$= (0.972)*(0.975)*(0.746)*(1.000)$$
$$= 0.707$$

$$V = \frac{3150}{\sqrt{0.707}} = 3750 \text{ fpm}$$

3.2.6 Estimating Airflow from Hood Static Pressure.

Since static pressure is proportional to velocity pressure, it follows that airflow is proportional to the square root of static pressure and inversely proportional to square root of density. Therefore, the airflow at time "2" can be computed from the observed Q, df, and static pressure at time "1" if air density is not expected to change over time:

$$\frac{Q_1}{Q_2} = \sqrt{\frac{SP_1/df_1}{SP_2/df_2}} \qquad \textbf{[3.9]}$$

It does not matter if the hood is compound (i.e., slot/plenum) or if the measurement was taken downstream of an elbow or other disturbance. However, the estimate will be inaccurate if the resistance to flow upstream of the hood has changed from Time 1 to Time 2 (for example, if the hood were damaged or modified or if a damper position upstream of the measurement were to change).

If air density is not expected to change over time, Equation 3.9 simplifies as Equation [3.10].

$$\frac{Q_1}{Q_2} = \sqrt{\frac{SP_1}{SP_2}} \qquad \textbf{[3.10]}$$

For example, if the airflow were 2150 acfm when the hood static pressure was 1.32 "wg and now the pressure is 1.01 "wg, then if the hood has not been obstructed or altered, the airflow can be computed as:

$$Q = 2150 * \sqrt{1.01/1.32} = 1880 \text{ acfm}$$

3.2.7 Using Tracer Gases to Estimate Airflow.

The principle of dilution is sometimes used to determine the rate of airflow in a duct or hood.[3.1] A tracer gas of known concentration (C_{feed}) is metered (Q_{feed}) continuously as it is released into the hood or into the duct downstream of the hood. The diluted tracer gas concentration in the duct (C_{duct}) is measured 10 diameters distance farther downstream. Since the mass flow rate of the tracer gas in the duct downstream must equal the rate of the tracer gas that was released upstream, then:

$$Q_{feed} * C_{feed} = Q_{duct} * C_{duct}$$

$$Q_{duct} = Q_{feed} * \left(C_{feed}/C_{duct}\right) \qquad \textbf{[3.11]}$$

The tracer gas should usually be selected for the following characteristics:

1. Ease of feeding into the air stream (i.e., a gas at room temperature)

2. Convenience and accuracy of measurement at both the feed concentration and the diluted concentration

3. Not otherwise present in the process being studied

4. Not absorbed chemically or physically in the duct system

5. Non-reactive with other constituents of the gas stream

6. Measurable at safe concentrations, (non-explosive, and does not interfere with the process)

Sulfur hexafluoride, nitrous oxide, and carbon dioxide are used frequently as tracer gases. Note that Equation 3.11 must be modified to subtract background concentrations when carbon dioxide is used as a tracer gas.

3.3   REPRESENTATIVE SAMPLING FOR PRESSURES AND VELOCITIES

Air flowing through a duct is not uniform across the duct at any given cross-section. Frictional drag along the ducts causes the air near the surface of the duct to flow slower than the air in the center of the duct. Duct fittings and obstacles – such as elbows, branch entries, contractions, dampers, or fans – cause significant distortion of the velocity profile. Consequently, it is important to use the average of readings at many different points to estimate the average velocity.

3.3.1 Traverse Insertion Depths for Determining Duct Velocities.

Measuring duct velocity pressures (or velocities) has two important differences from measuring static pressure. First, a single reading is almost never adequate. Second, the location of the measurement does not matter as long as the conditions for the measurement are good.

The velocity in a duct changes substantially with distance from the inner surface of the duct. The velocity generally will be lowest at the surface of the duct. Under ideal conditions, the velocity will increase with distance from the inner surface to a maximum value at the center of the duct (see Figure 3-4). Since the velocity varies everywhere across the duct (or hood face), take readings at many points and average them to obtain an accurate estimate of the true velocity. Using the centerline velocity will tend to over-estimate the average velocity since the center often has the highest velocity.

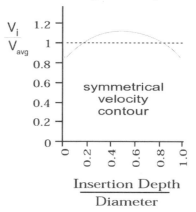

FIGURE 3-4. "Ideal" velocity contour

To accurately estimate the average velocity, take measurements at representative points across the entire cross-section of the duct. To do this, drill a hole in the duct, insert a Pitot tube and take readings at different "insertion" depths along a diameter (a "traverse"). It is possible to do a traverse with a thermal anemometer, but Pitot tubes and pressure sensors are better choices for three reasons:

1. A thermal anemometer probe is easily damaged

2. Thermal anemometers are not "intrinsically safe" in flammable atmospheres

3. There is some concern that at high velocities thermal anemometer traverses give higher velocity readings than do Pitot traverses

For sampling locations to be representative, every area of the duct should have an equal chance of being sampled. For that reason, the traverse points are not evenly spaced, but instead are chosen so that each point represents close to the same amount of airflow. The measurement locations listed in Table 3-3 for rectangular ducts and Table 3-4 for round ducts provide the greatest accuracy for the least number of measurement locations for rectangular and round ducts respectively.[3.2] Figures 3-5 and 3-6 show a graphical representation of the insertion depths.

Note that the locations for test points have changed slightly since the 24th Edition of the Design Manual. Previously there had been the use of the "Equal Area" method in which a duct cross section was divided into equal area segments and a reading taken at the center of each segment. Research has indicated that the newer points indicated in Tables 3-3 and 3-4 are somewhat more accurate. However, the insertion depths may differ from some published standards, such as those used by

USEPA for stack tests. For compliance testing, care is required to ensure that the insertion depths meet the requirements of the testing protocol. However, the insertion depths in this Manual agree with other standards, such as those published by ASHRAE.[3.2]

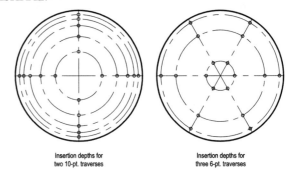

Insertion depths for two 10-pt. traverses   Insertion depths for three 6-pt. traverses

FIGURE 3-5. Insertion depths for round ducts

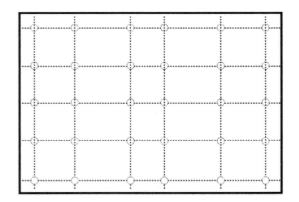

FIGURE 3-6. Insertion depths for rectangular ducts

TABLE 3-3. Recommended Traverse Insertion Depths for Round Ducts

Number of Insertions	Distance from wall in fractions of a duct diameter, log-linear rule Traverse Position									
	1	2	3	4	5	6	7	8	9	10
4	0.043	0.290	0.710	0.957						
6	0.032	0.135	0.321	0.679	0.865	0.968				
8	0.021	0.117	0.184	0.345	0.655	0.816	0.883	0.979		
10	0.019	0.077	0.153	0.217	0.361	0.639	0.783	0.847	0.923	0.981

TABLE 3-4. Recommended Traverse Insertion Depths for Rectangular Ducts

Number of Insertions	Distance from the wall in fractions of a duct diameter Traverse Point						
	1	2	3	4	5	6	7
5	0.074	0.288	0.0500	0.712	0.926		
6	0.061	0.235	0.437	0.563	0.765	0.939	
7	0.053	0.203	0.366	0.0500	0.634	0.797	0.947

3.3.2 Round Ducts Insertion Depths.

For round ducts, Table 3-3 shows recommended insertion depths based on fractions of the duct diameter. Tables 3-5, 3-6, and 3-7 show insertion depths for 6-, 8-, and 10-point traverses for some common round duct diameters listed in decimal inches. If we inserted the Pitot tube in even increments (e.g., 0.5"), the areas represented by the insertions close to the wall would be much larger than the areas near the center. To avoid that problem, more readings are taken close to the wall and fewer near the center of the duct.

In ideal condition, the velocity profile is symmetric and it may be acceptable to traverse only one diameter. If the velocity is skewed in one direction (a typical situation in fieldwork), a single traverse will not represent the true average of the flow. In that case or if accuracy is important, use two perpendicular diameters (see Figure 3-5). If unusually high accuracy is important, use three equally separated traverse diameters.

Taking more measurements on the same diameter is less useful than using a second or third diameter. For example, three 6-point traverses are much more accurate than one 20-point traverse. If only one traverse diameter is done, a10-point traverse should be measured. For two perpendicular traverses, 8- or 10-point traverses should be used (see Figure 3-5). When traversing three diameters in the same cross-section, 6- or 8-point traverses are acceptable.

3.3.3 Rectangular Ducts.

Determining the minimum number of measurement points for rectangular ducts is more complicated since the aspect ratio can vary from 1:1 to 5:1 or higher. ASHRAE[3.1] recommends a minimum of 25 points. The maximum distance between any two points should be 8 inches. Table 3-4 shows traverse insertion depths for 5, 6, and 7-point traverses for rectangular ducts (see Figure 3-6).

3.3.4 Where to Perform Pitot Tube Traverses.

Elbows, junction fittings, dampers, fans, and other obstructions skew the airflow to one side of the duct. At seven or more diameters downstream for most upstream elements, the airflow often has reached symmetry reasonably similar to Figure 3-4. The exceptions are dampers and fans, which can disturb the flow for more than 10 duct diameters. Since airflow starts to change direction before encountering an elbow, damper, or other disturbances, it is important to take readings at least one duct diameter upstream of them. Table 3-8 suggests some reasonable distances downstream and upstream from different disturbances.[3.3]

If it is not possible to find or use a location that meets those restrictions, there is no other choice than to use the best available location. For such relatively poor conditions, it is crucial to do two perpendicular traverses instead of relying on a single diameter traverse. A two-diameter traverse can be surprisingly accurate even when velocity contours are highly asymmetric. For example, in laboratory tests, the use of two diameter traverses should produce less than 6% error when taken only two diameters distance downstream from smooth elbows

TABLE 3-5. 6-Point Log-linear Traverse Points

Dia.	No. 1	No. 2	No. 3		No. 4	No. 5	No. 6
1.0	0.032	0.135	0.321		0.679	0.865	0.968
3.0	0.10	0.41	0.96		2.04	2.60	2.90
3.5	0.11	0.47	1.12		2.38	3.03	3.39
4.0	0.13	0.54	1.28		2.72	3.46	3.87
4.5	0.14	0.61	1.44		3.06	3.89	4.36
5.0	0.16	0.68	1.61		3.40	4.33	4.84
5.5	0.18	0.74	1.77		3.73	4.76	5.32
6.0	0.19	0.81	1.93		4.07	5.19	5.81
7.0	0.22	0.95	2.25		4.75	6.06	6.78
8.0	0.26	1.08	2.57		5.43	6.92	7.74

Note: Do not include midpoint in determining average velocity.

and less than 3% error when taken at least seven diameters distance downstream from obstructions.[3.3] Field measurements will have more variability.

The shape of the velocity contour can provide important information. If 10 diameters or more of straight duct is upstream of the measurement point, the contour should be nearly symmetrical. If it is skewed to one side or the other, it is likely that an obstruction is hidden just upstream or at the measurement location, particularly if readings on one side are much higher than the other side.

If a junction fitting or damper is less than seven diameters upstream, then the velocity contour will not be symmetrical. If an elbow is upstream, the shape of the contour will depend on whether the traverse is perpendicular to the plane of the elbow or in the same plane (see Figure 3-7). If perpendicular, the contour will be symmetrical. If in the same plane, the profile in the plane can be highly asymmetric. The variability shown in Figure 3-7 shows the need to conduct two perpendicular traverses.

If the duct is large (e.g., 24" or larger diameter), it may be

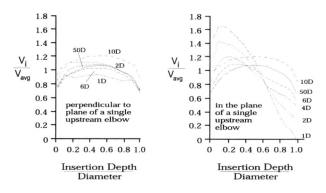

FIGURE 3-7. Velocity profiles at different distances from upstream elbows

advisable to drill from both sides and insert from the wall towards the center from each side rather than traversing all the way across from one side. Hence, the Pitot tube does not extend past centerline for any traverse.

3.3.5 Velocity Traverses of Hood Faces. It is likely that a hood airflow that is substantially lower than design values will be associated with inadequate performance for a given hood. For that reason, it is important to maintain hood exhaust vol-umes velocities at levels that meet or slightly exceed recom-mended levels.

In many cases, the most accurate way to determine the aver-age velocity at an open hood face is to determine the airflow using Pitot traverses of the branch duct connected to the hood, and then divide the airflow by the open cross-sectional area of the hood face. Traverses of the hood face can be highly inac-curate due to the inaccuracies of measurement devices at such

TABLE 3-6. 8-Point Log-linear Traverse Points

Dia.	No. 1	No. 2	No. 3	No. 4		No. 5	No. 6	No. 7	No. 8
1.0	0.021	0.117	0.184	0.345		0.655	0.816	0.883	0.979
3.0	0.06	0.55	0.5	1.04		1.97	2.45	2.65	2.94
3.5	0.07	0.41	0.64	1.21		2.29	2.86	3.09	3.43
4.0	0.08	0.47	0.74	1.38		2.62	3.26	3.53	3.92
4.5	0.09	0.53	0.83	1.55		2.95	3.67	3.97	4.41
5.0	0.11	0.59	0.92	1.73		3.28	4.08	4.42	4.90
5.5	0.12	0.64	1.01	1.90		3.60	4.49	4.86	5.38
6.0	0.13	0.70	1.10	2.07		3.93	4.90	5.30	5.87
7.0	0.15	0.82	1.29	2.42		4.59	5.71	6.18	6.85
8.0	0.17	0.94	1.47	2.76		5.24	6.53	7.06	7.83
9.0	0.19	1.05	1.66	3.11		5.90	7.34	7.95	8.81
10	0.21	1.17	1.84	3.45		6.55	8.16	8.83	9.79
11	0.23	1.29	2.02	3.80		7.21	8.98	9.71	10.8
12	0.25	1.40	2.21	4.14		7.86	9.79	10.6	11.7
13	0.27	1.52	2.39	4.49		8.52	10.6	11.5	12.7
14	0.29	1.64	2.58	4.83		9.17	11.4	12.4	13.7
15	0.32	1.76	2.76	5.18		9.83	12.2	13.2	14.7
16	0.34	1.87	2.94	5.52		10.5	13.1	14.1	15.7
18	0.38	2.11	3.31	6.21		11.8	14.7	15.9	17.6
20	0.42	2.34	3.68	6.90		13.1	16.3	17.7	19.6
22	0.46	2.57	4.05	7.59		14.4	18.0	19.4	21.5
24	0.50	2.81	4.42	8.28		15.7	19.6	21.2	23.5
26	0.55	3.04	4.78	8.97		17.0	21.2	23.0	25.5
28	0.59	3.28	5.15	9.66		18.3	22.8	24.7	27.4
30	0.63	3.51	5.52	10.4		19.7	24.5	26.5	29.4
32	0.67	3.74	5.89	11.0		21.0	26.1	28.3	31.3
34	0.71	3.98	6.26	11.7		22.3	27.7	30.0	33.3
36	0.76	4.21	6.62	12.4		23.6	29.4	31.8	35.2
38	0.80	4.45	6.99	13.1		24.9	31.0	33.6	37.2
40	0.84	4.68	7.36	13.8		26.2	32.6	35.3	39.2
42	0.88	4.91	7.73	14.5		27.5	34.3	37.1	41.1
44	0.92	5.15	8.10	15.2		28.8	35.9	38.9	43.1
46	0.97	5.38	8.46	15.9		30.1	37.5	40.6	45.0
48	1.01	5.62	8.83	16.6		31.4	39.2	42.4	47.0
50	1.05	5.85	9.20	17.3		32.8	40.8	44.2	49.0

Note: Do not include midpoint in determining average velocity.

low velocities and due to the high variability of low velocities. However, it can be desirable to measure velocities directly at the hood face if:

1. The duct is difficult to access

2. There are no appropriate locations for a Pitot traverse

3. The duct velocity is too low for accurate VP measurement in Pitot traverses (e.g., less than 1500 fpm)

4. Regulatory or in-house requirements specify a face velocity

In addition, a traverse of the hood face provides information on the uniformity and stability of the velocities at the hood face. The following points should be considered in evaluating such data:

1. A mean face velocity that is moderately higher (e.g., < 20%) than recommended values may produce lower exposures, and is unlikely to increase exposures compared to those that would have existed at recommended levels for the same conditions.

TABLE 3-7. 10-Point Log-linear Traverse Points

Dia.	No. 1	No. 2	No. 3	No. 4	No. 5		No. 6	No. 7	No. 8	No. 9	No. 10
1.0	0.019	0.077	0.153	0.217	0.361		0.639	0.783	0.847	0.923	0.981
3.0	0.06	0.23	0.46	0.65	1.08		1.92	2.35	2.54	2.77	2.94
3.5	0.07	0.27	0.54	0.76	1.26		2.24	2.74	2.96	3.23	3.43
4.0	0.08	0.31	0.61	0.87	1.44		2.56	3.3	3.39	3.69	3.92
4.5	0.09	0.35	0.69	0.98	1.62		2.88	3.52	3.81	4.15	4.41
5.0	0.10	0.39	0.00	1.09	1.81		3.20	3.92	4.24	4.62	4.91
5.5	0.10	0.42	0.84	1.19	1.99		3.51	4.31	4.66	5.08	5.40
6.0	0.11	0.46	0.92	1.30	2.17		3.83	4.70	5.08	5.54	5.89
7.0	0.13	0.54	1.07	1.52	2.53		4.47	5.48	5.93	6.46	6.87
8.0	0.15	0.62	1.22	1.74	2.89		5.11	6.26	6.78	7.38	7.85
9.0	0.17	0.69	1.38	1.95	3.25		5.75	7.05	7.62	8.31	8.83
10	0.19	0.77	1.53	2.17	3.61		6.39	7.83	8.47	9.23	9.81
11	0.21	0.85	1.68	2.39	3.97		7.03	8.61	9.32	10.15	10.8
12	0.23	0.92	1.84	2.60	4.33		7.67	9.40	10.16	11.1	11.8
13	0.25	1.00	1.99	2.82	4.69		8.31	10.18	11.0	12.0	12.8
14	0.27	1.08	2.14	3.04	5.05		8.95	10.96	11.9	12.9	13.7
15	0.29	1.16	2.30	3.26	5.42		9.59	11.75	12.7	13.8	14.7
16	0.30	1.23	2.45	3.47	5.78		10.22	12.5	13.6	14.8	15.7
18	0.34	1.39	2.75	3.91	6.50		11.50	14.1	15.2	16.6	17.7
20	0.38	1.54	3.06	4.34	7.22		12.78	15.7	16.9	18.5	19.6
22	0.42	1.69	3.37	4.77	7.94		14.06	17.2	18.6	20.3	21.6
24	0.46	1.85	3.67	5.21	8.66		15.34	18.8	20.3	22.2	23.5
26	0.49	2.00	3.98	5.64	9.39		16.61	20.4	22.0	24.0	25.5
28	0.53	2.16	4.28	6.08	10.11		17.89	21.9	23.7	25.8	27.5
30	0.57	2.31	4.59	6.5	10.83		19.17	23.5	25.4	27.7	29.4
32	0.61	2.46	4.90	6.9	11.55		20.45	25.1	27.1	29.5	31.4
34	0.65	2.62	5.20	7.4	12.27		21.73	26.6	28.8	31.4	33.4
36	0.68	2.77	5.51	7.8	13.00		23.00	28.2	30.5	33.2	35.3
38	0.72	2.93	5.81	8.2	13.72		24.28	29.8	32.2	35.1	37.3
40	0.76	3.08	6.12	8.7	14.44		25.56	31.3	33.9	36.9	39.2
42	0.80	3.23	6.43	9.1	15.16		26.84	32.9	35.6	38.8	41.2
44	0.84	3.39	6.73	9.5	15.88		28.12	34.5	37.3	40.6	43.2
46	0.87	3.54	7.04	10.0	16.61		29.39	36.0	39.0	42.5	45.1
48	0.91	3.70	7.34	10.4	17.33		30.67	37.6	40.7	44.3	47.1
50	0.95	3.85	7.65	10.9	18.05		31.95	39.2	42.4	46.2	49.1

Note: Do not include midpoint in determining average velocity.

TABLE 3-8. Minimum Distances for Velocity Measurement Locations

Location of Measurement Point in Multiples of the Duct Diameter, D			
Condition	Downstream of Condition for VP or V Traverse	Downstream of Condition for SP	Upstream of Condition
45° Tapered Hood Connection	6	2	N/A
Flanged Hood Connection or Takeoff	7	3	N/A
90° Radius Elbow	7	4	1
Junction Fitting	7	6	3
Damper or Fan	12-20*	6-20*	2-4*

* Use the lower end of the range if an elbow is between the damper or fan and the measurement point.

2. It is generally better if velocities across the hood face all fall within + 20% of the average value (spatial uniformity).

3. It also is better if readings taken one after the other at the same location all fall within ± 20% of the mean value (temporal uniformity).

Large changes across the hood face or with time are often due to turbulent conditions outside of the hood, replacement air approaching the hood face at a high velocity or with obstructions inside the hood, especially those near the face. In some cases, large eddies at the face of the hood can be energetic enough to push flow out of the hood at specific locations, making the hood ineffective. The best way to detect this is by releasing a test smoke at the face of the hood and watching for it to drift out instead of in.

Measuring face velocities is similar to measuring duct velocities in some respects. It is important to:

1. Divide an enclosing hood face into equal areas and sample the center points of each area (see Figure 3-8). Note that one would NOT use the log-linear traverse values shown in Table 3-3 since the objective is to assess non-uniformity.

2. Measure all velocities in the same plane while orienting the probe properly.

3. For reasonable accuracy in determining the average velocity, take velocities at each point then repeat every reading, then repeat again. The median of the three values at each point is used to represent the average velocity at that point.

4. A velocity traverse of a hood face is difficult to do unless the probe is held by a camera tripod or microphone stand or something similar.

5. To determine the variability at a point, place the probe in position and record several readings (for example 20 readings at one second intervals).

Many electronic devices measure values several times over a set interval and compute the moving average for that interval before displaying it. The so-called "time constant" should be 3-10 seconds. Longer periods provide "diminishing returns." For additional precision, it is much better to do additional complete traverses rather than to sample repeatedly at the same location. It also is important to note that the "hold" function on some electronic devices causes the peak value to be displayed, not this moving average.

The location and orientation of the probe is also important. Keeping the probe in the correct plane is important and can be difficult for enclosing hoods:

1. It is not always clear what plane is appropriate. As a practical matter, for unobstructed openings it should always be at least one inch inside the enclosure (see Figure 3-9). For hoods with sashes (e.g., laboratory hoods), the plane should be at the center of the sash

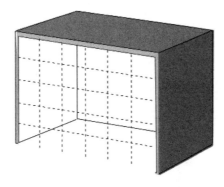

FIGURE 3-8. Enclosing hood with imaginary gridlines

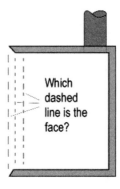

FIGURE 3-9. Face of the hood

depth. For walk-in booths where workers are completely inside the hood, it should be at the cross-section where workers would stand while exposed to contaminants.

2. Values generally fall rapidly if the probe wanders outside the face of enclosing hoods. Since it is difficult to hold a probe in one place without it wandering, the probe should be fixed on a tripod to hold the probe steady.

3. Avoiding distortion of the probe readings due to probe movement or obstructions to flow is also important. If the arm is fully extended, arm tremor can introduce enough movement to the probe tip to inflate the instrument reading of air velocity. The solution is to avoid supporting the wand or probe solely by hand. For example, one can press the base of a thermal anemometer wand or the forearm holding the wand against one edge of the hood face. A better solution is to mount the probe on a camera tripod.

4. Some instruments have no detachable probe. They cannot be read unless one is standing in the hood or at the face of the hood. The body changes the airflow patterns, making interpretation of readings difficult. These types of instruments should not be used.

Although any low-velocity anemometer can be used to measure the low velocities typically found at hood faces, thermal anemometers are the most frequently used because of their convenience and quick responses. The wand and probe are thin enough to have little effect on airflow patterns and the wand's length allows one to keep one's body out of the air stream near the probe.

The airflow through any cross-section can be computed the same way as ducts. For example, consider an enclosing hood face with the measured velocities shown in Figure 3-10. The average velocity for it would be:

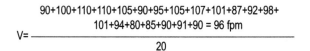

$$V = \frac{\begin{array}{c}90+100+110+110+105+90+95+105+107+101+87+92+98+\\101+94+80+85+90+91+90 = 96 \text{ fpm}\end{array}}{20}$$

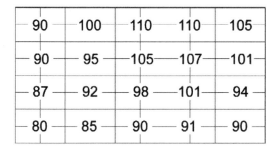

90	100	110	110	105
90	95	105	107	101
87	92	98	101	94
80	85	90	91	90

FIGURE 3-10. Average velocity and velocity profile

3.3.6 Velocity Measurements Near Close Capture Hoods.
For close capture hoods, the important value is the velocity at the source locations, not the average face velocity (which has no direct relevance). Measure the air velocities at the sources. Note the direction of the airflow using smoke visualization methods. Many of the issues and problems associated with enclosing hoods apply in measuring velocities near close capture hoods:

1. Select the measurement locations just over the source. For a diffuse source, identifying the proper location may be difficult. For a plating tank, the velocity measurements may be in the plane parallel to the face of the exhaust hood. For a grinding hood, the proper location may be where the swarf (grinding dust) is thrown by the grinding wheel. Often smoke visualization techniques are necessary to define the proper measuring point.

2. The lowest velocity in the region of contaminant release may be of greater interest than the average velocity.

3. As with enclosing hoods, avoid blocking the flow with the instrument or your body. Although it seems unrealistic to do so, it may be best to determine velocities without the worker in place. It simply is not clear how to interpret the effects of the worker's body on velocity profiles. To investigate effects of the worker's body on the effectiveness of the hood, release a non-irritating smoke at the source while the workers are working in their normal location.

4. As with enclosing hoods, the probe should be held steadily in place, ideally with a camera tripod.

In some cases, additional information can be obtained by measuring the velocity where the worker's face would be. The interpretation must be made carefully as the velocity may be caused by factors other than the capture hood.

3.4   STATIC PRESSURE MEASUREMENTS

It is possible to measure static pressure accurately using either a wall pressure tap or a Pitot tube probe. As with velocity measurements, it is important when measuring static pressures that the probe is aligned correctly with airflow and that the measurement location is chosen to avoid conditions that are difficult to measure accurately. Three conditions produce error:

1. Flow disturbances at the opening of the probe

2. Measurement error due to the probe not being perpendicular to the duct

3. Turbulence inside the duct

To avoid the latter, take readings several diameters downstream of the source of the turbulence (e.g., elbow, hood, branch entries).

Pressure readings can be taken using a wall tap (Figure 3-11) or with a Pitot tube inserted to the centerline of the duct.

3.4.1 Wall Pressure Measurements. For a highly accurate estimate of the mean static pressure at a cross-section of duct, average three static pressure measurements taken at wall taps equally spaced around the perimeter of the duct. However, if there are no disturbances for seven diameters upstream or more, a single wall reading generally will accurately represent the average value across the duct. A wall reading as close as three duct diameters downstream of a rounded elbow probably will be reasonably accurate.

If wall pressure data are taken, the static pressure opening should be flush with the inner surface of the pipe wall and there should be no burrs or projections on the inner surface. This is extremely difficult to do with a punch and very difficult to do with a drill especially for holes larger than 1/16 inch (Figure 3-11). The hole should be as small as possible both to avoid reducing projections inside the duct and to avoid Venturi effects due to air flowing over the hole. Note that the holes can fill quickly with particulate contaminants. Care should also be taken not to widen the hole when cleaning it out.

Wall pressures are sometimes measured through a small clean hole in a duct, which is covered by a "suction cup" probe. The suction cup is then connected to a sensor using plastic tubing. Such suction cup probes are often used with thermal anemometers, velometers, and other devices that cannot sense pressure but report it by measuring airflow through a calibrated orifice. It is important that the suction cup cover the hole in the duct completely to prevent leakage. In practice, it is difficult to determine whether the suction cup is tightly sealed on the duct and such readings may be unreliable.

3.4.2 Pitot Tubes Used for Static Pressure Measurements. Pitot tubes (see Section 3.5.1) can be used to measure the static pressure in a duct. Given the difficulties in creating and maintaining clean holes in the duct, taking measurements with a Pitot tube is often more convenient than wall taps — unless continuous monitoring is desired. Some practitioners may believe that a Pitot tube is not necessary and that a hollow tube pushed into the duct will work just as well. It will not. In fact, such readings can be grossly inaccurate.

3.5   SELECTION AND USE OF INSTRUMENTS

The selection of pressure or flow sensors should depend on the range of values to be measured, the required accuracy, and the conditions of measurement. Important conditions include vulnerability to high temperatures, presence of corrosive gases and contaminated atmospheres, required portability and ruggedness, and the size of the measuring probe relative to the available sampling port. A brief summary of the uses of the most important instruments is given in Table 3-9.

Inclined manometers are difficult to use accurately under field conditions, especially if they must be moved from location to location to take measurements. For that reason, they are

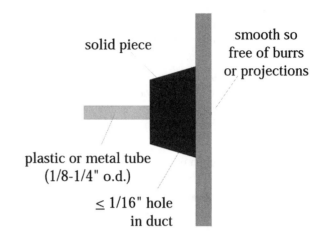

FIGURE 3-11. Wall pressure mount

best suited to calibrating devices that are more convenient. Aneroid Gauge and digital manometers both are convenient and easily calibrated by the user, but digital manometers are generally more precise and more convenient.

3.5.1 Pitot Tubes. Pitot tubes are probes used to conduct pressure to a pressure sensor, such as an inclined, U-tube, or digital manometer. Pitot tubes are generally constructed of stainless steel, making them tough and durable. High particulate or mist levels can cause plugging. Although the plug can be removed, the plug may form so quickly that measurements are impracticable. Usually a larger diameter Pitot tube takes longer to plug than a smaller one. When plugging is a problem, an S-type Pitot tube (Section 3.5.2) should be considered. In addition, the ability of the pressure sensor to measure low pressures limits the use of Pitot tubes to duct velocities well above 1000 fpm.

The Pitot tube is actually a tube-within-a-tube. As shown in Figure 3-12, the inner tube is a conduit for total pressure while the outer tube conducts static pressure only. If the total pressure "leg" and the static pressure "leg" are connected to opposite sides of a manometer, the fluid level is affected by static pressure equally on both sides leaving only the effects of velocity pressure. Hence, velocity pressure can be observed simply by connecting both legs of the Pitot tube to a manometer (see Figure 3-13).

It is important that any probe or instrument inserted into the air stream be small compared to the duct cross-section. As a rule of thumb, the probe or device should have a cross-sectional area perpendicular to the flow that is less than 1/20 of the duct cross-section. For Pitot tubes, for example, one should select the thinnest, readily available Pitot tube long enough to traverse the diameter comfortably. On the other hand, thin-stemmed Pitot tubes plug more readily with liquid and particulates, forcing use of larger diameter stems for some conditions.

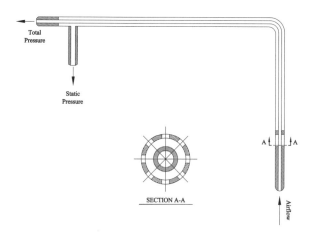

FIGURE 3-12. Pitot tube

Alignment with Airflow: For velocity (or static) pressure measurements to be accurate, the Pitot probe must be aligned with the airflow. This is particularly crucial when doing Pitot traverses to determine average velocity. To make sure that the probe is in line with the flow, keep the static pressure leg of the Pitot tube aligned with the duct and the Pitot tube stem perpendicular to the duct. Most critically, the probe should point upstream so that airflow impacts the opening of the probe. Figure 3-14 shows three common errors in inserting the Pitot probe. In the figure on the left, the probe is inserted at an angle. In the center figure, the probe is oriented correctly; however, it is not on the traverse line. In the figure on the right, the probe is inserted perpendicular to the duct, but twisted so that the probe in not parallel to the flow.

TABLE 3-9. Recommended Usage

Instrument	Parameter	Range	Comment
Pitot tube	SP	All SP	Measure at centerline
Pitot tube	VP	V >1500 fpm	Do two perpendicular 10-point traverses
Digital manometer	SP	Manufacturer's recommended range	"Wall" port or use with Pitot tube
Digital manometer	VP	V > 1500 fpm	Use with Pitot tube
Inclined manometer	SP	0 to 2 "wg typically	Use for calibration, not field readings
U-tube manometer	SP	1 to 20 "wg typically	Use for calibration for SP >2 "wg
Thermal anemometer	Velocity	30 to 400 fpm	Avoid using in ducts, especially if high temperatures or abrasive, sticky, or flammable contaminants
Aneroid gauges	SP	Range of particular device	Good for continuous monitoring

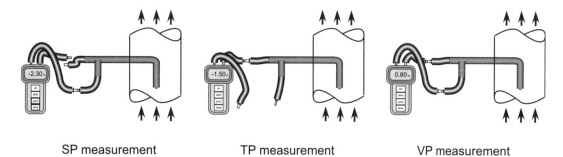

SP measurement   TP measurement   VP measurement

FIGURE 3-13. Pitot tubes connected for static, total and velocity pressure measurements

FIGURE 3-14. Different ways to misalign a Pitot tube

Using Pitot Tubes to Measure Static Pressure: For static pressure measurements, the Pitot tube should be inserted to the centerline of the duct (Figure 3-15). If poor uniformity is suspected, one can traverse the ducts for static pressure. If the values vary significantly, a location farther downstream should be employed if possible. At each point, one should wait for at least five seconds before recording the reading (longer if the manometer has a longer time constant) to give time for the sensor to reach its final value. As with velocity pressure traverses, one should use the smallest Pitot tube that can conveniently reach the desired insertion depths.

Using Pitot Tubes to Measure Velocity Pressure: For velocity pressure measurements, the Pitot tube should be inserted to each traverse depth in turn while keeping the Pitot tube probe aligned with the duct (Figure 3-16). At each point, one should wait for at least twice the time constant of the digital manometer, but at least five seconds before recording the reading to give time for the sensor to reach its final value. If there is variability in the reading – caused by variability in flow, vibration in the duct, or other cause – several readings may be required to obtain an accurate value.

Calculating Airflow from Pitot Traverse Data: The average velocity in a cross-section is simply the average of the velocities determined for the traverse points. An example is shown in the following table for a Pitot traverse of a 10-inch diameter duct (area is 0.5454 ft^2) and a df = 1.

Accuracy of Pitot Traverses: Many practitioners mistakenly believe that Pitot traverses cannot be accurate under "field" conditions because long, straight runs of duct are often not available to provide "good" measurement conditions. As is

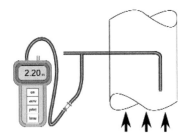

FIGURE 3-15. Static pressure measurement with Pitot tube

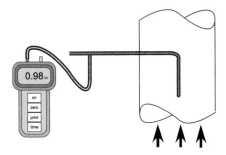

FIGURE 3-16. Measuring VP in a duct

Traverse Pt	Depth	VP, "wg	V, fpm		Traverse Pt	VP, "wg	V, fpm
1	0.2	0.38	2,469		1	0.44	2,657
2	0.8	0.42	2,596		2	0.5	2,832
3	1.5	0.48	2,775		3	0.55	2,970
4	2.2	0.54	2,943		4	0.59	3,076
5	3.6	0.6	3,102		5	0.61	3,128
6	6.4	0.62	3,154		6	0.62	3,154
7	7.8	0.68	3,303		7	0.58	3,050
8	8.5	0.64	3,204		8	0.54	2,943
9	9.2	0.52	2,888		9	0.49	2,804
10	9.8	0.43	2,626		10	0.44	2,657
	Average	2253				Average	2275
Average Velocity = 2916 fpm							
Volumetric Flow = VA = (0.5454)*(2916) = 1590 acfm							

suggested in earlier sections, Pitot traverses are generally reasonably accurate under surprisingly "bad" conditions.

A standard Pitot tube introduces very little error into measurements itself as long as the duct diameter is at least 20 times the Pitot tube stem diameter and the misalignment of the probe end with airflow is not much more than 5 degrees. The greatest concern is for conditions where the air is not aligned with the duct, making it impossible to align the probe ending correctly with the flow. This has lead to the belief that traverses can be accurate only if velocity profiles are highly symmetric. A laboratory study[3.4] demonstrated that Pitot traverse accuracies often deviated by less than 5% from true values even when velocity profiles were highly skewed. A single traverse produced less than 5% error when it was done at least seven duct diameters downstream from a hood, elbow, or junction fitting. The average of two perpendicular traverses produced errors less than 5% even when taken as close as two duct diameters from elbows. At seven duct diameters or more from elbows, hood openings, and junction fittings, errors were generally less than 3% if the average of two perpendicular traverses was used to determine average velocity. For the laboratory study, Pitot tubes were positioned with high precision.[3.4] The device fixed the Pitot tube at the correct insertion depth, ensured the tube was perpendicular to the duct, ensured the probe tip was directly into the airflow, and prevented any movement of the Pitot tube during the measurement.

Precision of measurements in the field is often less than the laboratory study discussed above. Instruments used in the field are not as accurate as the instruments used in the study above, especially at velocities less than 2,000 fpm. Most field instruments will give unacceptably high resolution errors at velocity pressure significantly less than 0.15 "wg. In addition, holding the Pitot tube by hand adds some error, due to the proper positioning and orientation of the probe and the inevitable movement of the probe during the measurement.

Conditions that can produce severe errors include:

1. If reverse flow exists over part of the velocity profile, the measurements will be in error. This condition should be suspected when the velocities measured near the duct is less than 20% of the centerline velocity.

2. The flow is highly disturbed due to objects in the duct or to a damper or fan within 10 duct diameters upstream.

Finally, it should be understood that the true average velocity may vary from hour to hour and day to day.[3.8] It sometimes may vary from minute to minute. Hence, finding different average velocities at different times does not necessarily indicate erroneous measurements. Airflows change with time due to:

1. Changes in line voltage (affecting the volumetric flow through the fan)

2. Change in damper position (either manual or automatic)

3. Change in resistance through the duct – for example, a movable hood with flex duct that has different loss depending on position of the hood

4. Changes to resistance at the air cleaning device, especially for devices with cleaning cycles (e.g., fabric filter)

5. Changes in fan speed due to control systems for the fan

Methods to Improve Accuracy: Holding a Pitot tube at a particular insertion depth while holding the stem perpendicular to the duct with its probe inline with flow can be difficult. However, some practical pointers may reduce the degree of difficulty if readings are frequently taken in the same size ducts:

1. Acquire a Pitot tube for each duct diameter you will frequently encounter. On each Pitot tube, mark the insertion depths for one of the duct diameters using a fine-tip permanent marker and mark the diameter on a tag affixed to the Pitot tube.

2. When the ink is dry, score a mark around the circumference of the shaft at each insertion mark using a straight edge and a sharp-edged file or equivalent (do not score so deeply that you create a leak).

3. Re-ink each insertion point using "permanent" inks. For example, the odd points could be blue (except for red for the centerline) and even points could be black or green.

4. Attach two feet of 0.25" plastic tubing to each "leg" of each Pitot tube. At the other end of each tube, insert a male plastic coupler to the static pressure leg and a female coupler to the total pressure leg (see Figure 3-17). Attach similar plastic tubes and couplers to the ports of all pressure measurement devices and never

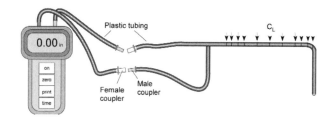

FIGURE 3-17. Attach plastic tubing and couplers to each sensor and Pitot tube

remove them. Use the couplers to connect and disconnect Pitot tubes from sensors.

5. Make a long extension with couplers at both ends matching the Pitot tube couplers. Mark the static pressure leg and "negative" ports with red ink.

Note: Avoid removing the plastic tubing from an instrument or Pitot tube and reattaching it because it will have stretched and may leak. If it is necessary to remove the tubing and use it again, cut off about 0.5" from the stretched end before reattaching.

Note: Avoid pinching the tube to the manometer, as this will result in erroneous readings.

3.5.2 S-Type Pitot Tube. The design of the Pitot tube includes a ring of small static pressure holes and a small total pressure port; consequently, it is prone to plugging. When inserted into a duct containing significant amounts of dust or mist, the standard Pitot tube can easily foul. To overcome this common occurrence, S-type (Staubscheide) Pitot tubes have been developed. S-type Pitot tubes usually take the form of two relatively large impact openings, one facing upstream and the other facing downstream (Figure 3-18). Such tubes are useful when thick walled ducts, such as boiler stacks, make it difficult or impossible to insert a conventional Pitot tube through any reasonably sized port opening. They are also often required for stack sampling using USEPA methods.

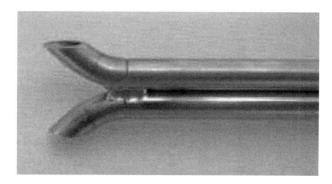

FIGURE 3-18. S-type Pitot Tube

Measurements made with an S-type Pitot tube cannot be used directly. The tube must be calibrated against a standard Pitot tube and the velocity pressure measured and corrected to the actual velocity pressure.

3.5.3 Pressure Sensors. Several types of pressure sensors can be used with a Pitot tube to measure velocity and static pressures within ventilation systems.

U-Tube Manometers: The vertical U-tube Manometer (Figure 3-19) is the simplest type of pressure gauge. Usually calibrated in inches water gauge, it is used with various fluid media such as alcohol, mercury, oil, water, kerosene, or special manometer fluids. The manufacturer specified gauge fluid must be used or the instrument will almost certainly be in error. The U-tube may be used for either portable or stationary applications. Available commercial units offer a wide variety of ranges and styles. Tubes are usually constructed of plastic to minimize breakage. One leg may be replaced by a reservoir or well (well-type manometer) for easier reading.

It is crucial that the U-tube be held perfectly vertical. Its verticality can be verified with a spirit level or plumb line. It is almost impossible to hold one vertical in your hand, so it must be mounted on a vertical surface.

Inclined Manometers: By inclining one leg of a U-tube manometer one spreads out the vertical rise in fluid level over a broader scale. This allows a more accurate visual discrimination of the true liquid levels (Figure 3-20). Manometers are designed to be inclined, and they have scales marked so that the vertical heights are correct.

It is important that the incline be at the correct angle. For that reason, most inclined manometers have a fixed angle to a horizontal section. A built in spirit level helps assure that the angle of incline is as intended. In commercial versions, only one tube is inclined and the other leg is replaced by a reservoir.

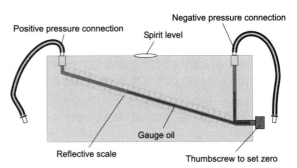

FIGURE 3-20. Inclined manometer

The better gauges are equipped with a built-in level, leveling adjustment, and a means of adjusting either the scale or the fluid level to zero. Some models include over-pressure safety traps to prevent loss of fluid in the event of pressure surges beyond the manometer range.

Under field conditions, even units marketed for field use are awkward to carry and set up and are time consuming and difficult to use. Ideally, one would mount a highly precise inclined manometer on the wall and use it to verify more convenient pressure sensing devices (e.g., electronic manometers) for use in the field.

A modification of the inclined manometer is the combined inclined and vertical gauge in which the indicator leg is bent or shaped to give both a vertical and inclined portion (Figure 3-21). The advantage is the greater upper range provided by the vertical section and higher precision in the crucial lower pressures covered by the inclined section. Although they are marketed for field use, they are best kept bolted to a wall for use in calibrating more convenient field instruments.

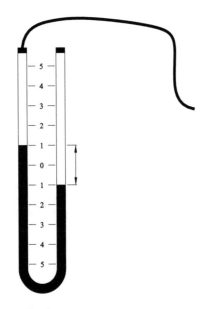

FIGURE 3-19. U-tube manometer

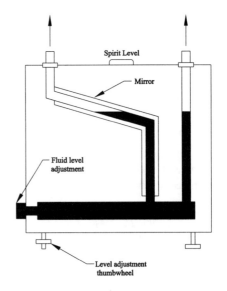

FIGURE 3-21. Inclined manometer with integrated vertical section

Whether on the wall or in the field, proper use of any manometer requires the following:

1. It must contain the correct gauge fluid and nothing else. Its chamber must have sufficient fluid. The fluid must be replaced periodically with clean fluid.

2. The manometer must be aligned with gravity, usually aided by a built-in spirit level.

3. The person who will use it (individuals read them differently) must zero it before each use.

4. The instrument cannot be read accurately until all bubbles in the fluid have been removed.

5. One must wait from several seconds to a minute for a stable reading depending on the size of the manometer and the magnitude of the pressure.

6. For inclined sections, the right-most edge of the meniscus should be read in both calibration and use. For vertical sections, the bottom of the meniscus should be read.

7. The meniscus and its mirror image on the device should be aligned before reading the scale. It is difficult to do this using both eyes, so shut one.

8. Values below 0.2 "wg are difficult to read with better than 10% precision.

Portable Digital (Electronic) Manometers: Digital manometers (see Figure 3-22) are electronic devices that sense pressure changes. The calibration is set within the electronics but their internal calibration must be verified periodically. These devices hold their calibration well, but do show zero drift, especially after first turning them on (wait 30 minutes to zero and use) and with temperature changes. Within their range of application, their advantages compared to other ventilation devices are compelling:

1. As is true for all pressure sensors, the contaminants inside the ducts are not allowed to flow through the device.

2. Battery powered versions can be small and lightweight enough to use in the field with much greater convenience than other pressure gauges. Some will fit in a shirt pocket.

3. Orientation to gravity and movement are irrelevant unlike mechanical devices.

4. They respond to pressure changes quickly (user selectable time averaging is a crucial feature).

5. Their accuracy often is superior to other devices suitable for field use.

6. Some have data logging and computer communication capabilities.

Aneroid Gauges: Perhaps the best known device of this type is the Magnehelic™ gauge (Figure 3-23). They are inexpensive, extremely rugged pressure sensing devices that keep their calibration well. They can be purchased in ranges from low to high and with scales for pressure, velocity, or both. For example, one could use a 0-0.5 "wg range for low velocities in ducts; 0-1 "wg for moderate velocities in ducts; 0-2 "wg for high velocities in ducts; 0-5 "wg for low static pressures; and 0-15 "wg for high static pressures.

In using these devices, you should:

1. Select the gauge with the mid-range value closest to the value you expect to measure.

2. Zero and use the device in the vertical orientation. Note that tilting the meter can change the reading substantially.

3. Zero the device before each use while it is positioned as it will be read (i.e., vertical or horizontal).

4. Verify readings against a manometer frequently.

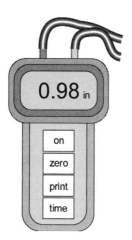

FIGURE 3-22. Digital manometer

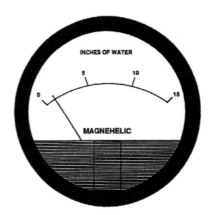

FIGURE 3-23. Aneroid gauge

5. Since an aneroid gauge measures pressures, the velocities displayed on the face are correct only for standard density. For non-standard densities, determine the density factor and calculate the velocity (Equation 3.5 or 3.6). Pressure readings are not affected by density and should not be "corrected." However, it is important to measure and record the temperature for other reasons.

3.5.4 *Air Velocity Instruments.* Many instruments can measure air velocity at a point. The accuracy of the average velocity depends on the accuracy of the measurement device, the correct use of the device, and how representative the samples are. All instruments should be handled and used in strict compliance with their manufacturers' recommendations.

One source of error is disturbance of the air stream by the instrument, its probe, and its user. That factor limits use of many of these devices to very large openings. Table 3-9 lists some characteristics of typical air velocity instruments designed for field use.

Thermal Anemometers: Thermal anemometers (Figure 3-24) respond to the amount of heat removed by an air stream passing a heated probe. The rate of heat removal corresponds to air velocity at standard density.

Air velocity often fluctuates rapidly and the instrument can respond much quicker than one can read the display. Many instruments have a "hold" button to display a value until the user releases the button. In some units, the user can set the time constant (i.e., averaging time) and later push a button to "hold" the running average just computed. However, some instruments display the instantaneous response when the hold button is activated, which is much less useful.

In using a thermal anemometer, the user should note that:

1. The sensor is fragile. Protect it from shock. It can be used in some ducts at low velocity ranges, but not in those ducts whose airflow are very hot or carry contaminants that are corrosive, explosive, abrasive, or whose concentrations are high enough to clog or coat the sensor.

2. Attachments are available to measure static pressure. The attachments allow air from a hole in the duct to pass through a calibrated orifice and the sensor. The velocity through the orifice is related to static pressure by calibration.

3. The probe diameter is small enough and the range of the instruments is high enough to allow use of the instrument in measuring duct velocities for ducts larger than 10 inches. For smaller ducts, the middle of the sensor is too far from the tip to reach points close to the wall of the duct opposite the insertion hole.

4. When used for low velocity measurements substantial error can be introduced by inadvertent movement of the probe tip. Movement of the sensor may produce values that represent hand tremor more than environmental conditions. For that reason, one should hold the probe in an adjustable stand (e.g., camera tripod or ring stand) to achieve the greatest accuracy. For cases where lower accuracy is acceptable, it may be sufficient to steady the wand by holding it against a fixed object (e.g., a side of the hood).

5. When used at hood faces it can be difficult both to decide which plane contains the face of the enclosing hood and how to hold the probe exactly in that plane. For many hoods, small deviations from the plane of the face can produce substantial changes in the measured velocity.

6. Like all other devices, it should be zeroed before use and its calibration should be verified frequently.

7. Measurements may become incorrect if the battery charge level is low.

8. Thermal anemometers can measure from 30 fpm and up with reasonable accuracy if properly calibrated. At velocities below 30 fpm, instrument response can be erratic or it may simply display zero.

9. Thermal anemometers used in the field have relatively poor accuracy or precision at velocities below 50 fpm (but so do all other field devices other than sonic anemometers).

10. One cannot determine the direction of airflow from the instrument readings.

Thermal anemometers can measure both high and low velocities — which is convenient. However, calibrating them requires production of a known velocity. A known velocity is much more difficult to verify than a known static pressure. Therefore, static pressure measuring devices are more reliable in measuring high velocities. If possible, one should measure airflow from Pitot traverses in ducts and compute average hood velocity from the measured airflow divided by the area of the hood face.

Rotating Vane Anemometers: Rotating vane anemometers (Figure 3-25) can be used to determine airflow through large (greater than 4 ft²) supply and exhaust openings. Where possible the cross-sectional area of the instrument should not exceed 5.0% of the cross-sectional area of the duct or hood opening. These instruments are fragile and are not suitable for dusty or corrosive atmospheres.

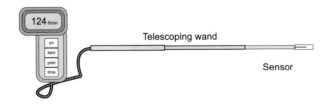

FIGURE 3-24. Thermal anemometer

FIGURE 3-25. Rotating vane anemometer

FIGURE 3-26. Swinging vane anemometer

The mechanical instrument consists of a propeller or revolving vane connected through a gear train to a set of recording dials that convert the number of rotations to total distance traveled by the air during the sampling time. By dividing the total distance by time recorded elsewhere (e.g., on a stop watch) one can compute the estimated velocity of the air that passed through the instrument. The dial readings are seldom accurate as read. General practice is to tape a table of conversions based on the most recent calibration to the side of the instrument. These values are used to "correct" dial readings. Note that the calibration is for one direction of flow only. The instrument can be made in various sizes with 2", 3", 4" and 6" being the most common for purely mechanical versions. The standard instrument can have a useful range of 50-3,000 fpm but specially built models can read lower velocities. It is not intended for use in small ducts but it can be used in very large ducts, mineshafts and large enclosing hoods.

Electronic rotating vane anemometers are also available. These instruments generally are much smaller than the mechanical devices but are too large for traversing any but the largest ducts (e.g., greater than 5 ft in diameter). These instruments record and count the number of revolutions of the vanes per time. Readings as low as 25 fpm can be measured and recorded. They are not suitable for dusty or explosive atmospheres. The size of the required opening for measurements in ducts is a serious issue.

Swinging Vane Anemometers: A swinging vane anemometer (Figure 3-26) was once used extensively in the field because of its portability, versatility and wide-scale range. However, it has been supplanted by thermal anemometers for low velocities and by digital manometers for both high velocities and static pressures. Calibration and maintenance of the instrument are concerns for the following reasons:

1. The presence of dust, moisture or corrosive material in the atmosphere presents a problem since the air passes through the instrument case. It does have filters to remove particulates, but dust loading of the filter changes instrument response as does removing and replacing the filter. Hence, filter loading is a source of error.

2. The instrument requires periodic calibration and adjustment but the instrument cannot be calibrated by the user.

3. The actual sensing device is a calibrated spring. For that reason, it is crucial that the instrument be held vertically while being calibrated and when used in the field – a difficult proposition while standing on a ladder. Furthermore, mechanical shocks can extend the spring, changing its calibration.

4. The length and inside diameter of the connecting tubing affect the calibration of the meter. When replacement is required, one can use only connecting tubing of the same length and inside diameter as that originally supplied with the meter.

5. The instrument does not actually measure static pressure. It measures the reduction in flow through the instrument when a fitting with a calibrated orifice impedes the flow. For that reason, loading of the filter also affects its static pressure readings and its readings must be corrected for air density.

The instrument has wide application. By use of a variety of fittings, it can be used to check static pressure and air velocity over a wide range of values. The instrument can be used to measure velocities through supply air grilles large enough (roughly 3 ft²) that the instrument does not introduce errors by blocking airflow. It is important to correct such readings using the calibration factors listed by the manufacturer for each grille type.

The instrument can be used to measure hood face velocities when the specified fitting is attached. However, the low velocity fitting is attached directly to the body of the instrument so that both must be placed in the air stream, introducing error as the air flows around it. Worse, the user often must place his or her head and torso into the air stream to read the instrument. Finally, the instrument must be held vertically so the minimum height above a surface at which one can measure is roughly six inches.

Before using this instrument, check the meter for zero setting by holding it horizontal and covering both ports so that no air can flow through. If the pointer does not come to rest at zero, adjust it to read zero.

Although the instrument includes a probe intended to measure velocities in ducts, its large size precludes accurate measurements in smaller ducts (less than 6 inches). Its large diameter blocks airflow excessively and its probe tip cannot reach the outermost traverse points. Used in place of a Pitot tube for velocity or total pressure measurements, it necessitates a much larger hole in the duct – a potential source of substantial leaks.

Like many other instruments, its readings must be corrected if air density is non-standard.

Sonic Anemometers: Sonic anemometers (Figure 3-27) measure the time required for sound to travel between the three "posts" of the instrument. Although currently almost three times the cost of a thermal anemometer, these instruments offer a capability achieved only with constant temperature anemometers and other "high-end" laboratory devices. The low-cost versions of these instruments may allow use of turbulence measurements to evaluate field conditions. The other compelling features of these devices are: 1) they do not require re-calibration once calibrated by the manufacturer, 2) unlike any other field instrument, they can measure very low velocities (2 ft/min) accurately, and 3) they can measure extremely high velocities (10,000 ft/min).

Flow Hoods: Flow hoods are devices that channel all air from a diffuser or other sources through the device (see Figure 3-28). By sensing the velocities at several points at a fixed

FIGURE 3-27. Sonic anemometer probe

FIGURE 3-28. Flow hood in use

cross-section of known area, it is possible for the devices to compute the airflow through them. The sensor in most instruments is a thermal anemometer, but units are available that measure a matrix of pressures across an orifice with a low pressure digital manometer. At least one manufacturer uses a rotating vane and timer to measure airflow.

It is important that all of the air from the source flow through the device so one should tightly seal the entrance of the device to the source outlet. The range of airflows a device can measure depends on the size of the device's entrance and the range of velocities it can measure with acceptable accuracy. A typical range is 25 to 2,000 acfm for devices using rotating vanes and timers to sense flow, but sizes capable of higher and lower ranges are available.

3.5.5 Density Correction. The readout of most instruments should be corrected for air density. See Section 3.2.5 for the appropriate correction equations.

3.5.6 Temperature Measurement Devices. Temperature is an important factor for determining air density. Since the output of many measuring devices needs to be corrected for density, temperatures must be field measured in most applications. There are many types of devices, or thermometers, commonly used to measure temperature, including liquid-in-glass, bimetallic, thermocouple, and resistance.

Liquid-in-glass thermometers are awkward to use in the field because they 1) are usually fragile, 2) respond slowly to changes in temperature, 3) must be kept upright, and 4) are often difficult to read, especially in poor light. The one advantage of liquid-in-glass thermometers is that their calibration should not change unless they are damaged. Other temperature measurement devices usually are more suitable for field use.

Other types of thermometers suffer from none of the disadvantages of liquid-in-glass but require frequent calibration. Bimetallic thermometers bind two metals with dissimilar thermal expansion coefficients at one end and measure the movement of the other ends due to different lengths of expansion as the temperature changes. Thermometers with dial indicators are often bimetallic. Resistance thermometers measure the changes in electrical resistance by sensing changes in temperature using a Wheatstone bridge or galvanometer. A typical resistance thermometer consists of a fine platinum wire wrapped around a mandrel and covered with a protective coating. A thermistor is a resistance thermometer whose sensor is a ceramic semiconductor. Thermistors release heat, which can interfere with measurements in still air. Their temperature range (-40 F to 300 F) is more limited than metallic resistance types.

Thermocouples respond to the voltage produced when two dissimilar metals join. The magnitude of the voltage varies with temperature. Thermocouples are frequently used in electronic devices.

Infrared "guns" emit a visible targeting laser beam and measure infrared light emitted from a surface. The emissions vary with the temperature of the surface according to Planck's radiation law. It also varies with the emissivity of the surface (i.e., how much the surface acts as a black body), so the gauge reading must be corrected, depending on the surface. The user must guess at the emissivity of the surface. Some instruments allow selection of emissivity and correct the readout accordingly. These instruments allow measurement of very high temperatures and are useful in measuring surfaces that are inconvenient to access due to location or movement.

Calibration: A two-point calibration can be done by the user over a range that is sufficient for most conditions inside both ducts and occupied spaces. The freezing point of distilled water is 32 F, a temperature achieved by letting ice come to equilibrium temperature in cold water. The boiling point of water at sea level is 212 F, providing the other test point. Since the boiling point temperature falls with barometric pressure, it is important to determine the boiling point at the altitude at which one is doing the calibration.

It is also possible to calibrate measurement devices over the range of temperatures of interest using a thermometer whose calibration over that range can be traced to a primary device.

3.5.7 Humidity Measurement Devices. Humidity usually is not an important factor in determining air density unless the air temperature is well above 100 F and the humidity is very high due to the process being measured. However, ambient levels of humidity are sometimes important for processes, comfort, and control of heat stress, especially when the temperature is also elevated.

Humidity can be determined indirectly with a psychrometer, which is a device that passes air over a dry-bulb and a wet-bulb thermometer at a controlled velocity. The velocity is controlled with a battery-operated fan in some devices and by the user forcing the device to swing about one end in "sling" psychrometers. Psychrometric charts provided by the manufacturer allow determination of relative humidity from the dry-bulb

and wet-bulb readings. In both types, air is driven across the thermometer bulbs until equilibrium is reached while taking care that the sock covering the Wet Bulb remains wet. In the battery powered devices, the fan speed may vary with battery charge so it is important to check the batteries before taking readings.

Hygrometers respond directly to the water vapor in the sampled air. Organic hygrometers are inexpensive and inaccurate devices that measure the change in length of organic materials with change in humidity. Electronic hygrometers, which can be much more accurate and are relatively expensive, measure the change in conductance of a sulfonated polystyrene strip or a similar material.

3.5.8 Tachometers. Tachometers are used to measure the rotational speed of fans. If the rotational speed is different from the expected speed, the cause should be investigated. The most common causes are discussed below.

1. Reduced rates may indicate belt slippage or the wrong type of belt. With the fan motor locked out, one should test whether the belt is as taut as the manufacturer recommended.

2. If pulleys are used, their sizes may be different from intended (check design specifications).

3. If a variable frequency drive is used, the frequency may be set incorrectly (check design specifications).

Tachometers may count rotations per time directly or stroboscopically (see Figure 3-29). The former should be placed on the center of the end of a rotating shaft. For the latter, white paint or chalk on the side of the shaft provides the reference point. It is important to verify both the motor and fan rotation rates when analyzing conditions.

3.5.9 Smoke Visualization. "Smoke" will follow the path of the air with little deviation, allowing the visualization of airflow. The trail of streaming smoke and the path of a single puff

FIGURE 3-29. Tachometer

of smoke are both useful in visualizing airflow behavior. They allow one to see cross-drafts, disruptive eddy currents, and stagnant zones – all of which are thought to be strongly associated with poor hood performance (Figure 3-30). They also can be used for checking air movement and direction in plant space.

In addition, low velocity measurements may be made by timing the travel of smoke clouds through a known distance. Smoke trail observations are limited to velocities less than 150 fpm since higher air velocities disperse the smoke too rapidly.

Instead of a true "smoke," it is best to use a fine powder. Smoke "guns" which have squeeze bulbs that allow one to puff a burst of white powder (e.g., asbestos-free talcum) are very low toxicity, non-irritating, and can be made to be explosive-proof.

Test smoke commonly is generated by heating a vegetable oil to sufficiently high temperatures or by reacting chemicals that give off a visible cloud of particulates. The former can generate great quantities of smoke for sustained periods, but the head of the cloud they release produces a vertical rise that makes interpretation more difficult. The chemically created smokes can be neutrally buoyant. A copious but short-term plug of smoke is released by smoke "bombs." Puffs of smoke are generated by manually pumping air through a tube filled with a reagent (e.g., titanium tetrachloride).

In using test smoke, it is important to note that:

1. The visible plumes from some smoke tubes are corrosive and should be used with care near people, sensitive processes, or food preparation. Avoid exposing others to the smoke or to skin or eye contact with the corrosive materials. Acetic acid may be less objectionable than the hydrogen chloride from titanium tetrachloride tubes. Smoke tubes should be disposed of properly.

2. Smoke candles are incendiary devices and thus cannot be used in flammable atmospheres and should not be hand held. All smoke sources (including smoke tubes) may set off fire alarms.

FIGURE 3-30. Using smoke to evaluate air movement

3. Alternative methods of observing airflow patterns include the use of soap bubbles, water vapor cooled by dry ice (CO_2) and heated vegetable oil. None of these methods creates neutrally buoyant "smokes."

4. Visible "smoke" will sometimes appear to show that a hood is functioning well when it is actually marginal or unacceptable. This is unfortunate but understandable if one considers that:

   a. Smoke that escapes the hood will mix with workroom air thus diluting the smoke concentration so that it is difficult to see. Unless lighting conditions are ideal, it is difficult to observe small amounts of smoke, leading to false "observation" that "virtually all" of the smoke entered the hood. Thus one can be misled into believing that one had "demonstrated" that a hood is highly effective in cases where it was only 90-95% effective.

   b. One may have observed "almost all" (i.e., 80-95%) of the smoke enter the hood and falsely conclude that the hood functions well. A 5-20% escape rate may be excessive in other cases. For example, if 99% collection efficiency is required, a 5% rate of escape is 5 times too high!

   c. The user may have released the smoke when the operator is not present and performing normal motions. Operator (and all other) motions almost always reduce the collection efficiency of a hood.

   d. It is quite possible to have over-exposure without any contaminant escaping the hood, especially if the worker's head is inside the hood and the contaminant is released close to the worker. An obvious example is a worker standing to the rear of a paint spray booth while the contaminant is released at the hood face. Less obvious, but extremely common, are cases where the workers are handling the contaminant source while leaning into or standing inside of the hood. Since air cannot flow through the worker's back, it must flow around him creating a stagnant zone in front of his body. Smoke released just in front of the worker's body will tend to linger in the stagnant zone. If the worker leans over or if the source is over waist high, then body and arm movements will spread the smoke into the worker's breathing zone.

Soap bubbles also can be very useful. They may survive and remain visible long after a puff of smoke would have dispersed to the point of invisibility. Their persistent visibility can be very helpful when evaluating large hoods or determining cross-draft velocities. A disadvantage is that bubbles created with air and soap are denser than air and will tend to fall to the floor. However, by creating very small bubbles (e.g., 1 mm diameter) with a helium-air mixture, it is possible to create neutrally buoyant bubbles. Since the durability of bubbles is inversely related to diameter, these small bubbles can be remarkably persistent, further enhancing their usefulness.

3.5.10 Borescope: Use in Examining the Interiors of Ventilation Components. Borescopes are devices designed to allow one to view down their length into otherwise hidden spaces (Figure 3-31). Typically, they employ fiberoptics to convey light into the space and arrangements of mirrors to allow reflection of the image back to the viewer. Those used for ventilation system inspections should have the following characteristics:

1. A 0.75 inch barrel, which is small enough that the access hole is reasonably small. Transmission losses increase dramatically with smaller diameters, increasing the required intensity from the light source and reducing the maximum clear viewing distance.

2. A view that is 90 degrees from the barrel.

3. A light source that is relatively light weight. Note that the light source requires too much power for battery operation so alternating current is required for ventilation applications.

4. If interior photography is desired, connections for still or video cameras should be available.

Although units can be extremely useful in detecting hidden objects and plugging, they can mislead the user into thinking that nothing is present in a duct when an obstruction is actually there. This can happen because:

1. Even light coatings of settled materials can make objects blend into the picture.

2. The optics can give the viewer the sense that he or she is viewing much further into a duct than is the case. The greatest distance for accurate impressions is probably less than 10 ft even in clean ducts and can be considerably less for ducts with coatings or settled material in

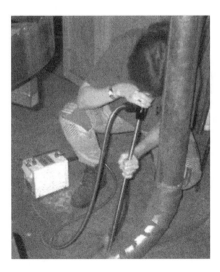

FIGURE 3-31. Boroscope

them. For borescopes with barrel diameters less than 0.75 inches, the useful viewing distance is dramatically reduced.

3.6   CALIBRATION

3.6.1 Need for Calibration. Almost everything except simple liquid manometers needs regular calibration because their responses can be changed by shock (dropping, jarring), dust, high temperatures, and corrosive atmospheres. Mechanical and electronic meters should be calibrated regularly. It may be prudent to calibrate them before each use if they will not adjust to zero properly or if they have been subjected to rough handling or adverse atmospheres.

To calibrate a device, you must have a way to produce known levels. For example, if you are calibrating a device that measures pressure, you should produce a pressure and measure it with a device you know is accurate and with the device you wish to calibrate. If they read the same for every level you check, then the device you are checking is in calibration.

A manometer can be good enough to calibrate field devices if it is zeroed, leveled, and filled with the correct fluid. For a manometer filled with distilled water to be accurate it is necessary only that the vertical distance be marked accurately. If gauge oil is used, then the scale on the manometer must be proportional to the density of the gauge oil. Commonly used gauge oils are colored red, blue, or green to make it clear which one should be used with a particular manometer.

Simple manometers are the only ventilation measurement devices currently in use that can be used as if they were primary standards. All others should be recalibrated periodically against a primary standard or against a secondary standard that is frequently calibrated against a primary standard.

An aneroid gauge, for example, should be periodically calibrated against a known level of pressure. Its spring is subject to metal fatigue and to mechanical dislocations, which could change the level displayed on its scale face. Since the gauge reading can drift between calibrations, it cannot be a primary standard. Likewise, so-called "velometers," which are calibrated orifices, vanes, etc., and thermal anemometers must be calibrated against primary standards.

If during calibration one finds the instrument has been reading incorrectly, one cannot be certain when the error appeared since the last calibration. Hence, all data taken since the last calibration is suspect until a new calibration check confirms the accuracy of the instrument. The optimal frequency of calibration depends on the cost of calibration as compared to the cost of incorrect measurements and the likelihood the instrument's accuracy will deteriorate unacceptably in the interim between calibration checks.

Some instruments may need certification (e.g., for National Environmental Balancing Bureau requirements) and must be sent to a company certified to calibrate them. However, it is still useful to do in-plant calibrations if they can be done with reasonably low cost and effort.

3.6.2 Calibrating Pressure Reading Devices. A great advantage of manometers is their ease of calibration. Practitioners can easily and quickly verify calibration in the office or lab using relatively inexpensive devices. This saves the cost of "factory" recalibration and reduces the time the instrument is out of service. Most digital manometers and aneroid gauges should not experience substantial errors unless subjected to sharp impacts or other harsh treatment or conditions. For that reason, unless the instrument has been dropped, immersed in liquids or otherwise abused, it may be adequate to rely on monthly calibration checks. However, given how easy it is to calibrate pressure devices, you should check calibration frequently – perhaps even before and after a day of use if the measurements are crucial or will be difficult to repeat.

All that is required is a device that can serve as a primary standard, a method to vary the test pressure, and connecting apparatus (i.e., plastic tubing). As shown in Figure 3-32, a typical setup would include a hand pump, an on-off air valve (e.g., needle valve), an inclined manometer, and the device to be calibrated.[3.4]

A standard field manometer is not truly a primary calibration device, but the potential for error using one is very low as long as the following are true:

1. The manometer is aligned vertically using an integrated spirit level or an external spirit level and a plumb line.

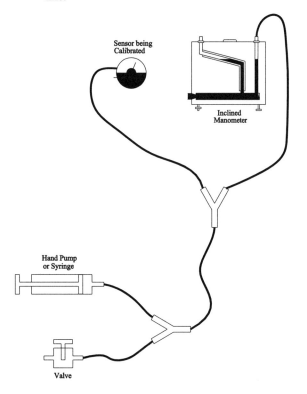

Sensor being Calibrated

Inclined Manometer

Hand Pump or Syringe

Valve

FIGURE 3-32. Pressure device calibration

2. The correct gauge fluid is used (follow manufacturer's specifications).

3. The internal volume is clean and the gauge fluid is free of debris.

4. The manometer is zeroed properly.

5. Inclined manometers with vertical elements are used only in the inclined range and not in the first values in vertical range, which can be inaccurate due to retention of fluid in the inclined section. For pressures above the inclined range it is better to use a separate simple U-tube manometer

3.6.3 Calibrating Velocity Measuring Devices. A great disadvantage of velocity devices is the difficulty of establishing a known velocity to verify calibration. Most practitioners will find it less costly to send the instrument back to the manufacturer for calibration rather than doing it themselves. The cost of "factory" calibration is typically very high (often greater than 22% of the cost of the instrument) and the turn-around times are very long – sometimes four to six weeks. For that reason, practitioners often have the calibration done annually or less frequently. Since vendors typically do not report the degree of error found prior to re-setting the device, the user generally has no idea whether the measurements taken prior to recalibration were accurate or not. It is possible to request that the company calibrating the instrument report the level of instrument error when they receive it. There may be an extra charge for that service.

3.6.4 Design of a Calibrating Wind Tunnel for Practitioner Use. With the exception of sonic anemometers, air velocity instruments must be calibrated against a known velocity. This requires that one must be able to produce a range of airflows and measure their velocities with a different instrument that is known to be accurate and precise for that velocity range. For high velocities (above 1500 fpm), readings from a velocity instrument can be compared to values in ducts determined using a Pitot tube and a calibrated pressure sensor. The difficulty is in calibrating velocity instruments for much lower velocities.

The best course may be to pay the manufacturer to check and recalibrate the instruments. For those with many instruments to check, it may be worthwhile to find or construct a small wind tunnel to calibrate instruments. The wind tunnel setup must include the following:[3.5, 3.6]

1. A relatively large, low velocity section for testing low velocity instruments. This chamber must have highly uniform airflow at the test cross-section, and the velocities should vary little if the measurement location is moved short distances up or downstream. The latter precludes use of laboratory hoods. Their face velocities can vary radically as the measurement device is moved into or out of the plane of the opening.

2. The chamber inlet should have a smooth curved, bell

shaped entry, which directs the air into the duct over a 180 degree angle (Figure 3-33). It must be free of obstructions and the air entering it should have no significant momentum lateral or vertical to the open face.

3. For calibrating larger instruments such as the lower velocity swinging vane anemometer and the rotating vane anemometer, a large rectangular test section of transparent plastic at least 2.5 ft^2 in cross-sectional area can be constructed with curved air foil inlets as shown in Figure 3-34. A fine mesh screen placed deep in the enclosure will assist in providing a uniform airflow in the test section.

4. Low velocities must be measured by a calibrated low velocity instrument that is placed in the test cross-section. If the low velocity section has uniform velocities, the test and tested instruments may be used side-by-side if one takes care not to obstruct the movement of air with one's body or with the instrument. Otherwise, a traverse should be performed using each instrument and the average values compared.

5. If the low-velocity section does not have uniform velocities, the average from a traverse by the low velocity device should be used to estimate the airflow through the test cross-section and that value should be compared to the result of a velocity pressure traverse in the high velocity section.

6. A high velocity section, preferably downstream of the low velocity section, and a Pitot tube and calibrated pressure sensor to conduct a velocity pressure traverse. For velocity measurements below 2,000 fpm, a micro-manometer (e.g., hook gauge) should be used to measure pressures.[3.7]

7. A fan and control system that allows variation of air velocities over the desired range in the test section. A variable frequency drive controller is preferred but a damper (e.g., slide-gate damper) may be employed if it is located well downstream of the low velocity and high velocity test sections.

8. Apparatus to measure temperature, barometric pressure, and humidity in the test room.

Note that the tested instrument should be supported in such a way that the support does not change the velocity at the instrument inlet by its presence. The instrument should be oriented to the flow as specified by the manufacturer for taking measurements in the field.

A sharp-edged orifice, Venturi meter or a flow nozzle can be used as a metering device.[3.8] Of these, the sharp-edged orifice has more resistance to flow but is more easily constructed, and it can be designed to be readily interchangeable for several orifice sizes. The orifice can be mounted between two flanged sections sealed with gaskets as shown in Figure 3-34. Each orifice should be calibrated using a standard Pitot tube and

manometer prior to use. The airflow for a sharp-edged orifice with pipe taps located 1" on either side of the orifice can be computed from the following equation for 2" to 14" diameter ducts:

$$Q = 6KD_o\sqrt{SP_o/\rho} \qquad [3.12]$$

Where: Q = Airflow rate, acfm
K = Coefficient of airflow
D_o = Diameter of open portion of orifice, inches
SP_o = Pressure drop across orifice, "wg
ρ = Density, lbm/ft^3

The coefficient, K, is affected by the Reynolds number, R_e. The Reynolds number is a dimensionless value expressing flow conditions in a duct. For standard air, the Reynolds number is given by:

$$Re = 8.4 \times D_oV_o \qquad [3.13]$$

Where: V_o = Velocity through the orifice, acfm
The coefficient, K, can be selected from Table 3-10.

3.7 PRACTICAL ISSUES IN VENTILATION SYSTEM MEASUREMENT

In addition to all of the considerations described in preceding sections, it is important to consider the effects of air contaminants, low-velocities, and system variability. In addition, there are errors that are so common that it is worthwhile to list them and review them from time to time. Finally, while collecting information, it is always wise to prepare the site and to develop means of organizing the information. This section reviews all of those issues.

TABLE 3-10. Values of K in Equation 3.13 for Different Orifice Sizes

D_o/D	Reynolds Number in Thousands						
	25	50	100	230	500	1,000	10,000
0.100	0.605	0.601	0.598	0.597	0.596	0.595	0.595
0.200	0.607	0.603	0.600	0.599	0.598	0.597	0.597
0.300	0.611	0.606	0.603	0.603	0.601	0.600	0.600
0.400	0.621	0.615	0.611	0.610	0.609	0.608	0.608
0.450	0.631	0.624	0.619	0.617	0.615	0.615	0.615
0.500	0.644	0.634	0.628	0.626	0.624	0.623	0.623
0.550	0.663	0.649	0.641	0.637	0.635	0.634	0.634
0.600	0.686	0.668	0.658	0.653	0.650	0.649	0.649
0.650	0.717	0.695	0.680	0.674	0.670	0.668	0.667
0.700	0.755	0.723	0.707	0.699	0.694	0.692	0.691
0.750	0.826	0.773	0.747	0.734	0.726	0.723	0.721

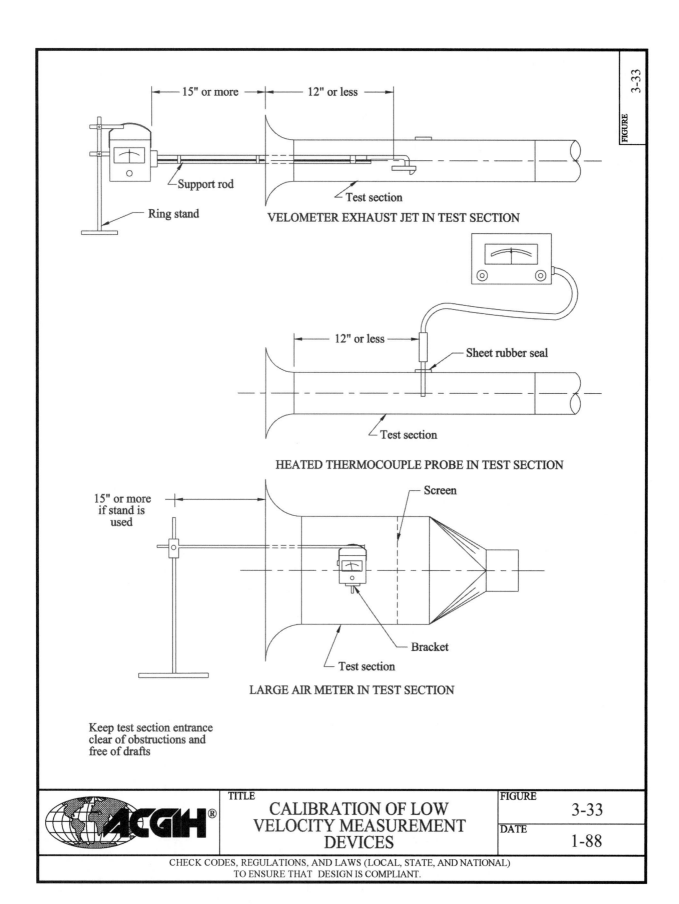

15" or more — 12" or less

Support rod

Ring stand

VELOMETER EXHAUST JET IN TEST SECTION

12" or less

Sheet rubber seal

Test section

HEATED THERMOCOUPLE PROBE IN TEST SECTION

15" or more
if stand is
used

Screen

Bracket

Test section

LARGE AIR METER IN TEST SECTION

Keep test section entrance
clear of obstructions and
free of drafts

FIGURE
3-33

	TITLE	FIGURE	
ACGIH®	CALIBRATION OF LOW VELOCITY MEASUREMENT DEVICES	3-33	
		DATE	1-88

CHECK CODES, REGULATIONS, AND LAWS (LOCAL, STATE, AND NATIONAL)
TO ENSURE THAT DESIGN IS COMPLIANT.

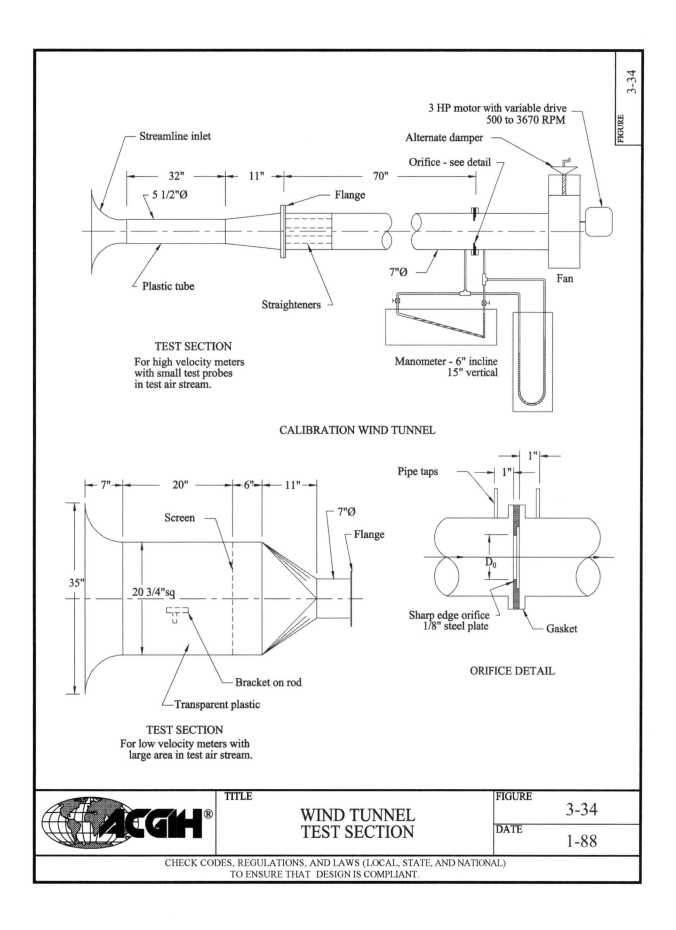

Streamline inlet

32"

11"

70"

5 1/2"Ø

Flange

Plastic tube

Straighteners

TEST SECTION
For high velocity meters
with small test probes
in test air stream.

3 HP motor with variable drive
500 to 3670 RPM

Alternate damper

Orifice - see detail

7"Ø

Fan

Manometer - 6" incline
15" vertical

FIGURE 3-34

CALIBRATION WIND TUNNEL

7"

20"

6"

11"

Screen

7"Ø

Flange

35"

20 3/4"sq

Bracket on rod

Transparent plastic

TEST SECTION
For low velocity meters with
large area in test air stream.

Pipe taps

1"

1"

D_0

Sharp edge orifice
1/8" steel plate

Gasket

ORIFICE DETAIL

TITLE	FIGURE	
WIND TUNNEL **TEST SECTION**	3-34	
	DATE	
	1-88	

®ACGIH

3.7.1 Measurement Conditions. Conditions inside ducts are important in considering the type of device to use and the corrections that should be made to its readings:

1. Air heavily contaminated with corrosive gases, dusts, fumes, mists, or products of combustion cannot be measured using some devices and presents problems in using all instruments. Drilling into those ducts can be hazardous, so it can be critical to know the properties of the chemicals and particulates that may be inside the duct. Fragile probes can be corroded, abraded, or otherwise damaged by airborne contaminants in the duct. Probes that contain sensors may report values incorrectly if coated with dust or other materials. Probes that act as a conduit for gases to reach the sensor may become blocked or allow these deleterious materials to reach the instrument where they block, coat, or damage it. Probes that conduct pressure only will pass along very little contaminant to the sensor, but they can become plugged.

2. High temperature conditions require density corrections for most devices (see Equations 3.2 and 3.3), and some sensors can be damaged if high temperature gases reach them.

3. High concentrations of water vapor and mist can plug probes so quickly that measurement becomes impracticable.

4. All field instruments have difficulty with very low velocities. Devices that measure pressure (including velocity pressure) for field use generally have degraded accuracy at static or velocity pressures below 0.1 "wg. Thermal anemometers developed for the field become increasingly unreliable below 30 fpm.

5. It is difficult to measure accurately where airflows are non-uniform. Such locations include near the discharges of process equipment and fans and near elbows, sudden expansions or contractions, and less than seven duct diameters downstream of junction fittings. However, this is typical of many field conditions.

6. In some systems, measurements may vary substantially over relatively short periods. Systems with automatic control of dampers or fan speeds sometimes change so frequently that the measurements taken on the same day at different locations in the system may present a misleading picture of system behavior. Velocity sampling for isokinetic sampling of stacks is often plagued by variable air volume systems, particularly when one stack is used in common for several fans. It is, therefore, important to log the insertion depth or setting of all dampers before tests are done and confirm that they have not changed during the tests.

3.7.2 Common Errors in Testing and Measurements. It is important to use measurement instruments properly. Errors in measurement usually occur when any of the following "short cuts" are used:

1. Using a single reading at the center of the duct and then multiplying it by some factor such as '0.9' (called the Centerline Method).

2. Using more than the centerline but still taking fewer readings than recommended.

3. Using instruments not intended for measurement in industrial air streams. For example, one should avoid using thermal anemometers, standard Pitot tube or similar devices in dust laden air streams or those with high moisture or heat.

4. Doing Pitot traverses in locations where the airflow has eddies, such as immediately downstream of elbows, hoods, etc.

5. Failure to consider heat, moisture or elevation corrections when calculating velocities and flows from measured data.

6. Using hood face velocities to determine branch airflows when it is possible to do a Pitot traverse in the duct instead.

7. Blocking hood airflows with the body or with bulky instruments when measuring hood face velocities (Figure 3-35).

8. Failing to calibrate measurement devices.

3.7.3 Ventilation Measurements. This section describes procedures for ventilation measurements. It is oriented to using a Pitot tube with a digital manometer; however, it would apply to velocity traverses of ducts done with a thermal anemometer or other devices.

Prepare Measurement Locations

1. Select locations for measurements. Table 3-8 provides some guidance.

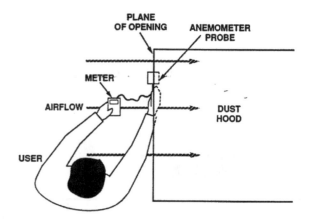

FIGURE 3-35. Blocking airflow at a hood

2. Drill the entry hole using a drill bit that is slightly larger than the Pitot tube's stem diameter. Larger holes are unnecessary. When using an existing hole that is unnecessarily large, cover the hole with duct tape and cut a longitudinal slit to allow entry of the Pitot tube.

3. Label measurement points on a sketch or drawing of the system.

4. Label each measurement location with

   a. Initials or name of individual responsible

   b. Date

   c. Notes on operating conditions

   d. Item or test-point number

   e. ID of duct

   f. Diameter of the duct

   g. Desired measurement values (for example SP_h, SP_{end}, VP)

Immediate Preparation Each Day of Measurement

1. Turn on digital manometer (if one is used) at least 30 minutes before use.

2. Check Pitot stems for alignment.

3. Prepare computer (if used) or data collection sheet

4. Zero manometer

5. Verify calibration of equipment (see Section 3.6)

Taking Measurements

1. To avoid subconscious bias, when reading an instrument with fluctuating values, look away then look back and record the second value you see. If the instrument demonstrated variability, collect several readings and average the readings.

2. Insertion depths for measurements:

   a. For static pressures, measure at centerline or at installed fitting.

   b. For velocity or velocity pressures, conduct an 8 or 10-point traverse of each traverse diameter. Conduct two perpendicular traverses.

3. Time constants for digital manometers:

   a. For static pressure measurements, average over five seconds (digital manometer) or take the median of three readings taken at least 2 seconds apart. If the instrument has a time constant, the duration between readings should exceed the time constant.

   b. For velocity or velocity pressure measurements, average over 1.5 to 2 times the instrument time constant.

4. Input or write comments on:

   a. Measurement conditions if not good

   b. Condition of duct (defects, wear, plugging)

   c. Known or suspected alterations

   d. Expected and observed pressure differential across the air cleaning device

   e. Special loss factors

   f. Setting of blast gate or other damper (e.g., percent open)

   g. Pressure differential across air cleaners

   h. Other notes

5. Compare to previous values if available. If substantially different (possibly greater than 10 percent):

   a. Re-measure

   b. Note need to investigate for alterations

6. Recheck zero as frequently as experience with the device suggests.

7. Cover test ports with duct tape or a rubber or plastic stopper.

Recording Values

It is important to prepare a means to log data in advance on a computer with software, on a computerized spreadsheet customized for the purpose, or on a paper form. The data sheet shown as Figure 3-36 is useful for recording Pitot traverse and static pressure observations. The same form can be set up in a spreadsheet program for direct input while taking measurements or for later data entry from completed paper forms.

It is crucial to write down any comments or information one wishes to remember immediately after the observation. What may have seemed clear and easy to remember early in the day can become a source of confusion if entered hours later. In this regard, it is important to take great care when data logging into digital manometers and other electronic devices. When data that has been logged are later downloaded, it is useless if one cannot associate specific measurement conditions and their locations with the specific data downloaded into the computer. Ideally, data logging devices will automatically time and date-stamp each datum, allowing one to keep track of data by writing down what was occurring at the specific time of each measurement. It is much less desirable if the electronic device simply segregates the data into different groupings or memory locations. For that strategy, one should log the value on paper as well as the device to be sure that each datum can be related to the conditions and location of the measurement.

REFERENCES

3.1   American Society of Heating, Refrigerating and Air Conditioning Engineers. ASHRAE Handbook–1997 Fundamentals.

3.2   American Society of Heating, Refrigerating and Air Conditioning Engineers. Practices for Measurement,

VELOCITY TRAVERSE
DATA FORM

Process Location/Description	Duct/Traverse Schematic

Duct Description _____ Shape ☐ Round   ☐ Rectangular   ☐ _____

Orientation _____ Dimensions D = _____ L= ___ W = ____   _____

Area

Density factor

Elevation = _____ : $df_e = [1-(6.73*10^{-6})(\text{elevation})]^{5.258}$ = _____

Static Pressure = ____ : $df_P = (407 + SP)/407$ = _____

Temperature = ____ F : $df_T = 530/(\text{Temp} + 460)$ = _____

Moisture ω = _____ : $df_m = (1 + \omega)/(1 + 1.607*\omega)$ = _____

$df = (df_e)(df_P)(df_T)(df_m)$ = _____

Traverse	☐ Vertical	☐ North-South		Traverse	☐ Vertical	☐ North-South	
Point	Distance	VP "wg	V, fpm	Point	Distance	VP "wg	V, fpm
1				1			
2				2			
3				3			
4				4			
5				5			
6				6			
7				7			
8				8			
9				9			
10				10			
Velocity Subtotal				Velocity Subtotal			

Average Velocity = _____

Area = _____

Volumetric flow = _____

Note: Calculate Velocity from $V = 4005*\sqrt{VP*K/df}$

FIGURE 3-36. Sample Pitot traverse data sheet

Testing, Adjusting, and Balancing of Building Heating, Ventilation, Air Conditioning and Refrigeration Systems, ANSI/ASHRAE Standard 111-1988.

3.3   Guffey, S.E. and Booth, D.W.: Comparison of Pitot Traverses Taken at Varying Distances Downstream of Obstructions. Am. Ind. Hyg. Assoc. J., 60(2): 165-174 (1999).

3.4   Guffey, S.E.: Simplifying Pitot Traverses. Applied Occup. Environ. Hyg., 5(2): 95-100 (1990).

3.5   Hama, G.: A Calibrating Wind Tunnel for Measuring Instruments. Air Engr. 41:18-20, (December, 1967).

3.6   Hama, G.: Calibration of Alnor Velometers. Am. Ind. Hyg. Assoc. J., (December, 1958).

3.7   Hama, G. and Curley, L.S.: Instrumentation for the Measurement of Low Velocities with a Pitot Tube. Air Engr. (July, 1967) and Am. Ind. Hyg. Assoc. J. (May-June, 1967).

3.8   Wang L.S.: Repeatability of Velocity Pressure and Static Pressure Measurements in Five Working Ventilation Systems. MS Thesis, Department of Environmental Health. University of Washington, Seattle, WA (1997).

Chapter 4
BALANCING DUCT SYSTEMS WITH DAMPERS

4.1   INTRODUCTION

Dampers are ventilation devices used to adjust the airflows through the branches in a duct system. A damper reduces the airflow to a given branch by adding to its resistance to flow. As its resistance to flow increases, airflow is diverted to alternate pathways in proportions that can be predicted mathematically.[4.1]

By judicious adjustment of all dampers in a system, a technician can force the relative airflows through the branches to achieve a desired distribution. This is called "balancing" with dampers. If each branch receives the correct fraction of the fan airflow, then by changing the fan rotation rate one can raise or lower all branch airflows to the desired levels. Alternatively, one can insert every damper still further until the additional cumulative resistance "chokes the fan down" to the desired level.

This chapter discusses how dampers work, when they should be used, when they should be adjusted, and how to adjust them. The chapter describes three methods of air balancing with dampers. An example is included with each method as well as a discussion of advantages and disadvantages. Each successive method uses less field measurement and adjustment but also requires more calculations. For simple systems of only a few branches, the Basic Method could be used. As the system becomes more complicated two more methods are shown that require more computations but fewer re-adjustments of dampers. This could represent a time savings.

In balancing methods presented in this chapter, VP_{cl} (measurement of Velocity Pressure at the center of duct) is sometimes used for intermediate steps of measurement. This is done because it represents an approximate relative value when doing quick adjustments in the setting of dampers. To be valid, a complete traverse must be performed to determine actual airflow but approximations may be used for intermediate steps. All initial and final readings must be done with complete traverse readings as recommended in this Manual and the Ventilation Manual. The most accurate readings during the balance will also be accomplished by full traverses in the intermediate steps of balancing but for large systems, V_{cl} (if properly determined) can be used.

4.2   BALANCING BY DESIGN

As is shown in the Design chapter of the Ventilation Manual, it is quite possible to design systems that have distributions that are acceptably close to the desired levels without employing dampers. This is done by judicious selection of components (e.g., elbows with higher or lower loss coefficients) and duct "sizes" (i.e., cross-sectional areas) as a part of normal duct system design. The advantage of systems designed to be balanced without dampers is that they should keep the same distribution unless duct diameters or fittings are modified in some way. One can be reasonably certain that the

distribution remains at the level for which it was designed. With dampers, there is always the concern that someone will change the damper settings when they should not.

The primary disadvantage of systems balanced without dampers is the same as their primary advantage: the distribution cannot be changed easily. If changing conditions or requirements necessitate a change in distribution, it is costly to achieve by substitutions of fittings with higher or lower loss coefficients or by changing duct diameters. Aside from cost considerations, replacing fittings is not likely to add enough resistance to shift airflow substantially. Likewise, rebalancing systems by changing duct sizes generally requires replacement of whole branches and submains. Such replacements are costly and disruptive enough that managers are understandably reluctant to authorize the necessary expenditures, especially when balancing with dampers is much less expensive and disruptive. In some cases (as specified by the National Fire Protection Association — NFPA), there may not be an option to use blast gates or dampers and the system must be installed using the Balance by Design Method. The designer must check NFPA requirements and other specifications to determine which method should be used.

4.3   PROBLEMS WITH DAMPERS AND POTENTIAL SOLUTIONS

Not all airflow distribution problems can be solved solely by adjusting dampers, and there are many problems practitioners might associate with dampers:

1. *The pressure required at the fan is substantially higher if dampers are used instead of balance by design.* This is true only if the fan speed is unnecessarily high and one adjusts the dampers to "choke down" the fan airflow without changing the fan speed. If dampers are employed only to produce the desired distribution and the fan is adjusted properly, the pressure requirement for the system will nearly always be lower than the same system balanced "by design."[4.1]

   However, the pressure requirements with or without dampers may be excessive if the airflow in any branch must be increased more than about 20-30%. If a large increase is needed, one should consider increasing the duct diameter of the branch duct and at least the first submain downstream of it.

2. *Operators and others tend to open dampers on one branch without considering the effect on airflows in other branches.* Since opening a damper on one branch increases its flow but reduces the airflow to all other branches, opening dampers can be a way of "stealing" additional airflow from everyone else. This can produce a "race to the bottom" where all operators fully open their dampers, making the dampers useless for all.

   This problem can be avoided by locking the dampers (using padlocks, welding blades in place, etc.). If the contaminants appear to be poorly controlled, no security system will protect the dampers. Hence, it is critical to provide adequate control.

3. *Plugging is likely due to sticky or stringy contaminants becoming caught on the dampers.* This may be an insuperable problem for some systems unless one is willing to clean the dampers frequently, perhaps even daily. This maintenance can be encouraged by connecting the damper fitting with easily removed clamps and by locating cleanouts near dampers.

4. Flammable materials caught on a damper could create or exacerbate a fire or explosion hazard. This may be an insuperable problem for highly flammable contaminants.

5. *If airflow is reduced using a damper, the velocity in some ducts may fall below the minimum velocities needed to prevent rapid settling.* This can certainly happen if the duct diameters are larger than needed. To avoid this problem, one should either replace oversized ducts or increase the target airflows to ensure sufficient duct velocities.

Some authorities[4.2] strongly urge "balance by design" instead of balancing with dampers because of the many disadvantages listed above (*See also* Ventilation Manual, Chapter 5). That may be a wise policy when first installing a new system, but the high direct and indirect costs of replacing system components to obtain a new balance "by design" may discourage the re-balancing of systems, leading to prolonged periods of inadequate airflows to hoods.

4.4   LIMITATIONS OF DAMPER EFFECTIVENESS

Care must be taken when attempting to make large changes to airflow distributions. There is no specific "limit," but as dampers are inserted farther, the fan pressure requirement can increase. Furthermore, if the system carries particulates, care must be taken to ensure that duct velocities do not fall below minimum levels required to prevent plugging.

At the same time the placement of the damper is important to proper operation. The blade should never be located at the bottom of the duct or near elbows and other disturbances that may influence the pressure drop and reliability. Damper blades can become sources for material buildup if not properly located.

If large changes in airflow to certain branches are required, it may be necessary to replace with either a larger or smaller diameter duct.

1. If particulates are involved and the airflow through a branch duct is to be reduced, it may be necessary to replace the duct with a smaller diameter in order to maintain sufficiently high velocities at the reduced airflow.

2. If particulates are not involved, then airflows can be reduced without changing duct sizes. Unless a majority of branches are virtually closed off, it is unlikely that the fan pressure will rise to extreme levels (i.e., maximum fan pressure). Note that fan motor power requirements will decline if centrifugal fans are used.

3. Increasing airflows to a given branch with dampers is much more difficult unless one increases fan speed. The possible increase to a given branch is limited by two factors: 1) Fan airflow falls as dampers are inserted so that the amount available to other branches is somewhat reduced, and 2) The airflow shifted from an adjusted branch to other branches is shared by all other branches (but especially those just upstream). Hence, it is difficult to sharply increase the airflow to any given branch unless the airflows to almost all other branches are reduced. As a rule of thumb, if the airflow through a branch must be increased by more than about 20%, it is likely that damper adjustments will not be sufficient.

If large increases in airflow are required for a given branch (especially if the other branch airflows are at desired levels), one should consider replacing the branch duct with a larger size before adjusting dampers and the fan speed. As a first approximation, the new duct size can be determined using traditional methods of duct sizing. That is, the duct area should be the largest duct size whose area is less than the target air volume divided by the minimum air velocity.

4.4.1 Characteristics of Blastgates. There are many designs and variants of designs of adjustable dampers used in exhaust ventilation systems, but the most common (and most suitable for contaminant control ventilation) are "blastgate or cutoff" dampers (see Figure 4-1). The slide is inserted perpendicular to the flow. As the air flows around the damper blade (see Figure 4-2), it separates from the duct downstream of the blade. Energy losses in the separation region vary with the fraction of the duct cross-section blocked by the damper, the sharpness of the damper, and the velocity pressure (VP) of the airflow upstream of the damper. It may also vary with the proximity of upstream and downstream disturbances, such as elbows, hood connections, etc.

These energy changes produce static pressure changes downstream of the damper. The resistance of the damper, X_{damper},[4.1] can be determined from the change in total pressure due to the damper divided by the upstream velocity pressure. Since it is difficult to measure pressure across a damper accurately, the most feasible way to determine the resistance of a damper is to determine the difference in the resistance at the end of the branch duct with and without the damper. Since the value of both the total pressure and velocity pressure would both change as the damper is inserted, this would be computed as:[4.1]

Plan View

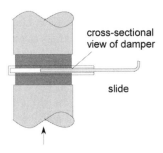

Elevation

FIGURE 4-1. Blastgate damper

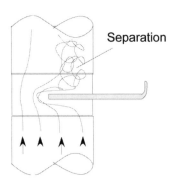

FIGURE 4-2. Flow around a damper

$$X_{damper} = \left(\frac{VP_2 + SP_2}{VP_2}\right) - \left(\frac{VP_1 + SP_1}{VP_1}\right) \qquad [4.1]$$

where: 1 = without damper inserted

  2 = with damper inserted some amount

  SP = static pressure measured well downstream of the damper

  VP = mean velocity pressure at the same location

The more the required reduction in flow, the greater the value of X_{damper} that is needed. Required values of X_{damper} on the same system for different branches typically range[4.1] from 0.2 to 5. Values less than 0.2 would have little effect on airflow, suggesting that the damper is not needed. For a duct that has a diameter that is much larger than needed, the value of X_{damper} could reach 100 or more.

While it is clear that the greater the insertion depth of the damper the greater the value of X_{damper}, very little has been published on the relationship of X_{damper} to insertion depth. Crowder and Lowdermilk[4.3] published a table of insertion depths to achieve different pressures at a given velocity. Idel'chik[4.4] provided a table of recommended values for a damper with a flat edge. Plotting them shows a highly non-linear relationship (see Figure 4-3). The resistance increases much more than linearly, perhaps because: 1) as one increasingly inserts the damper, the unoccluded opening becomes progressively smaller, increasing the air velocity past the edge of the slide, and 2) the region of separation becomes larger (see Figure 4-2).

As shown in Figure 4-3, the resistance due to a damper changes little until the damper is more than one-third closed.

At insertions greater than three-quarters of the diameter, large swings in airflow may occur with small additional changes in insertion depth, making adjustments frustrating and time-consuming. It is much easier to balance a system if the balancing methodology minimizes necessary insertion depths so that the operation is in a more level part of the curve in Figure 4-3.

Figure 4-3 represents values for one damper. Other dampers may have different curves based on blade design and blastgate location. For example, the leading edge of the slide (see Figure 4-4) can be straight or it can be rounded so that it follows the shape of the duct (convex) or rounded in the opposite direction (concave). Note that the concave shape precludes complete blockage of flow, a sometimes desirable trait. All dampers would have relatively low X_{damper} values when slightly inserted, but higher values as damper blades are inserted farther.

As is known by analogy to orifice plates used for airflow measurement, the sharper the leading edge of the damper the greater the value of X_{damper} at a given insertion depth, especially if the beveled edge faces downstream. Since abrasive particles in the air can round the edge of the damper, it is possible

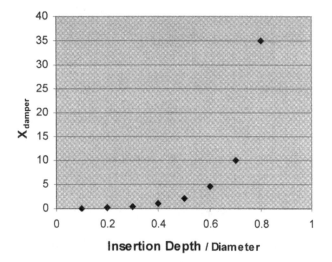

FIGURE 4-3. Graph of Idel'chik (1972) values

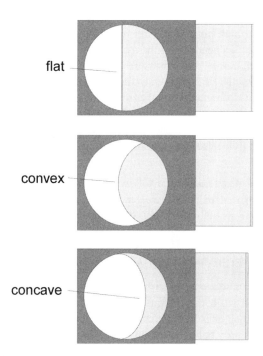

FIGURE 4-4. Different leading edges

that the resistance of the damper at a given insertion depth can decline over time with abrasive wear. It is also possible that the resistance would vary due to accumulation of contamination on the blade or just upstream or downstream of the blade. By creating a smoother path for the air around the damper, it is likely that an accumulation of contaminant in the duct would greatly reduce (not increase) the resistance, especially if it is on the downstream side. On the other hand, if contaminant buildup reduced the unoccluded area, it is likely that resistance would increase.

Once the required resistance of a given damper is known, it is also possible to use an orifice plate or other fixed obstruction with the same resistance in place of a conventional damper.

So-called "butterfly" dampers swivel about an axis to partially or fully block airflows. If the blade is aligned to the duct then the obstruction is minimal. If it is perpendicular then it will nearly or completely block the flow. These dampers are probably more likely to promote plugging than blastgates. They can be more difficult to adjust precisely than blastgates, especially when used to achieve substantial airflow reductions. For high velocities they may vibrate unless sturdily constructed, and they can easily shift if they are not tightened very securely.

4.5   STRATEGIC GOALS IN ADJUSTING DAMPERS

Dampers and fans should be adjusted together to provide sufficient airflows to each hood while minimizing energy costs. It is prudent to assume that for a hood to be reliably effective its airflow should not fall below some minimum reli-

able value (Q_{goal}). If Q_{goal} is selected appropriately for a given hood, then any amount of airflow above Q_{goal} is unnecessary and wasteful. Hence, for the example data listed as Table 4-1 (see Figure 4-5), Branches 2-A, 4-C, 5-C, and 6-D have excessive flows that should be reduced while the airflows in Branches 1-A and 3-B should be increased. The total airflow through the fan is 40% above the level that should exist if the system were perfectly balanced.

4.5.1 Overall Goal. The appropriate overall goal in balancing system airflows is to minimize the system airflow (i.e., the airflow at the fan) without allowing any hood airflow to become insufficient. This can be done by forcing the airflow (Q) in each branch to be as close as possible to its goal without falling below its Q_{goal}. For the example data shown in Table 4-1, the overall airflow before balancing was 40% above desired levels, a substantial excess. More importantly, some hoods have less than their goal airflows.

4.5.2 Distribution Goal. The level of airflow in each branch is determined both by the fan and by the damper adjustments. The purpose of the dampers is to achieve the desired distribution of airflows (i.e., each hood receives the desired fraction of the total airflow). The desired level of airflows can then be achieved by adjusting the fan output. Thus, the goal when adjusting dampers should be to force each branch duct to carry the same fraction (Q_{ratio}) of its Q_{goal} as all other branch ducts. For a given branch:

$$Q_{ratio} = (Q/Q_{goal}) \qquad \text{[4.2]}$$

For the example data shown in Table 4-1, values of Q_{ratio} before balancing vary from 0.82 to 2.57. Values of Q_{ratio} below 1.0 indicate insufficient airflow. Values above 1.0 indicate unnecessary airflow.

4.5.3 Total Airflow Goal. For the system as a whole, the least energy is consumed if the fan airflow is the minimum possible value ($Q_{goal-fan}$) and the fan pressure is the minimum that can exist when the fan airflow equals $Q_{goal-fan}$.[4.10] The first is achieved when all branches have airflows exactly equal to their respective Q_{goal} values. Since densities could vary throughout the systems, this minimum fan airflow can be computed only from mass balance:

TABLE 4-1. First Example Problem

ID	Dia	$Q_{meas.}$	Q_{goal}	Q_{ratio}
1-A	4	328	400	0.82
2-A	5	529	400	1.32
3-B	4	362	400	0.91
4-C	5	554	400	1.39
5-C	5	554	400	1.39
6-D	7	1030	400	2.57
Total		3357	2400	1.40

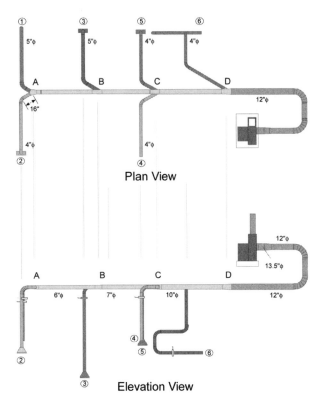

Plan View

Elevation View

FIGURE 4-5. Example duct system

$$Q_{fan-goal} = \left(\frac{1}{df_{fan}}\right)\sum_{i=1}^{n} df_i Q_{goal_i}$$ [4.3]

where: i = i^{th} branch duct

n = total number of branch ducts in the system

df = density factor of the air

$Q_{(fan-goal)}$ = airflow goal for the fan

If the static pressures upstream of the fan are less than 10 "wg and if the temperatures in each branch duct are within a 30 F range, the density factor is approximately the same throughout the system. Equation 4.3 can be simplified as:

$$Q_{fan-goal} = \sum_{i=1}^{n} Q_{goal_i}$$ [4.4]

For the example data shown in Table 4-1, the value of $Q_{fan-goal}$ is 2400 acfm.

4.5.4 System Pressure Goal. The second goal in balancing should be to minimize the fan static pressure. In addition to increasing energy costs, unnecessarily high static pressures stress the ducts and air cleaning device and may make damper adjustment more difficult. Fan motor loads are roughly pro-

portional to both airflow and total pressure. Hence, an unnecessarily high total pressure requires unnecessary energy expenses. Depending on the system resistance and the fan's operating curve, high pressures could also have substantial effects on the fan's efficiency and its noise level. A high static pressure also requires a higher rotation rate, possibly at a level beyond the current fan's upper limit. The minimum possible system pressure will occur if the system is successfully balanced while also leaving at least one damper completely open.[(4.1)]

As is discussed in the following sections, the interaction between system resistance, fan output and branch airflows complicates both adjusting the fan output and adjusting dampers.

4.6   DETERMINING INITIAL CONDITIONS

Some practitioners start balancing with some dampers partially closed. If the airflow in each of those branches is just below Q_{goal} or is higher than Q_{goal}, then opening all of those dampers fully before beginning to adjust may be unnecessary. However, it is probably safest to always determine initial airflows (Q_{open}) with all dampers fully open. In those cases, it is necessary to protect the fan from electrical overload since the airflow and power requirement will increase when dampers are open.

It is also important to measure hood static pressure, SP_h, and other key variables (e.g., fabric filter pressure drop).

4.6.1 Determining Airflow Goals for Each Hood. The airflow required for each branch and hood (Q_{goal}) should be no less than the values recommended in ventilation texts (e.g., *Industrial Ventilation: A Manual of Recommended Practice for Design*). In addition, the airflow should be high enough that the duct velocity exceeds minimum recommended values for adequate transport velocity. If the velocity is low, then either the duct must be replaced with a smaller one or the Q_{goal} value must be increased to:

$$Q_{goal} = Area * V_t$$ [4.5]

where: V_t = minimum velocity necessary to prevent settling

A = Cross-sectional area

If a hood has substantially low airflow and is ineffective, its airflow should be increased to the recommended value. If a hood already has at least the recommended airflow and its performance is poor, then it is possible that the recommended level is inadequate. However, one should first look to improving the hood design and the work practices since higher levels of airflow with the same design and conditions may also prove ineffective.

If the hood design and work practices are reasonably optimal, the airflow exceeds recommended levels, and the hood is ineffective, consider setting the value of Q_{goal} to be higher than the recommended level. It is important to not exaggerate the amount of increase. If the level of airflow is already high, it is quite possible that increasing the airflows will not solve the problem.

The next sections list three damper adjustment methods with a common example application for each.

4.6.2 Determining Adjustment Goals During Balancing. Although the goal in balancing is to provide the desired airflow for each branch, when actually adjusting dampers, it may be more convenient to use measured values that should be proportional to airflow, such as velocity, or proportional to airflow squared, such as the centerline velocity pressure or hood static pressure. Mean duct velocities can be determined from full 10 or 20-point Pitot traverses of each branch (see Chapter 3).

4.6.3 Centerline Velocity Pressure Goals. Since velocity pressure is proportional to the volumetric flow squared (Q^2), it is possible to use the mean velocity pressure as the indicator that the airflow has been adjusted to Q_{goal}. Likewise, since the ratio of the centerline velocity pressure (VP_{cl}) to VP_{avg} should be reasonably constant for a given measurement location, then VP_{cl} also can be used as a surrogate for airflow. Thus, one could adjust the damper until the observed value of VP_{cl} is the same as $VP_{cl\text{-}goal}$:

$$VP_{cl-goal} = VP_{cl-open} \left(\frac{Q_{goal}}{Q_{open}} \right)^2 \qquad [4.6]$$

where: $VP_{cl-goal}$ =   velocity pressure that should exist when the observed airflow equals Q_{goal}

   $VP_{cl-open}$ =   velocity pressure measured with all dampers open

The centerline velocity pressure can be a poor surrogate for the volumetric flow if: 1) its values are low (e.g., less than 0.15 "wg) due to low velocity in the duct or to pressure sensor error, 2) the velocity profile varies due to changing conditions upstream of the measurement, or 3) the velocity profile is highly asymmetrical. The latter is likely if VP_{avg}/VP_{cl} falls below 0.8 or exceeds 1.0. If three measured values of VP at the center of the duct are greater than the other values it is likely that errors due to use of VP_{cl} will not be excessive for purposes of adjustment when used in the manner described for this method.

Its accuracy also is suspect if a single reading is taken. It should be measured three times, each time removing the Pitot tube from the duct and re-inserting it before taking the next measurement. The median of the three values should be used as VP_{cl}.

Use of Equation 4.5 is not the same as employing the pipe factor (i.e., VP_{avg}/VP_{cl}) with the assumption that it is always

0.9, a common practice. Although 0.9 is reasonably accurate under ideal measurement conditions,[4.5] under varying measurement conditions pipe factor may deviate substantially from 0.9. Wang[4.6] found in a study of five working duct systems that airflow estimates based on pipe factors done for a diverse range of conditions deviated by -25% to +10% from values based on 20-point Pitot traverses. Nearly half of all airflows that were estimated using a pipe factor of 0.9 deviated from traverse values by 5% or more. For those reasons, it is very important that VP_{cl} be measured at least 5D downstream of any disturbance (e.g., elbow) and at least 3D upstream of any disturbance (especially the damper).

4.6.4 Hood Static Pressure Goals. Since hood static pressures (SP_h) are proportional to velocity pressures for a broad range of airflows[4.7] a goal hood static pressure can also be computed based on the SP_h value prior to damper adjustments:

$$SP_{h-goal} = SP_{h-open} \left(\frac{df_{goal} \; Q_{goal}}{df_{open} \; Q_{open}} \right)^2 \qquad [4.7]$$

where: SP_{h-goal} =   value of hood static pressure that would exist at $Q = Q_{goal}$

   SP_{h-open} =   hood static pressure measured with all dampers open

Note: When measuring SP_h, accuracy is improved by taking the median of three observations.

If density does not vary significantly from the time prior to adjustments to the time the dampers are adjusted, Equation 4.7 simplifies to:

$$SP_{h-goal} = SP_{h-open} \left(\frac{Q_{goal}}{Q_{open}} \right)^2 \qquad [4.8]$$

Since Q_{ratio} equals Q/Q_{goal}, Equation 4.8 can be re-stated as:

$$SP_{h-goal} = SP_{h-open}/(Q_{ratio})^2$$

Hood static pressure values are a somewhat more reliable surrogate for volumetric flow than are centerline velocity pressure values, but they, too, must: 1) be high enough for the pressure sensor to measure accurately, and 2) be measured at least 5D downstream and 4D upstream of disturbances. Like VP_{cl} values, it is prudent to measure SP_h three times and use the median value for computations.

4.7   WHEN THE DISTRIBUTION SHOULD BE RE-BALANCED

If the airflows are all high in every branch, it may be only necessary to adjust the fan airflow. Since every hood should have sufficient airflow, the ideal fan speed would be such that the lowest value of Q_{ratio} was 1.0. The desired airflow can also be obtained by adjusting the fan outlet damper if one is used.

This achieves the goal of ensuring that every hood has enough airflow, but it does not minimize the airflow requirement since some hoods may receive much more airflow than needed. Given the direct and indirect costs of balancing efforts, a good result can be achieved if the final fan volume (Q_{fan}) exceeds $Q_{fan-goal}$ by less than 10%.

The excess system flow is affected by a variety of factors. It is likely to be high if:

1. The original airflow distribution was inappropriate.

2. The airflow requirement for one or more hoods changes.

3. A branch is added or removed from a system.

4. A duct is replaced with one having a larger or smaller diameter or other changes are made that dramatically change resistance to flow.

5. One or more hoods are re-positioned in a manner that substantially changes the lengths and number of elbows in branch ducts, or if it changes how and where the branch and submains are connected to each other.

Most systems may have to be balanced several times over their useful life, even with stable operating conditions and no major duct changes. When there are changes to operating conditions or major duct changes, systems are very likely to require re-balancing.

4.7.1 Measures of Effectiveness of Damper Adjustments.
An obvious but misleading way to rate the effectiveness of damper adjustments is to compute the relative difference between the sum of observed airflows and the sum of goal airflows. It would be misleading because a system with excessive airflows in some branches and counterbalancing insufficient airflows in others could have a zero "error." Indeed the total airflow could be made to match the total sum of goals by setting the fan speed without using dampers at all.

Clearly, any measure of effectiveness should consider the deviations of values of Q_{ratio} from a value of 1.0. For example, one could employ the range of deviations from a value 1.0 in Example 1. If that were done and values of Q_{ratio} ranged from 0.82 to 2.57, then the errors for individual branches would range from -18% to +157%. One problem with that is that no hood should be allowed to receive insufficient airflow. If that were remedied by increasing the fan speed to 1/0.82 times its previous value, the lowest value would be satisfied but the highest value would be 191% of design.

The most useful measure is the relative difference between the lowest airflow at which the minimum Q_{ratio} is 1.0 and Q_{fan} = $Q_{fan-goal}$. Since the former is simply current fan airflow divided by the minimum value of Q_{ratio}, this can be computed after adjusting dampers from:

$$Q_{excess} = [1/min(Q_{ratio}) * Q_{fan}/Q_{fan-goal} -1]* 100\% \qquad \text{[4.10]}$$

where: $min(Q_{ratio})$ = minimum ratio of actual to desired airflow among all branches

Q_{fan} = airflow at the fan determined at any stage

In the previous example, $Q_{fan}/Q_{fan-goal} = 1.40$ and $min(Q_{ratio})$ is 0.82. The total Q_{excess} computed using Equation 4.10 is $(1/0.82*1.4 - 1)*100\% = 71\%$, a large amount of wasted airflow.

4.8   BASIC AIR BALANCE METHOD

The Basic method is the most commonly used balancing procedure. Different individuals may have somewhat different strategies but the basic idea is to adjust the first damper so that for it $Q = Q_{goal}$, then adjust the second damper so that for it $Q = Q_{goal}$, and so on until all dampers have been adjusted to achieve the desired airflows. However, since VP_{cl} is proportional to airflow squared, one can use VP_{cl} as a surrogate for Q during adjustments. This method is the least accurate of those discussed in this chapter, but if the procedure listed below is followed, each hood should receive airflow greater than or equal to Q_{goal}.

4.8.1 Procedure for Basic Method. The following is a version of the Basic balancing procedure:

1. Determine the desired airflow (Q_{goal}) for each hood. Compute $Q_{fan-goal}$ from Equation 4.3 or 4.4.

2. Open all dampers, taking care to protect the fan motor since the power it requires may increase substantially. Optional: partially close dampers for ducts whose airflows are known to be highly excessive.

3. Conduct Pitot traverses and measure VP_{cl} and SP_h for each branch duct, compute the "open" damper value of airflow (Q_{open}) for each branch.

4. Compute the initial $Q_{fan-open}$ from the sum of the observed airflows.

5. If necessary, adjust the fan's airflow until $Q_{fan-open}/Q_{fan-goal}$ exceeds or is equal to 1.15 and is below 1.40. A value of 1.2 is probably the most prudent adjustment goal if that is done.

6. Compute $VP_{cl-goal}$ for each branch duct using Equation 4.6.

7. Determine the order to adjust dampers based on convenience, decreasing duct size, or increasing insufficiency of airflow.

8. Adjust each damper in turn until it is observed that VP_{cl} equals $VP_{cl-goal}$ for that branch. Note that only the last damper adjusted will have the desired airflow. All others will change as each damper is moved.

9. Repeat Step 8 (i.e., 2nd round).

10. If necessary, repeat Step 8 again (i.e., 3rd round).

11. Do a full Pitot traverse for each branch duct to determine the final observed airflows (Q) and all Q_{ratio} values (Equation 4.2).

12. If the lowest value of Q_{ratio} (min(Q_{ratio})) is less than 1.0, increase the fan speed based on:

$$\omega_2 = \frac{\omega_1}{\min Q_{ratio}}$$

Note that it may be prudent to set the fan airflow to 5% above the minimum level as a safety factor.

If the initial total airflow is adequately high but not excessive (e.g., 115% to 150% of $Q_{fan\text{-}goal}$), this procedure should ensure that every hood has enough airflow and produce close to the desired distribution in two or three rounds of adjustment. Using this method, Balasubramian[4.5] found the excess airflow volume to be approximately 4.8% to 8.5% in two rounds of adjustments of a system with seven branches. For these tests, the measurement conditions were ideal and initial airflows were sufficient. The test started with all dampers fully open, then adjusted dampers in the order of most excessive to least excessive Q_{ratio} values. Under field conditions the excess airflow is likely to be somewhat higher in many cases.

4.8.2 Example 1 (Basic Method). The example application listed here is intended to illustrate the use of the Basic method. There are other methods that will also show relative advantages and disadvantages.

Following the steps of the Basic Method, the results would be as follows:

1. *Determine the desired airflow (Q_{goal}) for each hood. Compute $Q_{fan\text{-}goal}$ from Equation 4.4.*

   Note, if the density changes within the system, use Equation 4.3. The values shown in Table 4-2 were selected arbitrarily for this example.

TABLE 4-2. Initial Measurements and Airflow Goals for Example Problem

Branch	Dia	Q_{open}	Q_{goal}	Q_{ratio}	SP_h
1-A	4	328	400	0.82	1.18
2-A	5	529	400	1.32	1.51
3-B	4	362	400	0.91	1.44
4-C	5	554	400	1.39	1.66
5-C	5	554	400	1.39	1.66
6-D	7	1030	400	2.57	1.92
Fan	14	3357	2400	1.40	
Fan speed = 598 rpm					

2. *Open all dampers. Optional: partially close dampers for ducts whose airflows are known to be highly excessive.*

   In this example, all dampers were opened fully.

3. *Do Pitot traverses and measure VP_{cl} and SP_h for each branch duct, then compute the "open" damper value of airflow (Q_{open}) for each branch.*

   The results are shown in Table 4-2, $Q_{fan\text{-}goal}$ = 2400 acfm.

4. *Compute the initial $Q_{fan\text{-}open}$ from the sum of the observed airflows.*

   From Table 4-2, $Q_{fan\text{-}open}$ = 3357 acfm for $Q_{fan\text{-}open}$.

5. *If necessary, adjust the fan's airflow until $Q_{fan\text{-}open}/Q_{fan\text{-}goal}$ exceeds or is equal to 1.15 and is below 1.40. A value of 1.2 is probably the most prudent adjustment goal if that is done.*

   In this example

   $Q_{fan\text{-}open}/Q_{goal\text{-}fan}$ = 3357 acfm / 2400 acfm = 1.40

   Hence, the fan output was not adjusted.

6. *Compute $VP_{cl\text{-}goal}$ for each branch duct using Equation 4.6.*

   Table 4-3 shows the measured values for this example. For Branch 1-A, the measured VP_{cl} was 0.98 "wg. Since Q_{ratio} was 0.82, $VP_{cl\text{-}goal}$ = 0.98/(0.82)² = 1.46 "wg.

   The remaining values are shown in Table 4-3.

7. *Determine the order to adjust dampers based on convenience, decreasing duct size, or increasing insufficiency of airflow.*

   The order is shown on Table 4-3.

8. *Adjust each damper in turn until it is observed that VP_{cl} equals $VP_{cl\text{-}goal}$ for that branch. Note that only the last damper adjusted will have the desired airflow. All others will change as each damper is moved.*

   For a given damper, increase and decrease the damper insertion depth until the observed VP_{cl} is as close as possible to $VP_{cl\text{-}goal}$. As can be seen in Table 4-3, Branch 1-A was deficient in airflow, so its damper was not adjusted in Round 1. Note also, VP_{cl} was less than $VP_{cl\text{-}goal}$. Since the damper was full open, any change in the damper position would decrease VP_{cl}, a worse condition. Next, Branch 2-A was adjusted until it was 401 acfm, (very close to the goal of 400 acfm). After that adjustment, all other branch airflows would have increased but the airflow through the fan would have fallen slightly. If measured, it is probable that Branch 3-B had risen above 400 acfm.

TABLE 4-3. Basic Method – Initial Round

		Measured	Goal		1st Round	
Branch	Q_{ratio}	VP_{cl}	$VP_{cl\text{-}goal}$	Order	Resulting Q	Q_{ratio}
1-A	0.82	0.98	1.46	1	524	1.31
2-A	1.32	1.05	0.60	2	572	1.43
3-B	0.91	1.20	1.46	3	552	1.38
4-C	1.39	1.15	0.60	4	540	1.35
5-C	1.39	1.15	0.60	5	500	1.25
6-D	2.57	1.06	0.16	6	404	1.01
Total	1.40				3092	1.29

TABLE 4-4. Basic Method – Second and Third Rounds

		2nd Round			3rd Round	
ID	Order	Resulting Q	Qratio	Order	Resulting Q	Qratio
1-A	1	480	1.20	1	412	1.03
2-A	2	448	1.12	2	408	1.02
3-B	3	436	1.09	3	404	1.01
4-C	4	420	1.05	4	404	1.01
5-C	5	408	1.02	5	404	1.01
6-D	6	400	1.00	6	400	1.00
Total		2692	1.08		2432	1.01

If Branch 3-B was now higher than originally but still below 400 acfm (or at least VP_{cl} was less than $VP_{cl\text{-}goal}$), we would leave its damper alone. Otherwise, we would reduce the damper opening until VP_{cl} equals $VP_{cl\text{-}goal}$. If we now measured the airflows in Branches 1-A, 2-A and 3-B, it would have indicated that Branch 1-A was higher than originally measured but still below 400 acfm, Branch 2-A had risen even further above 400 acfm, and Branch 3-B was somewhat above 400 acfm.

Adjusting Branch 4-C set its airflow temporarily at 400 acfm but increased airflow through the other branches. In particular, the airflow in the branches previously adjusted to 400 acfm will increase above 400 acfm. A similar result occurs when adjusting Branch 5-C. Adjusting Branch 6-D required inserting its damper more than 90% into the duct. Much of the airflow from Branch 6 was diverted to other branches, producing the results seen in Table 4-3 at the end of Round 1. The column "Resulting Q" contains the airflow values after the first round of damper adjustments. Note that the total airflow is now 29% above the sum of Q_{goal} values and

that the Q_{ratio} for all but Branch 6-D was at least 25% above goal levels. A 29% excess volume would indicate another round should be attempted.

There is no point in doing Pitot traverses yet, but if they were done the results would be the values of Q_{ratio} shown on Table 4-4.

9. *Repeat Step 8 (i.e., 2nd round).*

    Complete the second round of adjustments. As in the first round, each branch airflow is adjusted in turn until it reaches Q_{goal}, but as each damper is adjusted the airflows in previously adjusted branches rise increasingly above Q_{goal} levels except the last damper adjusted, Branch 6-D. As shown in Table 4-4, Branch 1-A has a 20% excess in flow but the fan airflow is now only 8% over goal values.

    Since the "worst" branch is 20% above the goal, a third round was begun.

10. *If necessary, repeat Step 8 again (i.e., 3rd round).*

    As shown in Table 4-4 , at the end of the third round,

all branch airflows were within about 3% of goal levels and the overall excess is roughly 1%. No more rounds were required.

11. *Conduct a full Pitot traverse for each branch duct to determine the final observed airflows (Q) and all Q_{ratio} values (Equation 4.1).*

The resulting Q_{ratio} values are shown after Round 3 on Table 4-4.

12. *If the lowest value of Q_{ratio} (min(Q_{ratio})) is less than 1.0, increase the fan speed based on:*

$$\omega_2 = \frac{\omega_1}{\min Q_{ratio}}$$

In this example the lowest Q_{ratio} had a value of 1.0, which should always be the case if the initial fan speed exceeded ideal levels. No fan adjustment is needed.

Notes:

After the third round of adjustments, the error was about 1%, well within normal expectations. Although a good balance was achieved after three rounds of adjustments, this can be very time-consuming. To achieve the required resistance through the dampers, especially on branch 6-E, the damper must be nearly completely closed. In that case, even the slightest change in insertion depth would have large effects on airflow, making it very difficult to set the damper so that the airflow equaled Q_{goal}. Finally, a by-product of such high resistances is a high estimated fan total pressure of 14.4 "wg, a relatively high value.

Some practitioners have used the short cut of taking a centerline reading for VP and then applying a factor to estimate velocity (and volume) in a duct. As discussed earlier, the errors from that estimate can be quite large. It is important to take full Pitot traverses after balancing to document the final results.

In a system that was originally balanced for which re-balancing is required, it may be reasonable to start with the dampers at the position found, rather than beginning by opening all the dampers. The effort to balance the system may be considerably less. However, this approach may not optimize the performance of the balanced system. The additional effort of balancing associated with opening all dampers is often justified.

4.8.3 Advantages and Disadvantages of Basic Method.
The procedure's advantages are that it is easy to understand and it requires little preparation. Its disadvantages are:

1. The procedure will fail if the fan output before balancing is not sufficient. Otherwise, as the damper blades are inserted and the fan airflow declines, there is not enough airflow for the last branches adjusted. If this occurs, one must increase the fan speed and begin again.

2. Conversely, if the total airflow is initially significantly higher (e.g., more than 50%) than design, the damper adjustments will be more difficult because the dampers must be inserted more, perhaps to the point where even small changes in insertion depths have substantial effects on flow (see Figure 4-3).

3. As each damper's insertion depth is changed so that the current branch has the desired airflow, airflows in all other branches are increasing from the originally adjusted levels. In addition, the fan airflow declines with each damper blade that is inserted, possibly to levels that are insufficient for the system or that produce velocities in some submains and mains that are too low.

4. It is time-consuming. To achieve acceptable airflows, it is almost always necessary to conduct two and sometimes three rounds of adjustments. For each round, airflows may have to be calculated several times.

5. Because the dampers are being used to "choke down" the fan airflows in most cases, the fan pressures and fan motor operating costs are typically higher than could have been achieved with methods that separate achieving the desired relative airflows from controlling the fan output.

4.9   INTERACTIONS BETWEEN THE SYSTEM AND THE FAN

The airflow output of a fan varies inversely with resistance to flow.[4.8] A damper adds resistance to the duct in which it is installed and thus to the entire system. As dampers are inserted farther into a duct, the fan airflow (Q_{fan}) also decreases. At any change in system resistance, the change in fan airflow depends on the slope of the fan's airflow-pressure curve at that level of system resistance. The efficiency of a fan also varies with resistance of the system and therefore with changes to damper insertion depths.

Some air cleaning devices (e.g., fabric filters) also are variable sources of resistance. They complicate balancing because they produce changes in system pressure and airflows independently of the damper.

4.9.1 Throttling the Fan Airflow. The resistance added by a damper not only changes the proportion of the fan airflow going to that branch, but also the total airflow delivered by the fan (see Figure 4-6). This interaction complicates the adjustment process. It also makes it possible to reduce the fan airflow to a desired total output using the dampers while also achieving the desired distribution.

Although fan inlet or outlet dampers can be utilized to reduce the total fan airflow to desired levels, there are disadvantages for this method when compared to changing the fan speed:

1) Higher fan pressures result in resistance that is higher than necessary for distribution purposes, increasing

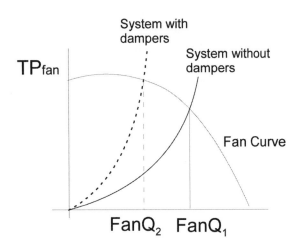

FIGURE 4-6. Effect of dampers on fan airflows

operating costs and fan speed. Fan speed increases can possibly exceed the safe maximum for the fan.

2) Fan efficiency may be affected adversely if the fan was initially selected without allowing for the additional resistance of the system due to the dampers, increasing operating costs.

3) Dampers must be inserted farther, possibly making adjustment more difficult and increasing the chances for material build-up.

Instead of "throttling" down the fan with the dampers, it is possible to separate damper adjustment and fan airflow regulation. This is done by adjusting branch duct dampers to achieve the desired distribution (i.e., fraction) of airflows instead of the desired level of airflows. Once that distribution is achieved, then adjust the fan airflows (ideally by changing the rotation rate) to obtain the desired total fan output. Since the distribution of airflows is independent of the level of airflows,[4.9] changing the fan speed does not ordinarily affect the distribution.

4.9.2 Optimum Initial Fan Output. Fan airflows will decrease as dampers are inserted. It would be very helpful to be able to predict the airflow that the fan would produce after all dampers had been adjusted. If the Basic or Modified Basic Method is used, it would allow setting the fan rotation rate to an optimum value before adjusting dampers. For the Target Method, discussed in a later section, the prediction would allow more accurate determination of target parameters (e.g., SP_h or VP_{cl}).

It may be possible to estimate the final fan airflow ($Q_{fan\text{-}final}$) that would exist if the dampers were adjusted to produce a perfect relative distribution at the lowest possible damper insertions ($Q_{fan\text{-}ideal}$). The use of this predicted value would depend on the balancing strategy.

4.9.3 Estimating $Q_{fan\text{-}ideal}$. Without sophisticated models, one cannot reliably predict $Q_{fan\text{-}final}$, but it may be possible to estimate it reasonably well. For example, multiplying $Q_{fan\text{-}goal}$ by 1.2 (a 20% increase) provides a rough estimate. This simple estimate will probably be sufficient for most systems that are being re-balanced. For example, if the value of $Q_{fan\text{-}open}$ is 3300 acfm and the value of $Q_{fan\text{-}goal}$ is 3000 acfm, then the estimated value of $Q_{fan\text{-}ideal}$ would be 3600 acfm. The fan output should be increased to 3600 acfm before adjusting any dampers.

However, the ideal level of Q_{fan} may be much less than $1.2*Q_{fan\text{-}goal}$. For example, if the relative airflow distribution is already very close to ideal and $Q_{fan\text{-}open}$ is nearly the same as $Q_{fan\text{-}goal}$, then $Q_{fan\text{-}ideal}$ should be only slightly greater than $Q_{fan\text{-}goal}$.

It may be possible to estimate the final fan airflow ($Q_{fan\text{-}final}$) more closely or to at least put boundaries on the possible range of $Q_{fan\text{-}final}$ values. The lowest possible value would occur when the fan airflow is independent of damper resistance. In that case, the effect of inserting a damper is solely to shift airflows to other branches. The final value of Q_{fan} would equal $Q_{fan\text{-}open}$ and all Q_{ratio} values would be equal to $Q_{fan\text{-}open}/Q_{goal}$.

The other extreme occurs if the fan airflow is so affected by damper adjustments that the fan airflow falls exactly by the amount the airflow to a branch is reduced by adjusting its damper. In that case, the value of Q_{ratio} for all dampers must equal the lowest initial airflow ratio, $min(Q_{ratio})$ and the final value of Q_{fan} must equal the $Q_{fan\text{-}goal}$ divided by the $min(Q_{ratio})$.

The value of $Q_{fan\text{-}ideal}$ could fall anywhere between $Q_{fan\text{-}open}$ and $Q_{fan\text{-}goal}/min(Q_{ratio})$. Where it falls in that range would depend on the values of X_{damper} for all dampers as well as the fan curve. However, a value halfway between the two values,

$$Q_{fan\text{-}ideal} = (Q_{fan\text{-}open} + Q_{fan\text{-}goal}/min(Q_{ratio}))/2$$

may be a conservative estimate. A better, although more complicated estimate is given in Equation 4.11.

$$Q_{fan\text{-}ideal} = (Q_{fan\text{-}open}) / \tfrac{1}{2}*\{Q_{fan\text{-}open}/Q_{fan\text{-}goal} + min(Q_{ratio})\} \quad \text{[4.11]}$$

If Equation 4.11 were applied to the data in Table 4-2, the predicted minimum initial airflow should be:

$$Q_{fan\text{-}ideal} = 3357 / (0.5)*(3357/2400 + 0.82) = 3357/1.11 = 3026 \text{ acfm}$$

Since the initial measured value was 3357 acfm in this example, the ideal value is about 10% lower than the initial value, if one assumes that the fan output will be adjusted after adjusting all dampers.

A study of typical systems and fans selected for them would likely find a mean optimum value that is somewhat higher or lower, but the midpoint can serve as a reasonable estimate until a better estimate is determined.

4.9.4 Fan Adjustment After Balancing. After all dampers have been adjusted, all branch airflows should be measured and compared to Q_{goal} values. Since a primary goal is for each hood Q to match or exceed its Q_{goal} value, all values of Q_{ratio} should match or exceed 1.0. The fan speed should be adjusted from its current rotation rate (ω_1) so that the branch with the minimum Q_{ratio} value has sufficient airflow. That will be accomplished at a new rotation rate (ω_2) that can be computed from:

$$\omega_2 = \frac{\omega_1}{\min(Q_{ratio})} \qquad [4.12]$$

where: $\min(Q_{ratio})$ = minimum Q_{ratio} value after all dampers have been adjusted

For example, suppose that after all dampers have been adjusted, the values in Table 4-2 were measured. The total airflow through the fan is 40% above the minimum desirable amount, but the airflow through two branches are below 100% of their goals. To make sure that Branch 1-A has sufficient airflow, it would be necessary to increase the fan rotation rate using Equation 4.12:

$$\omega_2 = \omega_1 / \min(Q_{ratio}) = \omega_1 / 0.82 = 1.22\ \omega_1$$

4.10 MODIFIED BASIC METHOD

The most severe difficulties in the basic procedure generally are due to extremely high or low fan speeds and problems with estimating airflows using centerline velocity or velocity pressure readings. The Ventilation Manual strongly recommends against using the centerline velocity, V_{cl}, in calculating the average velocities and volumetric flow rate. However, the problems that occur from this can be addressed in this section in a modified version of the Basic procedure. Before adjusting the first damper, the fan speed is adjusted to achieve sufficient fan airflow. Alternatively, the target airflow can be adjusted to match the airflow available on the assumption that the fan speed will be adjusted after balancing the dampers.

To reduce the errors associated with using VP_{cl}, dampers are adjusted using measured hood static pressure values (SP_h) rather than VP_{cl}. SP_h has been shown to be highly correlated to airflow squared.[4.7] Another difference is that the fan airflow is always adjusted to the "ideal" value prior to adjusting any dampers.

4.10.1 Procedure for Modified Basic Method. The steps for the Modified Basic Method are:

1. Determine the desired airflow (Q_{goal}) for each hood. Compute $Q_{fan\text{-}goal}$ from Equation 4.3 or 4.4.

2. Open all dampers, taking care to protect the fan motor since the power it uses may increase substantially. Optional: partially close dampers for ducts whose airflows are known to be highly excessive.

3. Do Pitot traverses and measure the volumetric flow, Q, and static pressure, SP_h, for each branch duct, then compute the "open" damper value of airflow (Q_{open}) for each branch. Measure and record the amperage for the fan motor, the SP across the air cleaner (ΔP), and other values you may wish to document or use later.

4. Compute the initial $Q_{fan\text{-}open}$ from the sum of the observed airflows.

5. Determine the ideal fan airflow ($Q_{fan\text{-}ideal}$). This can be 1.2 * $Q_{fan\text{-}goal}$, the average of the $Q_{fan\text{-}goal}$ and $Q_{fan\text{-}open}$, or the value determined by Equation 4.11.

6. Adjust the fan speed from the current value, ω_1, to ω_2:
   $$\omega_2 = \omega_1 \times Q_{fan\text{-}ideal}/Q_{fan\text{-}open}$$

7. After adjusting the fan speed, measure SP_h for each branch duct.

8. Compute the desired final hood static pressure, $SP_{h\text{-}goal}$, for each branch from Equations 4.7 or 4.8. Compute the values of $SP_h/SP_{h\text{-}goal}$ using the values of SP_h measured after adjusting the fan speed.

9. Beginning with the largest ducts and continuing through to the smallest or with the highest value of $SP_h/SP_{h\text{-}goal}$ and ending with the lowest, adjust each damper in turn until the measured SP_h equals $SP_{h\text{-}goal}$ for that branch.

   Optional: adjust the first few dampers to achieve SP_h values that are 5-10% below the $SP_{h\text{-}goal}$ values. Adjusting the hood static pressures slightly lower than the goal compensates for the general airflow increase as subsequent dampers are closed.

10. Repeat Step 9 for a second round.

11. Repeat Step 9 for a third round, if necessary.

12. Do a Pitot traverse for each branch duct to determine the final observed airflows (Q) and Q_{ratio} values.

13. If the lowest value of Q_{ratio}, $\min(Q_{ratio})$, is less than 1.0, increase the fan speed based on:

$$\omega_2 = \left(\frac{\omega_1}{\min(Q_{ratio})} \right)$$

Note that it may be prudent to set the fan airflow to 5% above the minimum level (ω_2) as a safety factor.

4.10.2 Example 2 (Modified Basic Method). This example will once again use the data in Table 4-2, which represents the system in Figure 4-5. In the Modified Basic Method, one always adjusts the fan output to $Q_{fan-ideal}$ unless it is already close (e.g., no more than 5% in excess of $Q_{fan-ideal}$). That step should assure that airflow is adequate without being excessive.

(Steps 1 thru 4 are the same as Basic Method Example)

1. *Determine the desired airflow (Q_{goal}) for each hood. Compute $Q_{goal-fan}$ from Equation 4.3 or 4.4.*

   The values shown in Table 4-2 were selected arbitrarily for this example.

2. *Open all dampers. Optional: partially close dampers for ducts whose airflows are known to be highly excessive.*

   In this case, all dampers were opened fully.

3. *Do Pitot traverses and measure Q and SP_h for each branch duct, then compute the "open" damper value of airflow (Q_{open}) for each branch.*

   The results are shown in Table 4-2.

4. *Compute the initial Q_{fan} from the sum of the observed airflows.*

   In this example, $Q_{fan-open}$ = 3357 acfm and $Q_{fan-goal}$ = 2400 acfm.

5. *Determine the ideal fan airflow ($Q_{fan-ideal}$).*

   This can be 1.2 * $Q_{fan-goal}$, the average of the $Q_{fan-goal}$ and $Q_{fan-open}$, or the value determined by Equation 4.11.

   In this example set $Q_{fan-ideal}$ = 1.2 * $Q_{fan-goal}$. $Q_{fan-ideal}$ = 1.2*2400 = 2880 acfm. Different estimates of $Q_{fan-ideal}$ could be used. Some provide less adjustment as the method is used; however, they are all estimates of the ideal volumetric flow.

6. *Adjust the fan speed from the current value, ω_1, to ω_2:*

   Noting that the original rotation rate was 598 rpm and that $Q_{fan-open}$ was 3357 cfm, Equation 4.12 can be used to determine the "ideal" new fan rotation rate:

$$\omega_2 = \omega_1 \times Q_{fan-ideal}/Q_{fan-open}$$
$$= 598 \text{ rpm} \times 2880 \text{ acfm}/3357 \text{ acfm} = 513 \text{ rpm}$$

7. *After adjusting the fan speed, measure SP_h for each branch duct.*

   After adjusting the rotation rate to 513 rpm, the new values of SP_h that should exist are shown in Table 4-5 under the column headed "Measured after fan speed adjustment."

8. *Compute the desired final hood static pressure, SP_{h-goal}, for each branch from Equation 4.7 or 4.8. Compute the values of SP_h / SP_{h-goal} using the values of SP_h measured after adjusting the fan speed.*

   The resulting values are shown in Table 4-4 under column heading "Compute SP_{h-goal}."

9. *Beginning with the largest ducts and continuing through to the smallest or with the highest value of SP_h/SP_{h-goal} and ending with the lowest, adjust each damper in turn until the measured SP_h equals SP_{h-goal} for that branch.*

   Table 4-6 shows the measured results after the first damper adjustment.

   The calculated column $Q_{ratio-1} = Q_{h-1}/Q_{goal}$ shows a measure of how close the first round of adjustments is to achieving the goal. Since the ratio for 6-D is 1.21, additional adjustment should be made. In this example all the branches are adjusted. In a real world situation, only those that are above 1.05 or possibly 1.1 would be adjusted.

10. *Repeat Step 9 for a second round.*

    Adjust the dampers a second time. After adjustment, measure the volumetric flow and the static pressure in each branch. The results for the second round are shown in Table 4-6 under the column heading "Measured second round."

TABLE 4-5. Modified Method Example – Initial Adjustment

Branch	Goal	Measured		Calculated		Measured after fan adjustment	
	Q_{goal}	Q_{open}	SP_{h-open}	Q_{ratio}	SP_{h-goal}	$Q_{after-fan}$	SP_h
1-A	400	328	1.18	0.82	1.75	281	0.87
2-A	400	529	1.51	1.32	0.86	454	1.11
3-B	400	362	1.44	0.91	1.76	311	1.06
4-C	400	554	1.66	1.39	0.87	475	1.22
5-C	400	554	1.66	1.39	0.87	475	1.22
6-D	400	1030	1.92	2.58	0.29	884	1.41
Fan	2400	3357				2880	

TABLE 4-6. Modified Method Example – First and Second Rounds

| Branch | Measured first round | | Calculated | Measured second round | | Calculated |
	Q_{h-1}	SP_{h-1}	$Q_{ratio-1}$	Q_{h-2}	SP_{h-2}	$Q_{ratio-2}$
1-A	407	1.81	1.02	402	1.78	1.01
2-A	407	0.89	1.02	405	0.89	1.01
3-B	408	1.83	1.02	404	1.79	1.01
4-C	432	1.01	1.08	420	0.95	1.05
5-C	465	1.17	1.16	410	0.91	1.03
6-D	483	0.42	1.21	418	0.32	1.04
Fan	2603			2460		

11. *Repeat Step 9 for a third round, if necessary.*

    As shown in Table 4-6, the values of $Q_{ratio-2}$ (= Q_{h-2}/Q_{goal}) were all below 1.05. Consequently, it was not necessary to have a third round of adjustments.

12. *Do a Pitot traverse for each branch duct to determine the final observed airflows (Q) and Q_{ratio} values.*

    The results are shown in Table 4-6 (Q_{h-2} and $Q_{ratio-2}$).

13. *If the lowest value of Q_{ratio}, min(Q_{ratio}), is less than 1.0, increase the fan speed based on:*

$$\omega_2 = \left(\frac{\omega_1}{\min(Q_{ratio})} \right)$$

Since the minimum Q_{ratio} was 1.01, it was not necessary to change the fan speed. However, to demonstrate the approach, Table 4-7 shows the results when the fan is slowed down by 1%. (In reality, a change less than 5 percent would not be made.) After adjusting the fan speed, the results are shown in Table 4-7.

Notes on the procedures:

1) Although the procedure determines the required fan speed, it is often not practical to achieve exactly the desired fan speed. The sheaves (pulleys) are limited and only a few fan speeds can be achieved. Normal practice is to run the fan faster that the calculated value. This is less important on the first fan speed adjustment since a final speed will be required. The extra fan speed is essentially a safety factor. Care is required to ensure that safety factors do not compound resulting is an excessive exhaust rate.

2) Some designers adjust the final fan speed to a nominal 5% above that desired for an additional safety factor.

3) In the above example, the volumetric flow after each adjustment decreased from 3024 acfm after the first fan speed adjustment, to 2474 acfm after the first damper adjustment, to 2393 acfm after the second fan adjustment. This progression is typical with each damper adjustment as the dampers are inserted farther and the system resistance increases. The fan backs off on the fan curve.

4) The final speed increase was not to increase the flow through the fan to the goal, but rather to increase the flow through each branch to meet or exceed the goal for the branch.

5) The efficiency of the balancing is shown in Q_{excess}. If Q_{excess} is too large, it may be economical to continue the balancing. However, a single branch that significantly exceeds the goal may not warrant the rebalancing effort unless Q_{fan} is also excessive.

4.10.3 Using Adjustment Targets That Are Not Equal to the Goal Values. In many cases the target airflow (Q_t) during balancing should differ from Q_{goal} values for reasons discussed in this section. Balancing systems is complicated by the fact that airflows can change in a duct even when its damper is not touched. This can happen because: 1) Q_{fan} fluctuations due to the air-cleaner (ΔP changes as bags become dirty, etc.), 2) changes in resistance of branches due to external causes, 3)

TABLE 4-7. Modified Method Example – Final Conditions

| Modify fan | | |
Branch	Q	Error
1-A	400	0.0%
2-A	403	0.8%
3-B	402	0.4%
4-C	418	4.4%
5-C	408	2.0%
6-D	415	3.9%
Fan	2446	1.9%

changes in Q_{fan} due to adjusting other dampers, and 4) shifting of flows among branches due to other dampers being adjusted.

For example, suppose that the pressure across a fabric filter varies over its cleaning cycle from 2 to 5 "wg, producing a 10% change in fan airflow over the cycle. During damper adjustment, the airflow achieved would depend not only on the damper but where the fan was in the cleaning cycle. The same would be true if branch resistances changed for reasons having nothing to do with the dampers. For example, a flexible duct connected to a moving hood would experience changes in resistance. Its share of airflow would fall when its resistance increased and climb when the resistance decreased. All other airflows would change in the opposite direction in each case. A damper set to achieve $Q = Q_{goal}$ may only achieve it for one shape of the flexible duct.

In both of the cases above, it would be difficult to compensate exactly for these events. The best strategy may be simply to adjust to a target that is slightly greater (e.g., 5%) than Q_{goal}. Some airflow will be wasted some of the time, but hood airflows would seldom be insufficient.

4.10.4 Branch Airflow Changes. Changes in airflow through a branch due to other interactions can be both greater in effect and easier to compensate for accurately. The two most important interactions are those: 1) between branches and 2) between branches as a group and the fan. If one adjusts a damper to achieve a particular airflow in a given branch, the actual airflow will rise as each succeeding branch's damper is adjusted since their relative resistances are increasing. If one adjusts each damper to achieve Q_{goal}, only the last branch adjusted will have $Q = Q_{goal}$. For all others $Q > Q_{goal}$. Hence, the target during adjustments should be lower than the goal values for all except the last branch adjusted, and the branches adjusted first should have the greatest reduction. A trial and error experiment produced the following relationship:

For velocities or airflows: $k = (n/N)^{0.0.445}$ [4.14]

where: n   = rank order number of the branch

N   = total number of branch ducts

k   = order factor

Table 4-8 show approximate k values for ranges of the value of n/N.

Another correction can be made for insufficient or excessive fan airflows. If $Q_{fan-ideal}$ is defined as the value of Q_{fan} that would exist if dampers were adjusted perfectly and with the minimum system pressure, then the difference between $Q_{fan-open}$ and $Q_{fan-ideal}$ represents wasted airflow. Instead of reducing the fan speed before adjusting dampers, one could simply increase target airflow, Q_t, proportionately to the excess. This would allow damper adjustment to achieve a relative distribution which would then be followed by a change to fan airflow.

For example, if $Q_{fan-open}/Q_{fan-ideal} = 1.5$, one could set $Q_t = 1.5 \times Q_{goal}$ for each branch. The fan speed could be adjusted

after balancing instead of before. Hence, considering both the fan and branch-to-branch interactions, Q_{target} could be computed from:

$$Q_{target} = \left(\frac{k}{Q_{ratio}}\right)\left(\frac{Q_{fan-open}/Q_{fan-goal}+minQ_{br-goal}}{2}\right)Q_{open} \qquad [4.15]$$

Likewise, the target hood static pressure and the target centerline velocity can be given by:

$$SPh_{target} = \left[\left(\frac{k}{Q_{ratio}}\right)\left(\frac{Q_{fan-open}/Q_{fan-goal}+minQ_{br-goal}}{2}\right)\right]^2 SPh_{open} \qquad [4.16]$$

$$VPcl_{target} = \left[\left(\frac{k}{Q_{ratio}}\right)\left(\frac{Q_{fan-open}/Q_{fan-goal}+minQ_{br-goal}}{2}\right)\right]^2 VPcl_{open} \qquad [4.17]$$

Methods based on hood static pressure measures (SP_h) are more robust than those relying on centerline velocity pressures (VP_{cl}) because VP_{cl} measurement accuracy is strongly affected by disturbances. In addition, the ratio of VP_{cl} to Q^2 can vary somewhat from one measurement to another. SP_h is also easier to measure than VP_{cl} since it is not so critical in measuring SP_h values that the probe be in the exact center of the duct or that the probe be aligned perfectly with the airflow. Locations for SP_h measurements also typically are more easily accessible than good locations for VP_{cl} or for Pitot traverses. VP_{cl} should be used instead of SP_h only if measurement of SP_h is infeasible.

It is recommended that dampers be located three or more duct diameter lengths (3D) downstream of the SP_h measurement location.

4.11   TARGET METHOD

The third method is somewhat more complex mathematically than the second method but it reduces the measurement efforts. The method requires the same initial measurements. The method is the same as the Modified Basic Method through Step 4. Like that method, this one uses SP_h measurements to adjust dampers. Unlike the Modified Basic Method, the fan speed need not be re-set before adjusting dampers.

TABLE 4-8. Approximate k Values for Damper Adjustment

n/N	k	n/N	k
0 -0.10	0.90	0.51-0.60	0.98
0.11-0.20	0.93	0.61-0.70	0.98
0.21-0.30	0.95	0.71-0.80	0.99
0.31-0.40	0.96	0.81-0.90	1.00
0.41-0.50	0.97	0.91-1.00	1.00

4.11.1 Procedure for Target Method. The steps for the Target Method are:

1. Determine the desired airflow (Q_{goal}) for each hood. Compute $Q_{fan-goal}$ from Equation 4.3 or 4.4.

2. Open all dampers. Optional: partially close dampers for ducts whose airflows are known to be highly excessive. In this case, all dampers were opened fully.

3. Do Pitot traverses and measure VP_{cl} and SP_h for each branch duct, then compute the "open" damper value of airflow (Q_{open}) for each branch.

4. Compute the initial $Q_{fan-open}$ from the sum of the observed airflows.

5. Do NOT adjust the fan speed prior to balancing unless $Q_{fan-open}$ is less than 0.7 or greater than 1.5 times $Q_{fan-goal}$. If so, compute $Q_{fan-ideal}$ from Equation 4.11 and adjust the fan output to achieve that value, then re-measure values of SP_h.

6. Rank order and number the branches based on their Q_{ratio} values from 1 to N. Assign order factor (k) value for each branch duct based on its rank order number using either Equation 4.14 or Table 4-7.

7. Compute the desired final hood static pressure, SP_{h-goal}, from Equation 4.8 and the target hood static pressure ($SP_{h-target}$) for each branch from Equation 4.16.

8. Beginning with the branch with the lowest value of Q_{ratio} and continuing through to the next to smallest, adjust each damper in turn until the measured SP_h equals $SP_{h-target}$ for that branch. Leave the branch with n = N completely open for all steps.

9. After the first round is complete, measure SP_h for each branch again.

10. Compute $SP_{h-ratio} = SP_h/SP_{h-goal}$ for each branch and determine the median value of the ratios, median ($SP_{h-ratio}$).

11. Adjust each branch damper so that its measured hood static pressure equals:

    $$SP_h = SP_{h-goal} \times med(SP_{h-ratio})$$

    Begin with the duct whose $SP_{h-ratio}$ value is the greatest, followed by the least and alternate between next highest and next lowest until roughly one-half of dampers have been adjusted a second time. If necessary, adjust all dampers.

12. Do a Pitot traverse for each branch duct to determine the final observed airflows and Q_{ratio} values.

13. Using the minimum Q_{ratio} value determined above (min(Q_{ratio})), adjust the fan speed from the original rotation rate (ω_1) to:

    $$\omega_2 = \omega_1/min(Q_{ratio})$$

Note: Some designers set the fan airflow to 5% above the minimum level (ω_2) as a safety factor. Care should be used to avoid compounding safety factors.

4.11.2 Example 3 (Target Method). The same example used for the Basic Method and Modified Basic Method is used here to demonstrate the use of the procedure. Given the initial measurements and airflow goals listed in Table 4-2 and Figure 4-5, follow the procedure listed above to balance the dampers.

The step by step solution is as follows:

1. *Determine the desired airflow (Q_{goal}) for each hood. Compute $Q_{fan-goal}$ from Equation 4.3 or 4.4.*

   The values shown in Table 4-2 were selected arbitrarily for this example.

2. *Open all dampers.*

   Optional: Partially close dampers for ducts whose airflows are known to be highly excessive. In this case, all dampers were opened fully.

3. Do Pitot traverses and measure VP_{cl} and SP_h for each branch duct, then compute the "open" damper value of airflow (Q_{open}) for each branch.

   The results are shown in Table 4-8.

4. Compute the initial $Q_{fan-open}$ from the sum of the observed airflows.

   From Table 4-2, for $Q_{fan-open}$ = 3357 acfm.

5. Do NOT adjust the fan speed prior to balancing unless $Q_{fan-open}$ is less than 0.7 or greater than 1.5.

   In this example the ratio was 1.40, so no adjustment prior to balancing is necessary.

6. Rank order and number the branches based on their Q_{ratio} values from 1 to N. Assign order factor (k) value for each branch duct based on its rank order number using either Equation 4.14 or Table 4-8.

7. *Compute the desired final hood static pressure, SP_{h-goal}, and the target hood static pressure ($SP_{h-target}$) for each branch from Equation 4.8 and 4.15, respectively.*

   The results are shown under the column labeled "Compute Initial Target. For Branch 2-A:

   $$SP_{h-goal} = SP_{h-open} / Q_{ratio}^2 = 1.51 / 1.32^2 = 0.87\ \text{"wg}$$

   $$SP_{t\arg et} = \left[\left(\frac{k}{2Q_{ratio}} \right) \left(\frac{Q_{fan-open}}{Q_{fan-goal}} + \min Q_{ratio} \right) \right]^2 SP_{h_{open}}$$

   $$= \left[\left(\frac{0.98}{2(1.32)} \right) \left(\frac{3357\,cfm}{2400\,cfm} + 0.82 \right) \right]^2 1.51\ \text{"wg} = 1.02\ \text{"wg}$$

8. *Beginning with the branch with the lowest value of Q_{ratio} and continuing through to the next smallest, adjust each damper in turn until the measured SP_h equals $SP_{h-target}$ for that branch. Leave the branch with n = N completely open for all steps.*

9. *After the first round is complete, measure SP_h for each branch again.*

    The results are shown in Table 4-9. Note that the results are shown under the column labeled "Measured after first round." Note that the values are much larger than the goal values.

10. *Compute $SP_{h\text{-}ratio} = SP_h / SP_{h\text{-}goal}$ for each branch and determine the median value of the ratios, median ($SP_{h\text{-}ratio}$).*

    Note that the ratios of the hood static pressure to median range from 0.83 to 1.08.

11. *Adjust each branch damper so that its measured hood static pressure equals:*

    $$SP_{h\text{-}target} = SP_{h\text{-}goal} * median(SP_{h\text{-}ratio})$$

    Begin with the duct whose $SP_{h\text{-}ratio}$ value is the greatest, followed by the least and alternate between next highest and next lowest until roughly one-half of dampers have been adjusted a second time. If necessary, adjust all dampers.

The results are shown under the column labeled "After Second Round."

12. *Do a Pitot traverse for each branch duct to determine the final observed airflows and Q_{ratio} values.*

    The results are shown under the column labeled "After Second Round." Note that values of Q_{ratio} range from 1.18 to 1.23. Since the values are all about the same, the branch airflows have been adjusted to the correct relative distribution.

13. *Using minimum Q_{ratio} value determined above ("$min(Q_{ratio})$"), adjust the fan speed from the original rotation rate (ω_1) to:*

    $\omega_2 =$ $\omega_1/min(Q_{ratio})$

    $=$ 598 rpm/1.23 = 486 rpm

    The last columns in Table 4-9 show the resulting measured value after modifying the fan speed. The last column shows the percentage of excess air in each branch. Note that the Q_{excess} is only 1.4%, a very small level of wasted airflow.

TABLE 4-9. Target Method Example

	Goal		Measured		Computed				
Branch	Q_{goal}	$Q_{open\text{-}1}$	$SP_{h\text{-}1}$	Q_{ratio}	Rank	k	$SP_{h\text{-}goal}$	$SP_{h\text{-}target}$
1-A	400	328	1.18	0.82	6	1.00	1.75	2.16
2-A	400	529	1.51	1.32	4	0.98	0.87	1.02
3-B	400	362	1.44	0.91	5	0.99	1.76	2.11
4-C	400	554	1.66	1.39	3	0.97	0.87	0.99
5-C	400	554	1.66	1.39	2	0.95	0.87	0.96
6-D	400	1030	1.92	2.57	1	0.92	0.29	0.31
Fan	2400	3357		1.40				
	$Q_{fan\text{-}goal}$	2400	acfm	($Q_{fan\text{-}open}/Q_{fan\text{-}goal}$ + min(Q_{ratio}))/2 = 1.11				
	$Q_{fan\text{-}open\_1}$	3357	acfm					
	$Q_{fan\text{-}ideal}$	3026	acfm					

TABLE 4-9 (Cont.). Target Method Example

	Measured after first round		Computed				
Branch	Q_2	$SP_{h\text{-}2}$	$SP_h/SP_{h\text{-}goal}$	$SP_{h\text{-}ratio}$	Rank	k	$SP_{h\text{-}target}$
1-A	503	2.77	1.58	1.09	1	0.92	2.55
2-A	443	1.06	1.23	0.85	4	0.98	1.25
3-B	440	2.13	1.21	0.84	2	0.95	2.55
4-C	467	1.18	1.36	0.94	6	1.00	1.26
5-C	496	1.33	1.54	1.06	5	0.99	1.26
6-D	499	0.45	1.55	1.07	3	0.97	0.42
Fan	2848		1.45				

TABLE 4-9 (Cont.). Target Method Example

Branch	Measured		Computed		Measured	Computed	
	Q_3	SP_{h-3}	SP_{h-3} / SP_{h-goal}	$Q_{ratio-3}$	Q_4	Q_{ratio}	Q_{excess}
1-A	490	2.63	1.50	1.23	414	1.04	3.6%
2-A	480	1.24	1.44	1.20	406	1.01	1.5%
3-B	477	2.50	1.42	1.19	403	1.01	0.8%
4-C	483	1.26	1.46	1.21	408	1.02	2.1%
5-C	475	1.22	1.41	1.19	402	1.00	0.4%
6-D	473	0.40	1.40	1.18	400	1.00	0.0%
Fan	2878				2434		1.4%

Notes:

1) The example does not include measurement error in determining the static pressure and volumetric flow at each measurement point.

2) The changing of the fan speed assumes the sheaves are available to provide the desired fan speed.

4.11.3 Advantages of Target Method. The Target Method has the following advantages over the Modified Basic Method:

1. It does not require that the fan speed be adjusted before adjusting dampers.

2. It may require only 1.5 rounds of damper adjustment and should seldom, if ever, require more than two full rounds.

The disadvantage of this method compared to the Modified Basic Method is that it requires more mathematical operations.

Dodrill[4.11] found remarkably good distributions using the method to achieve two challenging distributions in an experimental 7-branch system. Only one and one-half rounds of adjustments were required to obtain Q_{excess} values less than 2% for every test. The results were comparable to those found by Geiger[4.12] for the "Static Pressure Ratio method."

REFERENCES

4.1   Guffey, S.E.: Airflow Redistribution in Exhaust Ventilation Systems Using Dampers and Static Pressure Ratios. Appl Occup. Environ. Hyg., 8(3):168-177 (1993).

4.2   Caplan, K.: Balance with blast gates – a precarious balance. Heating/Piping/Air Conditioning, February (2003).

4.3   Crowder, J.W.; Loudermilk, K.J.: Balancing of Industrial Ventilation Systems. Control Technology News, Vol. 32, No. 1 (1982).

4.4   Idel'chik, I.E.: Handbook of Hydraulic Resistance Coefficients of Local Resistance and Friction, "US Atomic Energy Commission, AEC-TR-6630 (1972).

4.5   Balasubramian, V.: Effectiveness of the common method of adjusting exhaust ventilation system dampers. Master's Thesis, West Virginia University (2005).

4.6   Wang, L.T.: Investigation of Measurement Error and Possible Shortcut Methods in Determining Mean Velocity in Ducts, Master's Thesis, University of Washington (1997).

4.7   McLoone, H.E.; Guffey, S.E.; Curran, J.C.: Effects of Shape, Size, and Air Velocity on Entry Loss Factors of Suction Hoods. Am. Ind. Hyg. Assoc. J., 54(3):87-94 (1993).

4.8   Jorgensen, R. (editor): Fan Engineering, Eighth Edition. Buffalo Forge Company (1983).

4.9   Guffey, S.E.; Spann, J.G.: Experimental Investigation of Power Loss Coefficients and Static Pressure Ratio in an Industrial Exhaust Ventilation System. Am. Ind. Hyg. Assoc. J., 60(3):367-376 (1999b).

4.10 Guffey, S.E.: Airflow Distribution in Exhaust Ventilation Systems. Am. Ind. Hyg. Assoc. J., 52(3):93-106 (1991).

4.11 Dodrill, M.W.: Experimental Validation of the "Target Hood Static Pressure" Balancing Method for Exhaust Ventilation Systems. Master's Thesis, West Virginia University (2004).

4.12 Geiger, H.M.: Evaluation of a Proposed Static Pressure Ratio Balancing Method. Master's Thesis, University of Washington (1999).

Chapter 5
VENTILATION SYSTEM MONITORING AND MAINTENANCE

5.1   INTRODUCTION

The capital funds spent to install industrial ventilation systems will not provide long-term protection and value if the systems do not have an active predictive maintenance program. Industrial ventilation systems fall outside of the design range of airflows that provide protection at the hoods and enclosures due to a variety of causes, such as sudden failures (e.g., broken fan belt), gradual degradation failures (e.g., dust buildup in the ducts), or management failures (e.g., unauthorized system changes). This chapter provides guidance on proactive measures to keep the industrial ventilation system within baseline limits. Additionally, this chapter provides recommended practice for ventilation system monitoring and maintenance by identifying nine key elements and associated guidance to implement the practice.

Monitoring and maintenance programs should focus on the inherent risks posed to employees by contaminants (i.e., toxicity, flammability, physical hazard) and the likelihood of rapid system degradation due to: contaminant characteristics, system capability, and system operability. A well-designed and correctly installed ventilation system can operate for months within baseline limits and without significant need for maintenance. However, a poorly designed system may operate within baseline limits for only a matter of days or weeks.

The overall performance goal is to operate and maintain the system within design parameters to ensure ongoing employee protection and predict when possible system failures may occur. For those contaminant sources within the influence of the local exhaust ventilation system, this minimizes the need for on-going air sampling. However, the impact of external system influences such as pedestal fans or powder spills from dumping bags outside the ventilation control hood must be understood as part of the total exposure profile for the operation supported by the ventilation system. The nine key elements of a successful ventilation system monitoring and maintenance program are listed below and explained in more detail later in this chapter.

Key Elements of a Monitoring and Maintenance Program:

1. Comply with OSHA and EPA regulatory limits and requirements.

2. Provide initial verification that the ventilation system is capable of providing the protection for which it was installed.

3. Take corrective action when the system monitoring data exceeds a set percent deviation of from baseline value.

4. Complete a maintenance risk assessment of the consequences of ventilation system failure by reviewing the inherent risks of the contaminants handled and risk factors that can lead to more rapid system degradation.

5. Establish on-going monitoring of the system to provide early warning of rapid changes that could potentially hurt system performance.

6. Establish on-going degradation and trend monitoring of the system to identify the places where and when the system routinely begins to degrade. This action will provide confidence that the monitoring locations give adequate early warning.

7. Document management expectations with a written monitoring and maintenance program.

8. Assure that adequate staffing is available to support the ventilation system monitoring and maintenance program.

9. Enable a continuous improvement philosophy for the ventilation system monitoring and maintenance program.

5.2   WHY MONITORING AND MAINTENANCE ARE NEEDED

The primary function of an industrial ventilation system is to provide a safe working environment by removing and controlling airborne hazards from the environment around the process. When systems are not routinely maintained, they eventually stop delivering the design exhaust airflow, sometimes within a few weeks of startup in the more extreme cases.[5.1]

In dust conveying systems, once transport velocities in the branches of the duct network are below acceptable ranges, some of the branches may become blocked by settled particles. Hood face velocities can drop at some capture points, resulting in a loss of worker protection. In some cases, transport velocities above the acceptable range can create problems if the contaminants smear at higher velocities and build up on the duct elbows or if they are abrasive and erode the ducts. If the collector develops operating problems, it can also cause general reduction of system airflow and loss of protection for the workers. Additionally, unacceptable environmental emissions might also occur. Therefore, management and facilities personnel must ensure the industrial ventilation systems operate properly.

A key practice to ensure on-going protection and avoid unexpected exposures is to manage systems within design parameters. One example would be to measure airflow and maintain a range of acceptable operation. A range such as within ± 10% of design airflow might be used. Smaller ranges may be employed for more toxic or dangerous materials and larger ranges for systems that have inherent variability. This is a proactive protection strategy rather than waiting for air samples that indicate out of limits operation – a reactive strategy.

Predictive maintenance procedures will assure the reliability of the system and expedite correction of degradations when they occur. When monitoring data are gathered, they become the basis for restoring the system to baseline or system troubleshooting as described in Chapter 7. The audit form (Figure 5-17) and the monitoring and maintenance schedules (Figures 5-18a through 15-8e) provide guidance on whether a site's technical documentation and maintenance program are effective.

The supply air system is an equally important component of the industrial ventilation system. The air exhausted by the local exhaust system, including process exhaust, must be replaced by the supply air system to keep the building from developing a high negative pressure. All exhaust ventilation systems will be significantly impacted by lack of or inadequate distribution of supply air. Excessive building negative pressure will reduce local exhaust system airflow, result in high draft velocities that can disrupt hood performance or cause operator discomfort, cause back-drafting in furnace flues, or other problems. Planned system maintenance is very important when replacement air is mechanically supplied. Operations and maintenance personnel must consider the correct performance of burners, chillers, condensers, coils, filters, etc., to keep the supply system delivering design airflows. Refer to the Supply Air Systems chapter in *Industrial Ventilation: A Manual of Recommended Practice for Design* for more information.

Responsibility for operation and maintenance functions differs among facilities and companies. Trained personnel who are knowledgeable about system purpose and maintenance procedures should perform industrial ventilation system repairs. The skills needed to perform system monitoring and maintenance are described in Chapter 9.

5.2.1 Why Ventilation System Performance Changes Over Time. Local exhaust ventilation systems are designed with target face or capture velocities at hoods, a set range of transport velocities and pressures in the duct network, and specific collector operating parameters. Systems degrade over time due to natural causes and unauthorized changes to components. Figure 5-1 graphically represents this loss in performance and protection over time.

Typical causes are explained below:

1. Over time, dust or other contaminants can build up in the duct network. This can be due to dropout from air moving too slowly to maintain suspension of the dust or smearing and buildup of contaminant at an elbow (see Figure 5-2) from going too fast (if the dust is sticky). The buildup of material restricts the open area of the duct at that point and partially obstructs the airflow. This reduces the airflow and velocity, adds more dust dropout, and magnifies the problem. Without intervention to clear the accumulated material, the duct branch could eventually become blocked.

2. Collector differential pressure can change over time. This causes total system airflow to drop and transport velocities to drop in all branches of the duct network and leads to the same failures described above. Fabric filter media can become blocked by dust buildup that adheres to the fabric during the cleaning cycle. Fabric filter hoppers can fill up with dust into the bags because of airlock valve or screw conveyor blockage, again reducing total system airflow.

3. Exhaust fan capability can change due to material buildup on the fan impeller that reduces its air moving performance. Reduced flow can also be caused by mechanical failures of the fan's bearings or pulley belts. Duct systems and exhaust fans can also deteriorate due to corrosion or erosion.

5.2.2 Impact of Unauthorized Changes. Local exhaust ventilation systems are designed to deliver a set amount of airflow at each hood or enclosure. These systems move that airflow within a defined range of velocities through each branch of the duct system. Each system's design performance should be verified at startup (see Chapter 2, Commissioning and Proof of Performance). The baseline values of airflow and static pressure will be needed as the reference values for mainte-

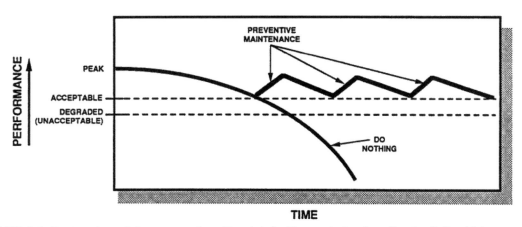

FIGURE 5-1. System degradation versus time (Reprinted with permission from Procter & Gamble)

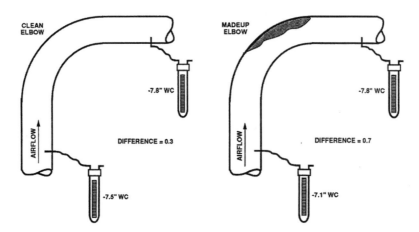

FIGURE 5-2. Duct buildup increases pressure drop (Reprinted with permission from Procter & Gamble)

nance. Drifting from the baseline values indicates time to clean or repair the ventilation system to return the performance back to baseline. There is very little flexibility in most ventilation system designs to make changes to the system without major redesign effort.

Common unauthorized changes that put the system out of baseline are listed below. It is important to use competent resources to make any system changes correctly the first time.

1. Removing a hood and closing the opening at the end of the duct (perhaps with a blank flange or with duct tape over a duct air bleed as shown in Figure 5-3). The airflow in the ducts closer to the fan will have airflows that can be reduced, promoting dust settling in them. The ventilation will be starved for air in that portion of the system. The exhaust fan will try to bring in air from all the other branches but typically it cannot draw enough to make up what was lost. Transport velocities will all be affected, the system will plug more rapidly, and the protective airflows at the hoods will be impacted.

2. Adding a hood and branch into an existing duct (see

FIGURE 5-3. Blocking branch airflow (Reprinted with permission from Procter & Gamble)

Figure 5-4). The same airflow will now be divided among more hoods, thereby reducing the flows to all hoods. The fan will pull air into the system from the new location starving air from other locations further away from the exhaust fan. The velocities in all branch ducts will drop (promoting plugging if the contaminant is particulate), but the duct velocities may increase downstream of the new duct (towards the fan) and decrease upstream of it (towards the hoods).

3. Enlarging the size of the hood opening, whether capturing or enclosing hood, without redesigning of the duct system (Figure 5-5). With a larger opening, the face velocity at the opening will decrease, reducing the protection provided by that hood.

4. Changing the configuration of the hood. A properly designed hood controls the flow of air to capture the contaminant from the source. Changes to airflow patterns (e.g., putting cardboard over the face of the hood, moving the hood further away from the contaminant source, putting equipment or other obstructions inside the opening to the hood, etc.) can disrupt the desired airflow patterns and adversely affect the protection provided by the hood.

5. Changing the position of the blast gates on one or more branches from the baseline position without careful consideration of changes to the resulting adjacent airflows. All parts of the ventilation system are connected through the duct system. The blast gate positions were carefully set at startup to deliver the right airflows to all hoods and enclosures. Although opening a damper might produce more airflow on one branch, it will reduce the airflow on other parts of the system and thus reduce the protection offered by those branches and hoods. Do not reposition blast gates once they have been set unless there is a plan that will result in improved performance at all branches and hoods.

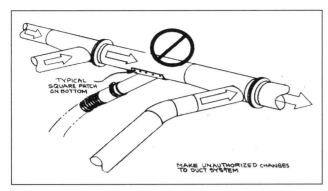

FIGURE 5-4. Unauthorized duct branch addition (Reprinted with permission from Procter & Gamble)

6. Removing an orifice or inserting the wrong size orifice (Figure 5-6) can cause the system to change from the baseline in the same way as changing a blast gate.

5.3 THE VALUE OF PREDICTIVE MAINTENANCE

Many systems today are maintained on a breakdown basis. Problems like dust escaping from the hoods, plating acids blowing out the exhaust stack or occupational health air samples out of limits prompt investigation to find the cause. By the time the problems are noticeable, the system could have degraded considerably. Investigation may show that several ducts are blocked, the collector is plugged or another similar problem exists – all which reduce system airflow and the employee protection it provides. It then takes unplanned work to clean the ducts or empty out the collector hopper to get the system back on line. Predictive maintenance is useful to forecast anticipated problems sufficiently early so that the interventions can be held to small jobs.

Better management and execution of proper procedures will help keep ventilation systems performing up to their intended

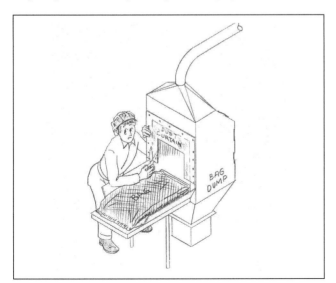

FIGURE 5-5. Enlarging of hood opening (Reprinted with permission from Procter & Gamble)

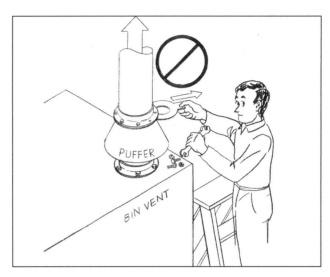

FIGURE 5-6. Changing balancing orifice (Reprinted with permission from Procter & Gamble)

design. There is a way to predict that a problem is developing, while the correction requires less cost and work to perform.[5.2] Three primary actions are needed:

1. Collect data from system startup (or its last planned change) to show the original airflows (or duct velocities) and static pressures throughout the system at the chosen test points. This is referred to as the "baseline" in this Manual. Some sources of baseline information include: as-built system engineering schematics, air balance reports, and static pressure balance calculations.

2. Subsequent to the baseline measurements, routinely measure and record system static pressures and airflows at the designated test points. This is referred to as "monitoring" in this Manual.

3. Evaluate the measured data and take corrective action based on a comparison of monitoring data to baseline data. This is referred to as "maintenance" or "troubleshooting" in this Manual. When the difference between the monitoring static pressure and the baseline static pressure varies by more than 20% (or some other set deviation), this is an indication of a developing system degradation or failure. The amount of buildup in a duct that can cause such a change is small and so cleaning the duct at this time is a smaller job. Delays can increase the magnitude of the problems and the remediation efforts.

By installing cleanout doors or similar methods to enter the duct and clean it, a large shutdown project, as shown in Figure 5-7 can be replaced by a smaller effort. Maintenance effort will be reduced by using measurement data to decide where to enter and clean rather than use a guessing approach.

The more productive method is often less disruptive to the

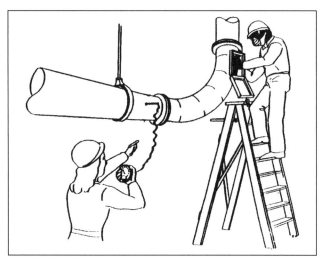

FIGURE 5-7. Predictive Maintenance: Installing clean out doors simplifies maintenance effort (Reprinted with permission from Procter & Gamble)

production process. Rather than dismantle a whole duct system, planned servicing of small areas can be performed on off-hours or even during breaks.

5.4   RECOMMENDED PRACTICE – KEY ELEMENTS

The overall industrial ventilation system performance goal is to operate and maintain the system within design parameters to ensure ongoing employee protection and predict when possible failures may occur. For those contaminant sources within the influence of the system, this minimizes the need for ongoing air sampling. However, the impact of external system influences such as pedestal fans or spills from outside the hood(s) must be understood as part of the total exposure profile for the operation supported by the system. The key elements of a successful system monitoring and maintenance program are explained in more detail below.

5.4.1 Comply With OSHA and EPA Regulatory Limits.
Operate the ventilation system so it consistently meets all U.S. Occupational Safety and Health Administration (OSHA) permissible exposure limits (e.g., TWAs, STELs, and ceiling limits) and other occupational exposure guideline limits (e.g., TLVs®, RELs, etc.) that apply to the operation. There are some specific OSHA regulations for some chemicals and for some industries which can be found in Title 29 of the Code of Federal Regulations or on the OSHA website (www.OSHA.gov). Additionally, some states have their own state occupational safety and health programs that may have air contaminant standards that take precedent over federal OSHA limits. Other countries, as well as various local entities (e.g., counties, Canadian territories, cities, etc.) may also establish local regulations that may apply to a facility's air emissions.

The U.S. Environmental Protection Agency (EPA) requires that air cleaning devices comply with all EPA regulations or environmental air emission permits. There are specific emission regulations for many chemicals and industries which can be found in Title 40 of the Code of Federal Regulations or on the EPA website (www.EPA.gov). The various states and territories in the United States also may have additional local regulations. Other countries may also have similar regulations covering environmental health issues.

The facility should have records that show that operations are within limits and that prompt actions are taken to correct problems that cause the system to operate outside of its baseline. A complete monitoring and maintenance program provides the data gathering direction and forms for keeping records. Facility records should be complete enough to show:

- Actions taken if visible stack emissions exceed permitted environmental limits (e.g., bag leaks, bubbles/mist from scrubbers, paint on roof, etc.)

- Continuous compliance with numerical permit limits for emissions (special stack testing, when required)

- Routine monitoring data for collector performance parameters (e.g., no visible stack emissions, fabric filter differential pressure, scrubber water flow, etc.) and any additional data required by the environmental permit

- Maintenance performed on internal components and subsystems (e.g., bag cleaning system operation, scrubber recirculation pump, etc.)

- Disposal of collected system wastes in accordance with regulations and disposal permits

5.4.2 Provide Baseline Verification.
Provide initial verification that the ventilation system is capable of providing the protection for which it was installed.[5.2] The objectives of the ventilation system baseline are to:

- Ensure that the ventilation system design intent (hood face velocities, duct airflows and corresponding static pressures, air cleaning device collection efficiencies, etc.) is met for all parts of the system and documented for reference for ventilation system monitoring and maintenance program.

- Demonstrate through an industrial hygiene assessment that appropriate employee contaminant exposure limits are not exceeded by contaminant sources under the control of the ventilation system.

- Update the baseline technical documentation for the ventilation system whenever the system is changed or modified.

5.4.3 Take Corrective Action on Deviation From Baseline.
The baseline shows the performance of the ventilation system when it is installed. Presumably, the system achieves the goal of providing adequate operator protection without excessive exhaust rates. Over time, however, the system will deteriorate. By setting realistic and measurable guide-

lines for the system, periodic monitoring can show when the system is not functioning as well as desired. For example, the volumetric flow or the hood static pressure can be monitored. In many systems, a decrease in volumetric flow of 10% can indicate initial deterioration of system performance. When the system is outside of the guidelines, a proactive program initiates an investigation of the cause(s) and implements corrective action(s).

5.4.4 Maintenance Risk Assessment. A maintenance risk assessment should be performed to assess the exposure consequences of ventilation system failure due to the inherent risk posed by the contaminants (i.e., health risk, fire, or explosion risk). Risk factors that lead to more rapid degradation include contaminant characteristics, ventilation system capability and operability, and operating experience. A multi-factor risk profile is used to determine the frequency of monitoring and maintenance for an industrial ventilation system to prevent those consequences.

Inherent Hazards of Contaminants. The consequences of unacceptable exposures in the workplace could lead to one or more of the following:

- Acute or chronic health effects,
- Fire/explosion hazards,
- Physical hazards due to runaway reactions, and
- Other hazards.

For some contaminants, only shorter duration exposures can be tolerated, implying that the system must function within limits for a very high percentage of the time. Other systems for highly toxic or combustible materials might need sensors and automatic shutdowns if significant levels of the contaminants are detected. In contrast, nuisance dusts would not require such immediate action.

Inherent contaminant risks can be assessed and communicated using a risk rating system. Such systems include the five-point (i.e., 4 – severe hazard, 3, 2, 1, 0 – minimal hazard) Hazardous Materials Identification System (HMIS – National Paint and Coatings Association), the National Fire Protection Association (NFPA), or some other similar rating system. Using one of these systems, assess the inherent risks for the contaminants. Some materials have a severe hazard in one, or more than one, of the three broadly accepted hazard categories (i.e., health, flammability, and reactive/physical hazard). Decide which of the following categories best describes the overall hazard of the contaminant(s) being controlled by the ventilation system as one of the components of the risk profile:

- Severe
- High
- Moderate
- Low

For more serious hazards that develop a higher overall rat-

ing (i.e., "severe" and "high"), the operator should know quickly if there has been a ventilation system failure. Alarms or strategically placed indicators on a system can alert the operators of a rapid system change, such as a fan belt break or debris sucked up into a branch and blocking airflow. The frequency of checking the indicators will extend over a longer period for less risky materials. Such alarms and indicators may not be necessary for "low" or "moderate" risk hazards.

Ventilation System Degradation. The performance of any ventilation system will degrade over time due to natural causes or operator error. Systems can more rapidly degrade from baseline performance depending on a combination of one or more of the following: the physical characteristics of the contaminants captured by the system, the design capability of the system, or the operability of the system. A higher rating under each heading indicates a greater likelihood of accelerated system degradation, hence the need for more frequent system monitoring and predictive maintenance.

The system is more likely to move outside of design ranges due to a combination of one or more of the following factors:

- Contaminant physical/chemical characteristics that cause accelerated plugging or corrosion of system ducts (Severe, High, Moderate or Low likelihood)
- Ventilation system design that does not consider contaminant characteristics such as minimum transport velocity (i.e., particulate system designs need more attention to detail than gas/vapor system designs). (Severe, High, Moderate or Low likelihood)
- System operability and layout considerations that make it difficult to operate the system (Severe, High, Moderate or Low likelihood)
- Production pressures that block getting the necessary system downtime for required maintenance (Severe, High, Moderate or Low likelihood)

Ventilation System Risk Profile. Each of the four hazard categories (i.e., health, flammability, reactivity/physical and other) has a separate impact and should be considered as a group as shown in Figure 5-8. An overall score is meaningless since a contaminant with an inherently "Severe" hazard rating might suggest a high maintenance frequency for a ventilation system with a "Low" risk of degradation (e.g., highly toxic gases). The system monitoring frequencies selected need to be adequate to alert for sudden failures and predict gradual degradation. Predictive maintenance will provide on-going protection by keeping system performance within design parameters.

5.4.5 Alert Monitoring. Establish on-going alert monitoring of the ventilation system to provide warning of rapid changes that may impact system performance. Make a judgment of the risk posed by the consequences of a system failure (e.g., employee exposure or environmental release of contaminants, etc.) to decide the frequency of alert monitoring. Some

Ventilation System Risk Factor	Hazard Rating (Severe, High, Medium, Low)	Start with Suggested frequencies in Alert Monitoring Section 5.4.5	Consider Increasing Time Between Data Measurements
Consequence of Contaminant Exposure:		HMIS level 3 or 4 and possibly level 2 for any risk category	HMIS levels 0 through 2
Health			
Flammability			
Reactivity/Physical Hazard			
Other Hazards			
Overall Rating			
Risk of Rapid Ventilation System Degradation Based On:		Start with the suggested frequencies in the Degradation Monitoring section 5.4.6	Consider increasing the time between data measurements
Contaminant characteristics		Sticky dust, heavy dust, abrasive dust, corrosive or condensing vapors	Vapors unlikely to condense, mists, lightweight dusts, fumes
Ventilation System Capability		More than 25% of the duct branches are outside conveying velocity limits	All system branches baselined to within ± 10% of design airflows
Ventilation System Operability			Trained resources on each shift

FIGURE 5-8. Ventilation System Risk Profile

possible alert monitoring frequencies from highest risk to lowest are: automatic (severe), per shift (high), daily (medium,) or weekly (low). Additionally, if a ventilation system failure is immediately dangerous to life and health (IDLH) or might result in a deflagration or explosion, a strategy of alarms and automatic system shutdown (e.g., equipment interlocks) may be required.

Strategically located visual indicators (i.e., alert monitoring indicators) at hoods or on ducts (e.g., Magnehelic gauges or liquid filled manometers) can warn of sudden changes in the system. Such changes may be due to damaged ducts, debris sucked into the system, slipping fan belts, etc. It is not necessary to put indicators on every part of the system. Well-placed indicators can warn of the beginning of degradation changes in major sections of the system as well as on individual hoods. However, they will not be able to pinpoint where the degradation is beginning. Training operators to read gauges and react when action limits are exceeded or when automatic sensors and alarms are triggered are two ways of providing alert monitoring. Additionally, note that gauges, sensors, and other automatic devices require routine maintenance and calibration to ensure their proper operation.

When performing alert monitoring, take the following actions and implement appropriate corrective measures if

action limits have been exceeded:

1. Record static pressure readings from strategically placed pressure indicators (see Figure 5-8) at hoods and ducts. This can be a routine activity for operators served by the hood(s) and a scheduled activity for the individual(s) responsible for the ventilation system operation.

2. Inspect the system physical changes in the duct network (e.g., unusual noises, duct damage, leaks, unauthorized changes, etc.).

3. Record air cleaning device parameters (e.g., fabric filter differential pressure or venturi scrubber water flow) required for environmental permit or local operating practice.

4. Record if unacceptable emissions were visible at the ventilation system stack.

5. Record other parameters based on site experience.

5.4.6 Degradation Monitoring. Establish on-going degradation and trend monitoring of the ventilation system to:

1. Identify the places where and when the system routinely begins to degrade, and

2. Provide confidence that the alert monitoring locations

in key element 5 (see Section 5.4.5) give adequate early warning.

Duct system measurements and trend tracking of static pressures in all duct branches and strategically chosen airflows reveal the locations in the system where system degradation begins. Degradation may be caused by buildup of debris inside the duct, corrosion or erosion causing leaks in ducts, filter media blinding, damaged ducts or fittings, etc. Corrective action might include design changes to eliminate the problem or routinely scheduled duct cleaning based on static pressure monitoring trends.

Determine the risk posed by the likelihood of rapid ventilation system degradation to decide the frequency of degradation monitoring. Some possible degradation monitoring frequencies from highest risk to lowest are: weekly (severe), monthly (high), quarterly (medium), or semi-annually (low). Record duct system and collector static pressure and airflow measurements to identify routine degradation points and verify that alert monitoring points provide adequate warning.

The following three-step process is recommended for gathering data on the ventilation and using the data to make decisions on the right monitoring points and frequency for your specific system. This assumes a "severe" risk of degradation based on the maintenance risk assessment in Section 5.4.4. Figure 5-8 offers factors for lower risk of degradation that would shift to a longer time between monitoring checks.

Startup Learning Period. Start by obtaining a three-month database of operating history (i.e., weekly static pressure data at all test points). Also measure airflows in strategic locations (see Section 5.4.6). The problem areas in the duct system will develop and trend plots will determine out-of-baseline locations within this timeframe. Take action either to make a design change to eliminate the problem or to determine the right corrective action (e.g., clean the third elbow in a system's branch every three weeks) to bring the system back into baseline condition. When the data show that the system runs within baseline limits (i.e., ± 10% of design airflow or face velocity, or ± 20% of baseline static pressure) with interventions/cleanouts at repeatable points, it is possible to move to the next step.

Strategic Test Points and Visual Controls. When the startup learning period has been completed, move to take bi-weekly static pressure data and monthly airflow data at identified strategic test points. Strategic test points (i.e., 20-25% of total test points) are selected based on locations where blockage is more likely to happen and are the points that, based on historical data, provide the earliest warning of system problems. The following are suggested locations for strategic test points:

- Branches with heavy dust loading (e.g., any branches with pneumatic conveying rather than just dust control). These might be additional checkpoints on the branches with visual controls (an installed static pressure gauge marked with action limits). No reduction in

test points should take place at the areas known to be "high risk."

- Branches with multiple elbows in quick succession.

- Branches where the airflow path through the connected equipment causes particulate to become airborne and pull excessive amounts of particulate into the ventilation system. This can have a negative impact on production as product is pulled into the ventilation system.

- Systems that may "inadvertently" pick up lightweight objects, such as gloves, wipe rags, drink cans, etc.

- Each duct branch that enters the air cleaning device.

- The fan inlet and outlet.

Reducing Strategic Test Point Monitoring Frequency. After three months of tracking bi-weekly strategic test points and taking corrective actions to prevent out-of-baseline operation, there will be proper control of the system within design parameters. This will allow reduction of monitoring to four-week periods. This assumes that key alert static pressure indicators are checked frequently, perhaps daily or weekly, to ensure that no surprise changes occur in the system. Strategic airflows can then possibly be measured at a quarterly, rather than monthly, frequency. To reduce monitoring frequency, the following conditions should be met:

- Select scheduled elbow cleanout inspections that give an early warning of developing system imbalance.

- Document the common causes of deviation (e.g., this elbow plugs every third week, this air bleed screen gets dirty, difference in measurements is known between filler door open and closed, etc.).

- Complete design modifications as appropriate to extend the length of time for deviations to develop when possible (e.g., larger mesh air bleed screens, longer radius elbows, reduce the source of dust so less is carried into the ventilation system, etc.).

- Install visual controls (e.g., Magnehelic gauges or other static pressure indicators with action limits indicated) on the branches with routine deviations (see Figure 5-9).

- Ensure that monitoring frequency is adequate to prevent problems from developing undetected.

Once the system has been balanced and baselined to demonstrate it can deliver design airflows, the static pressures taken at baseline with the airflows can be used to determine the actual system performance. When routinely scheduled static pressure readings indicate values 20% above or below the baseline limits, use of the Duct Network Troubleshooting Guide (see Chapter 7, Industrial Ventilation System Troubleshooting) offers guidance on where to look for the problem.

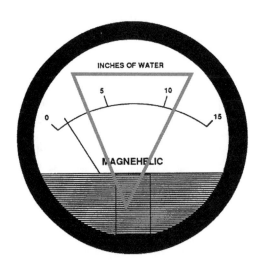

FIGURE 5-9. Visual controls example (installed gauges marked with action limits like "call xxx if needle is outside the green area") (Reprinted with permission from Procter & Gamble)

Static Pressure Measurement Strategy After System Modification. If a change is made to the system, start back at the shortest static pressure measurement frequency for approximately three months until it is demonstrated that the new baseline condition is controllable.

5.4.7 Document Management Expectations. Document management expectations with a written monitoring and maintenance plan. Ensure that the facility has a written plan for each industrial ventilation system and there is clear accountability for system performance results.[5.3] Ensure that all components of the ventilation system are included in the plan – both local exhaust as well as supply air systems.

5.4.8 Provide Adequate Staffing. Ensure adequate staffing is available to support industrial ventilation system monitoring and maintenance. Operating staff that are assigned responsibility for the system should have adequate time and training (see Chapter 9, Operator Skills and Training) to do the work necessary to keep the system operating within baseline limits.[5.3] Labor saving techniques such as the location of permanent monitoring devices (e.g., Magnehelic gauges, etc.) at key points in the system can save effort so that minimal time is required to acquire data.

5.4.9 Seek Continuous Improvement. Enable a continuous improvement philosophy for the industrial ventilation system monitoring and maintenance program. This includes looking for opportunities to increase system reliability and reduce maintenance-related exposures from duct cleanouts and other tasks that are potentially large magnitude exposure events. For example, use the data in a way that specifies elbow(s) or duct segments that build up first are cleaned while the particulate layer is small rather than waiting until there is major blockage requiring significant effort, exposure, and downtime. The process of monitoring and maintaining the system is effective in identifying the intervention points. It may not be necessary to investigate the entire system to discover the recurring problems.

5.5   MAINTENANCE RISK ASSESSMENT PROCESS

An industrial ventilation system can rapidly degrade due to a variety of factors. Systems controlling particulates typically degrade more rapidly than non-particulate systems. This section provides information for both particulate and non-particulate contaminant characteristics, ventilation system design characteristics contributing to system degradation, and operability issues that affect ventilation system reliability. These characteristics and issues should be considered when determining maintenance and monitoring frequencies.

5.5.1 Particulate Contaminant System Design Characteristics. In general, transporting particulate contaminants in a duct network requires more attention to design details than non-particulate contaminants. If the duct velocity is too low, the particulates will settle out of the air stream and fall to the bottom of the duct. When the duct velocity is too high it can cause duct erosion if the particles are abrasive or rapid smearing buildup on duct elbows if the particles are sticky. Duct transport velocity should be sustained through the tapered transition for dusty air streams that are joined in a "Y" fitting.

Additionally, more gradual transition angles are needed for sticky dusts than for non-sticky, lightweight dusts. If mists are present, ducts need to be sloped to low point drains to prevent liquid accumulation in the duct network.

Particulate contaminant characteristics that can contribute to ventilation system degradation include:

- Sticky, smearing dust (e.g., detergents)
- Hygroscopic dust (i.e., readily absorbs moisture)

- Process moisture sources in air streams

- High humidity in intake air and possible approach to the dew point

- Dust density extremes (e.g., heavy, high density dust such as lead or lightweight, low density dust such as paper dust or fiberglass fluff)

- Abrasive dust that wears elbows rapidly

- Dust loading (>10 grains to 0.5 pounds per pound of dry standard cubic foot of air)

Examples of problem particulates at the "high" end of the range include detergent (high inherent risk) and sugar dust (low health risk but a high flammability risk). Dry softwood sawdust is an example of a material with a "low" relative risk.

Ventilation system design details are a significant factor in system degradation. System design factors that can lead to rapid degradation of particulate ventilation systems include:

- More than 3 feet of flexible hose in any duct branch

- Elbows with centerline radius of less than 2.0 duct diameters

- Sequential elbows within 5 duct diameters of each other

- Welded elbows that cannot be removed for clean out

- Branch entries that join the main headers at an angle of more than 30 degrees

- Branch entries that do not enter the main header in a tapered section

- Branch entries that enter the main header at the bottom

- Ys: Blank flanges on branch instead of air bleed

- Branch adds more than 10% more air to main and downstream duct not larger diameter

- Sudden enlargement or contraction in duct diameter

- Mist systems do not have low point drains on duct network

- No intake to permit air entry at duct on sealed equipment

- Air cleaning device must be manually emptied

- No proof of operation for air cleaning device on dust removal equipment

- Varying differential pressure and system-wide airflow for air cleaning device

- Ventilation system fan operates within 10% of full load amp rating

- Ventilation system fan impeller has buildup or erosion from contaminants

- Large central ventilation system versus small ventilation system directly supporting process area

- No blast gates or other balancing devices installed (not balance by design system)

- Ventilation system baseline documentation not available or non-existent

- Supply air not balanced with local exhaust ventilation air volume

Examples of varying air cleaning device differential pressure for particulate ventilation systems include:

- Fabric filter element cleaning system allows more than 2 "wg between clean and dirty conditions (e.g., pulse jet filter bags plugged, shaker filter cleaned only off-line, etc.).

- Cyclone dust buildup/fouling or dust hopper backup.

5.5.2 Gas/Vapor Contaminant System Design Characteristics. Non-particulate industrial ventilation systems typically are not as concerned with material settling, therefore, transport velocities are much lower than those for particulates. However, these systems might have to deal with concerns about mixing incompatible materials, system corrosion, or developing an explosive concentration in the ventilation system. Ventilation systems for flammable vapors are typically operated at less than 25% of the lower explosive limit (LEL). Some locations operate the systems at less than 10% of the LEL, particularly in confined spaces or when working with dangerous materials.

Gas/vapor contaminant characteristics that can contribute to ventilation system degradation include:

- Contaminant changes from a vapor or fine mist in the duct system to a solid

- Contaminant may condense in the duct system

- Contaminant is corrosive (i.e., $5 < pH > 9$)

- Contaminant is a Class I, II, or IIIA flammable

- Contaminant is flammable and could exceed 25% of LEL in the ventilation system if not operating within the baseline specifications

- Contaminant is reactive if exposed to ambient air or moisture

System design factors that can lead to rapid degradation of gas/vapor ventilation systems include:

- More than 3 feet of flexible hose in any duct branch

- Duct system not sloped to low point drains when transporting condensing gases/vapors

- Duct liquid drains do not have an effective trap to prevent air entry

- Ventilation system materials not corrosion resistant

- Ventilation system depends on dilution with fresh air to keep flammable concentrations less than 25% of the LEL

- Air cleaning device – varying differential pressure and system-wide airflow

- No proof of operation device on air cleaning device

- Ventilation system shutdown does not automatically shut down process

- Ventilation system fan operates within 10% of full load amp rating

- Ventilation system fan impeller has corrosion from contaminants

- Large central ventilation system versus small ventilation system directly supporting process area

- No blast gates or other balancing devices installed (not balance by design system)

- Ventilation system baseline documentation not available or non-existent

- Supply air not balanced with local exhaust ventilation air volume

Examples of varying air cleaning device differential pressure for gas/vapor ventilation systems include:

- Oil mist collector drains back up into filter elements

- Carbon adsorber bed fouling

- Thermal or catalytic oxidizer bed fouling

5.5.3 *Ventilation System Operability and Degradation.*
As was described in Section 5.2, management and operator attitudes towards industrial ventilation systems in general can contribute to rapid degradation. Management must provide an atmosphere supporting the maintenance and monitoring programs in the plant. Operator productivity is affected by the difficulty required to access the equipment to perform monitoring tasks.

Ventilation system operability characteristics that can contribute to system degradation include:

- No formal ventilation system training for process operator or maintenance personnel

- Operators routinely adjust blast gate positions

- No local indicating gauges to alert operators of sudden changes

- Parts of the ventilation system that need routine cleanout are not easily accessible (e.g., platforms, cleanout doors, etc.)

- Need to find a ladder to access air cleaning device indicating gauges or controls or both

- Need to find a ladder to access ventilation system fan for routine inspections

- Air cleaning device and exhaust fan remote from process served

- No ventilation system-trained personnel on site during system operation

- No one designated accountable for ventilation system results

- No ventilation system change management program in place

Rating	Inherent Rating: Suggested ALERT monitoring frequencies	Inherent Hazard Rating from your Analysis	System Degradation: Suggested DEGRADATION monitoring frequencies	System Rapid Degradation Rating from your Analysis
Severe	Automatic or Per Shift		Weekly	
High	Daily		Monthly	
Moderate	Weekly		Quarterly	
Low	Monthly		Semi-annual	

FIGURE 5-10. Maintenance risk profile

Example: Use the maintenance risk profile shown in Figure 5-10 to complete this example.
Synthetic detergents (irritant) with enzymes (respiratory sensitizer)
- Inherent risk: High Risk
  - Health: 3
  - Flammability: 1
  - Reactivity: 0
- Rapid degradation risk:
  - Contaminant – Particulate: High Risk (smears at duct velocity > 4500 fpm, drops out at duct velocity < 3500 fpm)
  - System Capability (well designed system): Low Risk
  - System Operability (system integrated into process): Low Risk
- Alert Monitoring: High (Daily)
- Degradation Monitoring: High (Monthly)

- Downtime not available as necessary for ventilation system maintenance for known problem spots in system

5.5.4 Frequencies for Alert and Degradation Monitoring.
In order to make a holistic decision on monitoring frequencies, utilize the maintenance risk profile shown in Figure 5-10. This profile brings the information forward from both the inherent risk of the contaminants as well as the possible causes of rapid system degradation and lists the suggested risk-based frequencies for alert and degradation monitoring.

There is no "safe" or "unsafe" cutoff regarding risk. All systems should receive routine maintenance. Figure 5-10 merely assists facilities staff in determining the priority relative risk of delaying maintenance. Ultimately, judgments regarding the frequency of alert and degradation monitoring should be made based on experience with the contaminants and ventilation systems.

5.6   TECHNICAL DOCUMENTATION – BASELINE

To use predictive maintenance effectively, it is important to gather baseline data from the startup of the industrial ventilation system.[5.3] This includes key hood velocities, duct airflows and static pressures throughout the system. If the system is handling non-standard air, the temperature and moisture content are also required. Note that airflow and hood requirements at elevations above 1,000 feet must consider the effects of air density even if temperatures and moisture are at "standard" conditions. Whether the duct system consists of many hoods or just a single hood, technical documentation is necessary so an initial reference point exists for the system's monitoring and maintenance program.

5.6.1 Schematics. Develop a drawing of the entire system.
The drawing can be as simple as a single line drawing or as detailed as the isometric schematic shown in Figure 5-11. The design should be approximately to scale and should show: the

pick-up points (i.e., hoods, enclosures, hoppers, etc.); the duct system including diameters, elbows, branch entries, and special fittings; the filtering devices including component parts like rotary valves; and the fans including supply and exhaust fans. Additionally, the drawing should include the node numbers and the test point identification numbers or letters utilized for system balancing. The identification numbers or letters can also be the start and end points from the calculation sheet used to design the system. Test point identification numbers or letters should also be marked on the actual duct systems. A schematic drawing should be completed for each industrial ventilation system.

5.6.2 Hood and Duct System Baseline Data Sheets.
Hood performance is a critical issue to assess at system startup. Hood data, an industrial hygiene review and an employee exposure assessment provide the necessary information to assess whether the facility's exposure control strategy objectives were met. Figure 5-12 identifies recommended hood data that should be documented as part of the ventilation system monitoring and maintenance program.

5.6.3 Equipment Data Sheets.
Facilities professionals have developed various tables, spread sheets and computer-based maintenance management systems to record system data such as equipment make, models and serial numbers. It is important to note the performance and manufacturer's data for both the local exhaust ventilation and the supply air systems. Sometimes it is necessary to contact the original equipment manufacturer or replace original equipment. Capturing all the information in a single visit is essential when the evaluation team is traveling to a site away from their office. Figure 5-12 provides an example of the data needed to evaluate an industrial ventilation system.

Balance Orifice or Blast Gate Information. This information is typically provided in table format and shows the loca-

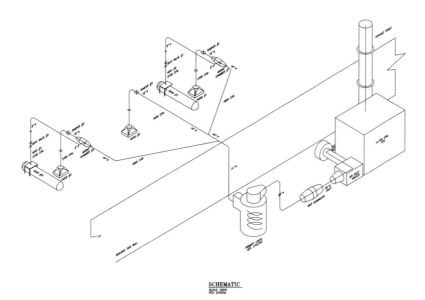

FIGURE 5-11. Isometric schematic with test points and nodes

Test Point	Common Name	Face Dimensions [width (ft) × height (ft)]	Face Surface Area (ft^2)	Design Face Velocity (fpm)	Design Airflow (acfm)	Measured Airflow (acfm)	Measured Air Temperature (F)	Measured Hood Static Pressure ("wg)

FIGURE 5-12. Hood and enclosure performance measurements

tion number and orifice size or blast gate position. It is identified as point "A" in Figure 5-13 and only orifice information is shown in this example.

Fan and Motor Information. This information is typically provided in table format and includes data on fan sizes, motor specifications, sheave sizes, belt information, etc. This information should include all supply and exhaust fans. It is identified as point "B" in Figure 5-13.

Test Point Data. This information is provided in table format and includes design information on static pressure and airflow at each test point in the system as well as the baseline airflow and pressure data measured during startup. This information is identified as point "C" in Figure 5-13. Additional space is available in the table for recording of static pressure and temperature values taken on fixed intervals at each test point. This document contains the details of how and when the static pressure balance was determined and what orifice sizes (or blast gate settings) will be used to balance the system. This calculation can be done manually or by computer and has to be updated any time the system design is changed.

Ambient Conditions. It is useful to collect data on the ambient conditions in the room(s) and outdoors; temperature, humidity and barometric pressure readings are usually sufficient. Hygroscopic or hydrophilic processes may require additional information.

Differential Pressure. Information should also be documented for the ΔP across the filter or scrubber especially if this value can change during normal operation of the system (e.g., bags become dirty, etc.).

5.6.4 Fan Specification Data. Data will typically include design information on fan, motor and drive components. It should also include a certified-vendor drawing showing the operating curve for the fan and the system. Specific information for various components is shown below:

- Exhaust Fan: Manufacturer, model number, serial number, and manufacturer's certified fabrication drawing number.

- Design condition: airflow, static pressure, air temperature and humidity, RPM, and BHP.

- Ultimate condition: airflow, static pressure, air temperature and humidity, RPM, and BHP.

- Motor: Manufacturer, model number, efficiency type, serial number, horsepower, voltage, frequency, frame size, service factor, RPM, and full load and typical amp loading.

- Drive: Belt type, size, length and number, sheave size and center-to-center distance.

5.6.5 Air Cleaning Device Specification Data. Data includes details about the design and construction of the various air cleaning devices and other components that may be used on the system. In general, this data should include manufacturer, model and serial numbers, product feed rates, airflows, piping and instrument diagram equipment numbers, plant property identification number, manufacturer's certified fabrication drawing numbers, design static pressure values, etc. Specifics for various unit devices are shown below:

- Fabric Filter: Manufacturer, model number, serial number, media (cloth) area, media (cloth) specification, air-to-cloth ratio, interstitial/can/tank velocity, equipment number, and manufacturer's certified fabrication drawing number.

- Screw Conveyor: Manufacturer, model number, serial number, type of screw flight, maximum mass flow rate, design mass flow rate, design powder bulk density, RPM, and motor drive (HP, frame size, RPM, and full load amps).

- Rotary Air Lock Valve: Manufacturer, model number, serial number, maximum mass flow rate, design mass flow rate, design powder bulk density, RPM, and motor drive (HP, frame size, RPM, and full load amps).

- Scrubber: Manufacturer, model number, serial number, equipment number, design airflow, design pressure drop, design water flow rate, chemical addition rate, control pH if required and manufacturer's certified fab-

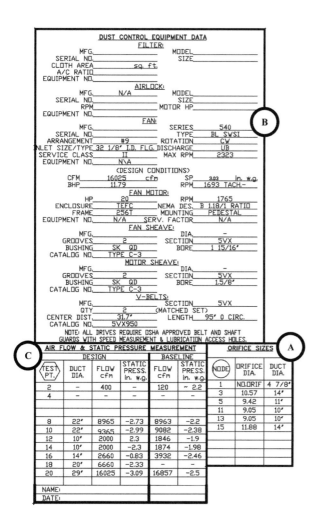

DUST CONTROL EQUIPMENT DATA

FILTER:
MFG.____ MODEL____
SERIAL NO.____ SIZE____
CLOTH AREA____ sq. ft.
A/C RATIO____
EQUIPMENT NO.____

AIRLOCK:
MFG. N/A MODEL____
SERIAL NO.____ SIZE____
RPM____ MOTOR HP____
EQUIPMENT NO.____

FAN:
MFG.____ SERIES 540
SERIAL NO.____ TYPE BL SWSI
ARRANGEMENT #9 ROTATION CW
INLET SIZE/TYPE 32 1/8" I.D. FLG. DISCHARGE UB
SERVICE CLASS II MAX RPM 2323
EQUIPMENT NO. N\A

(DESIGN CONDITIONS)
CFM 16025 cfm SP 3.03 in. w.g.
BHP 11.79 RPM 1693 TACH.-

FAN MOTOR:
HP 20 RPM 1765
ENCLOSURE TEFC NEMA DES. B 1.18/1 RATIO
FRAME 256T MOUNTING PEDESTAL
EQUIPMENT NO. N/A SERV. FACTOR N/A

FAN SHEAVE:
MFG.____ DIA. -
GROOVES 2 SECTION 5VX
BUSHING SK QD BORE 1 15/16"
CATALOG NO. TYPE C-3

MOTOR SHEAVE:
MFG.____ DIA. -
GROOVES 2 SECTION 5VX
BUSHING SK QD BORE 1.5/8"
CATALOG NO. TYPE C-3

V-BELTS:
MFG.____ SECTION 5VX
QTY 2 (MATCHED SET)
CENTER DIST. 31.7" LENGTH 95" 0 CIRC.
CATALOG NO. 5VX950

NOTE: ALL DRIVES REQUIRE OSHA APPROVED BELT AND SHAFT GUARDS WITH SPEED MEASUREMENT & LUBRICATION ACCESS HOLES.

AIR FLOW & STATIC PRESSURE MEASUREMENT

TEST PT.	DESIGN DUCT DIA.	DESIGN FLOW cfm	DESIGN STATIC PRESS. in. w.g.	BASELINE FLOW cfm	BASELINE STATIC PRESS. in. w.g.
2	-	400	-	120	~ 2.2
4	-	-	-	-	-
8	22'	8965	-2.73	8963	-2.2
10	22'	9365	-2.99	9082	-2.38
12	10'	2000	2.3	1846	-1.9
14	10'	2000	-2.3	1874	-1.98
16	14'	2660	-0.83	3932	-2.46
18	20'	6660	-2.33		
20	29'	16025	-3.09	16857	-2.5

NAME:
DATE:

ORIFICE SIZES

NODE	ORIFICE DIA.	DUCT DIA.
1	NO.ORIF	4 7/8'
3	10.57	14'
5	9.42	11'
11	9.05	10'
13	9.05	10'
15	11.88	14'

FIGURE 5-13. Ventilation system design information (Reprinted with permission from Procter & Gamble)

rication drawing number.

- Cyclone or Spark Arrester: Manufacturer, model number, serial number, manufacturer's certified fabrication drawing number, design airflow, design pressure drop (standard or actual conditions), and equipment number.

- Absorbers (e.g., mist eliminator, wet scrubbers, etc.): Manufacturer, model number, serial number, equipment number, design airflow, design pressure drop, manufacturer's fabrication drawing number, inlet and outlet temperature and difference, wash down liquid flow rate, and liquid inlet and outlet pH.

- Adsorption Bed (e.g., carbon bed): Manufacturer, model number, serial number, equipment number, design airflow, design pressure drop, design regeneration (recharge) frequency, and manufacturer's certified fabrication drawing number. Some evaluations may need inlet and outlet contaminant concentration.

- Condenser: Manufacturer, model number, serial num-

ber, equipment number, design airflow, design pressure drop, outlet gas stream temperature, coolant flow rate, coolant inlet and outlet temperature, and manufacturer's fabrication drawing number. Some evaluations may need outlet gas stream concentration.

- Electrostatic Precipitator: Manufacturer, model number, serial number, equipment number, design airflow, design pressure drop, voltage, amperage, outlet temperature, rapper intensity and frequency, manufacturer's fabrication drawing number, and chemical or detergent cleaning system. Some evaluations may need inlet and outlet gas stream and oxygen concentration.

- Thermal Oxidizers: Manufacturer, model number, serial number, equipment number, oxidizer type (regenerative, catalytic, etc.), design airflow, design pressure drop, inlet and outlet temperature, LEL of inlet gases, ignition gas flow rate and temperature, and manufacturer's certified fabrication drawing number.

5.7 SYSTEM MONITORING USING BASELINE DATA

5.7.1 System Test Points. To get representative values of airflow and static pressure, test points should be the proper distance from upstream and downstream disturbances and turbulence. Each test point should be labeled with its identification mark, duct diameter, and the baseline values of static pressure, airflow, and baseline date. When possible, locate test points where accessible from floors or existing platforms.

Remote static pressure sensing lines may be used in hard to access test point locations. A remote sensor tubing connector is fastened to cover the test point hole (see the guidelines below) in order to allow metal or plastic tubing to relay the static pressure reading to a more convenient location. Ensure the remote sensor tubing connector is sealed to the duct to avoid interference problems caused by air leakage around the connection point.

Remote Sensor Test Point Tips:

- Ensure that the remote sensor tubing is compatible with the conveyed material and the temperature conditions of the duct.

- Limit remote sensor tubing to not more than 20 m (60 ft).

- Use one-piece plastic or metal remote sensor tubing to avoid problems with leaks at tubing junctions.

- Protect remote sensor tubing from damage on its way from the test point to the monitoring location (e.g., guiding tubing through rigid duct) to avoid punctures, excessive bending, etc.

- Locate remote sensors on the top or the side of the duct, never on the bottom. Tubing of 3/16" (5mm) internal diameter has been successfully used for this purpose.

- Install the remote sensing point so its tip is flush with

the inside wall of the duct wall.

- Use duct connectors to anchor the end of the tubing to the duct wall.

- Watch out for product buildup and plugging, particularly in systems with high particulate loading and moisture. If the reading has not changed or does not slightly pulsate, the connection point might be plugged.

- Allow time for pressures to stabilize before recording readings when taking measurements. Time is directly related to the length of tubing – it may take a minute or two.

- Check the reading directly at the test point periodically and before taking any corrective action at the duct.

Velocity Measurements. Baseline or initial hood performance is established by face velocity or capture velocity measurements, smoke tests or tracer gas tests, and duct airflow for the hood. Some facilities utilize face velocity measurements at hood openings to provide a warning of poor system performance particularly when there is insufficient duct length (i.e., five duct diameters upstream from any fitting) to obtain reliable static pressure readings. However, face velocities can be difficult to obtain and interpret, only apply to the hood being assessed and do not provide enough information to accurately assess the system. More importantly, face velocity readings do not replace the need for static pressure monitoring and trend tracking.

Hood Static Pressure Monitoring. Hood static pressures measured at the same time as hood airflows, and in appropriate locations, become the basis for system monitoring. Any variability in the system (e.g., differential pressure across the collector) should also be documented when taking readings in the system. For instance, dirty filter media will give a more negative static pressure reading than clean media. Systems are designed to operate within a range between clean and dirty conditions. A hood that works correctly when the differential pressure is low may be out of baseline acceptability at a normally higher collector differential pressure.

Static Pressure Gauges. Static pressure gauges monitor the resistance of the system.

Static Pressure Gauge Tips:

- Inspect the gauges to ensure the industrial ventilation system is operating within its baseline range.

- Tap needle (i.e., analog) gauge to make sure the needle is not stuck.

- Ensure the gauge returns to zero when the gauge or system is off or the sensing line is disconnected. Three way gauges that have one port open to the atmosphere will be useful to zero the gauge.

- Inspect gauge lines and sensors for moisture and clogs.

- Check manometers for fluid flow by pinching the lines. Manometers (slack tube or inclined) may be used in place of gauges. Be sure to use the manometer fluid for which the scale is calibrated (typically water or red oil).

5.7.2 Static Pressure Data Gathering. Use a recording sheet similar to that found in Figure 5-14 to record static pressure measurements at all the test points for a system. The format displayed in Figure 5-14 provides space to list the baseline values as well as the action limit values for ± 20% of baseline. This helps to quickly identify which sections of the ventilation system are developing problems.

5.7.3 Duct Static Pressure Trend Tracking. The best parameter to track system performance is duct static pressure (SP_d). Duct static pressure is relatively easy to obtain (see Chapter 3, Testing and Measurement of Ventilation Systems) and allows personnel, with the proper use of trend tracking, to identify problems in the ventilation system. Total system airflow at the fan inlet, as well as airflows at major branches entering the collector, also provides valuable information about the status of the system. Additionally, where static pressure measurements vary more than 20% from baseline, airflow measurements can be obtained for verification. Note that systems containing heat sources may have static pressure changes that result from changes in density rather than system operation. Such systems require a more detailed investigation.

				Static Pressure Data Trend Tracking Form		
Company Name:				**System Name:**		
System Location:				**System Drawing Number:**		
Test Point	**Baseline SP ("wg)**	**Baseline +20%**	**Baseline -20%**	**Date___/___/___ list reading below SP ("wg) / T (F)**	**Date___/___/___ list reading below SP ("wg) / T (F)**	**Date___/___/___ list reading below SP ("wg) / T (F)**
				/	/	/
				/	/	/
				/	/	/
				/	/	/

FIGURE 5-14. Sample Static Pressure Data Trend Tracking Form

By plotting the static pressure values on a graph, the changes in system performance can be seen over time. This can be done on graph paper by hand or with a spreadsheet program by computer. More sophisticated methods can be used for remote or large systems. Such methods use electronic sensors that record the data as they are taken in the field and download the data into a program.

Refer to Chapter 7, Troubleshooting Ventilation Systems, for more details on how to analyze the data and take corrective action.

5.7.4 Recommended Ventilation System Maintenance Schedules.
Figures 5-16a through 5-16e provide ventilation system monitoring and maintenance program recommendations for a dust control system. Frequency recommendations are provided for hoods, duct systems, air cleaning devices, fans and fan motors, and supply air systems. Additional monitoring and maintenance recommendations for air cleaning devices can also be found in the appropriate section of Chapter 6. Exhaust fans, air cleaning devices, etc., are manufactured by different companies and will differ in parts and construction. Experience will determine an exact monitoring and maintenance frequency schedule. If more than one frequency is suggested for a component, perform that function at the most stringent frequency until it is determined what the data-based frequency should be. Always refer to the manufacturer's specifications for additional guidance in determining frequency schedules. Some equipment may require specific and documented maintenance schedules to maintain the warranty.

5.8 VENTILATION SYSTEM PROGRAM MANAGEMENT

5.8.1 Documenting Ventilation System Expectations.
Several people or departments normally do the work of monitoring and maintaining an industrial ventilation system. As such, keeping a system's records in a central location is beneficial to tracking the system's history and aids in troubleshooting the system.

5.8.2 Repair Records.
Recordkeeping provides a history of problems found with the ventilation system, solutions that worked, and costs of the repairs instituted. Figure 5-17 provides a sample format that could be used.

5.8.3 System Compliance Auditing.
Most facilities will have more than one industrial ventilation system. Therefore, ventilation system maintenance and monitoring data can be compiled and kept in notebook form with other pertinent information about the system. The checklist in Figure 5-18 provides a way to summarize the status of all site systems into a single document for management's review.

REFERENCES

5.1   Johnson, G.Q.: Cradle to Grave TLC for Your Industrial Ventilation System. The Synergist, pp. 35-36 (September 2004).

5.2   Johnson, G.Q.: Dust Control Design: Allowing for your range of process conditions and establishing baseline values. Powder & Bulk Engineering, pp. 39-48 (October 2005).

5.3   Johnson, G.Q.; Ostendorf, R.G.; Claucherty, D.G.; et al.: Improving Dust Control Systems Reliability. Ventilation '91, 3rd International Symposium on Ventilation for Contamination Control, pp. 57-62 (September 16-20, 1991).

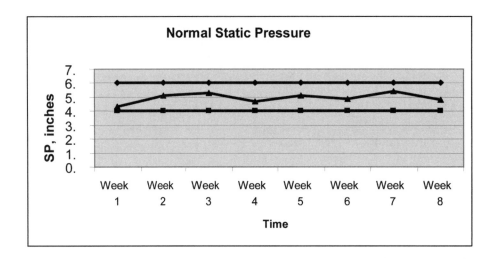

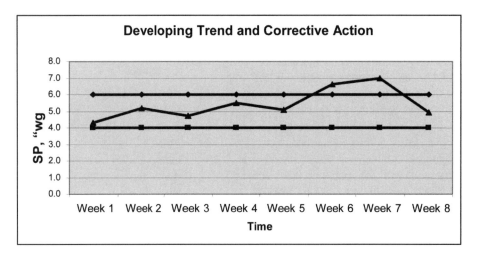

FIGURE 5-15. Static pressure trend plots (Reprinted with permission from Procter & Gamble)

Exhaust Hoods Monitoring and Maintenance Schedule								
Frequency Schedule[1]	D	W	BW	M	Q	SA	A	WR
Visual Inspection								
Hoods[2]								
Check all hoods and enclosures installed as per design and for signs of physical damage, leaks (i.e., ruptures, open access doors, etc.), rust, corrosion or erosion				X	X			
Inspect all hood components for clogs or obstructions				X	X			
Check all slots for debris and buildup (e.g., gloves, rags, hanging tools, etc.)		X		X				
Plenums								
Check access doors and determine if they are shut and sealed (i.e., no audible leaks)		X						
Clean out collected debris before it interferes with airflow		X		X				
Baffles and Flanges								
Check that they are clean and unobstructed		X		X				
Check for any interference with desired airflow pattern				X	X			
Take-Off or Duct Connections								
Check that they are clean and unobstructed		X		X				
Measurements								
Check and record the hood static pressure and ensure it is within the proper operating range	X	X						
Check manometer fluid level				X	X			
Check pressure gauge calibration					X	X		
Measure the hood capture velocity (at contaminant point of generation)				X	X	X		
Measure booth cross-sectional velocity					X	X		

[1] Frequency Schedule: D = daily, W = weekly, BW = bi-weekly, M = monthly, Q = quarterly, SA = semi-annually, A = annually, and WR = when required

[2] Since every hood type is different, an exact maintenance schedule can only be determined by experience

FIGURE 5-16a. Monitoring and Maintenance Schedule – Exhaust Hoods

Duct Systems Monitoring and Maintenance Schedule								
Frequency Schedule[1]	D	W	BW	M	Q	SA	A	WR
Visual Inspection								
Damaged ducts	X							
Open access doors	X							
Properly operating air bleeds	X							
Visible leakage of product or contaminant	X							
Inspect exhaust stack – ensure no-loss stack or rain deflection device in place				X	X			
Static Pressure and Airflow/Velocities								
Check and record static pressures at points with visual controls	X							
Check, record and trend plot airflows at the strategic test points			X					
Check, record and trend plot static pressures at the strategic test points			X	X^2				
Check, record and trend plot airflow or velocity at fan inlet duct				X	X^3			
Check, record and trend plot face velocity at strategic exhaust ventilation or dust controlled openings				X	X			
After Duct Disassembly for Clean-out								
Ensure duct, air bleeds, damper, and orifices have been correctly reassembled								X
Inspect, clean and repair access doors							X	
Audit of System Schematic or Isometric Diagrams								
Check the as-built condition against the diagram							X	
Annual System Performance Confirmation								
Static pressures at all test points							X	
Static pressures at all test points							X	

[1] Frequency Schedule: D = daily, W = weekly, BW = bi-weekly, M = monthly, Q = quarterly, SA = semi-annually, A = annually, and WR = when required

[2] After three months, go to a monthly schedule if deviations have been prevented

[3] After six months, go to a quarterly schedule if deviations have been prevented

FIGURE 5-16b. Monitoring and Maintenance Schedule – Duct Systems

Air Cleaning Device Monitoring and Maintenance Schedule								
Frequency Schedule[1]	D	W	BW	M	Q	SA	A	WR
Visual Inspection								
Check for exhaust stack visible emissions dust or other effluent on the roof	X							
Trend plot bag differential pressure	X							
Check for adequate and proper fluid in liquid filled manometer	X							
Check the bag cleaning system compressed air pressure	X							
Check the broken bag detector output, if installed	X							
Check for proper rotation of:								
- Rotary valve	X							
- Screw conveyor	X							
- Dust fines flow	X							
Check if the access doors are closed and leak free	X							
Determine if the bag cleaning system is operating properly (solenoid and diaphragm valves work for each row of bags)		X						
Check for plugs in the bag differential pressure sensing lines		X						
Check system compressed air pressure		X						
Clean and inspect bag differential pressure connections				X				
For rotary airlock valve and the screw conveyor								
Lubricate bearings				X	X			
Inspect pulley belts and drive sprockets/chains for tension and wear and replace as necessary					X	X		
Change the gearbox oil					X	X		
Clean air plenum								
Check if the blowpipes are in place							X	
Check for signs of leaking bags							X	
Look for signs of corrosion and/or moisture							X	
Calibrate the following instruments								
Compressed air pressure gauge							X	
Differential pressure instrument							X	
Broken bag detector (if installed)							X	
Secondary filter differential pressure alarm (if installed)							X	
Startup of new bags								
Use clean bag startup procedure (see Section 6.2.20 of Chapter 6, Monitoring and Maintenance – Air Cleaning Devices)								X

[1] Frequency Schedule: D = daily, W = weekly, BW = bi-weekly, M = monthly, Q = quarterly, SA = semi-annually, A = annually, and WR = when required

FIGURE 5-16c. Monitoring and Maintenance Schedule – Air Cleaning Devices

Fans and Motors Monitoring and Maintenance Schedule								
Frequency Schedule[1]	D	W	BW	M	Q	SA	A	WR
Visual Inspection								
Inspect fan blades for cleanliness, wear and damage				X	X			
Inspect fan blades for vibration, freedom and proper rotation direction					X		X	
Inspect impeller, fan housing and back plate for material buildup and wear				X	X			
Inspect fan housing for physical damage, rust and corrosion							X	
Inspect pulley or sheave belts for tension and wear and replace as necessary						X		
Drain water from fan housing and ensure drain hole is free flowing				X				
Lubrication								
Lubricate fan bearings (use manufacturer's specified lubricant, look at lubricant color and inspect viscosity) – DO NOT OVER LUBRICATE!!								X^2
Lubricate fan motor bearings only if fittings are provided and according to the manufacturer's recommendations								X^2
Lubricate moving louver or damper parts				X	X			
Motors								
Inspect and clean the exterior surface of the motor					X			
Ensure motor is securely fastened to the base plate and foundation							X	
Inspect sheaves and belts for proper alignment					X			
Ensure motor operating voltage is within 10% of the nameplate voltage							X	
Ensure the phase currents differ by no more that 5%							X	
Perform variable frequency drive checks per the manufacturer's recommendations					X		X	
Vibration Analysis								
Measure fan and motor shaft vibration amplitude, frequency, and phase; compare to industry recognized standards and plant maintenance history to determine necessary corrective action				X	X			
Inspect flexible connectors for tears, corrosion, and secure fitting					X			
Inspect the isolation foundation for vibration and secure fitting					X			
Ensure that the isolation foundation is level							X	
Inspect the condition of all rubber and spring fittings					X			

FIGURE 5-16d. Monitoring and Maintenance Schedule – Fans and Motors

Fans and Motors Monitoring and Maintenance Schedule								
Frequency Schedule[1]	**D**	**W**	**BW**	**M**	**Q**	**SA**	**A**	**WR**
Fan Belts (V-Belts)								
Inspect multiple belt drives for uneven amounts of vibration between the different belts; replace multiple belts only with matched sets from the same equipment vendor				X				
Inspect belts for surface wear cracking or a shiny, glazed or burnt appearance					X			
Inspect belts for tension and fit; V-belts should not ride on the bottom of the sheave groove (listen for belts squealing on fan startup)					X			
Inspect fan shafts and motor sheaves for alignment					X			
Inspect belt sheaves for nicks, burrs, wear, or shiny grooved bottoms					X			
Ensure the belt guard is clean, tight and secure					X			
Louvers or Dampers								
Ensure linkage connections are secure				X	X			
Inspect louver or damper for wear, rust and corrosion					X			
Inspect louver or damper for freedom of movement (ensure the louver or damper blades open and close according to design specifications)					X			
Ensure safety screens are free from debris				X				
Bearings								
Check for abnormally hot operation by feel (<140 F) or infrared		X		X				
Shafts[3]								
Inspect shaft for scoring or brown areas near bearings					X			
Inspect shaft size (at least 99.9% of its nominal diameter)							X	
Inspect alignment and straightness of shaft							X	
Ensure shaft guard is clean, properly aligned and secure					X			
Post Maintenance								
Ensure the inspection door does not leak air, is shut tightly and the fan belt guard is in place								X
Check proper motor rotation								X

1   Frequency Schedule: D = daily, W = weekly, BW = bi-weekly, M = monthly, Q = quarterly, SA = semi-annually, A = annually, and WR = when required

2   Since every bearing application is different, an exact lubrication schedule can only be determined by experience.

3   Inspect shaft size routinely only if the bearings run directly on the shaft – typical of plain babbit bearings. Ball, roller and needle bearings that run on an inner race usually do not need to be checked except when replacing the bearing.

FIGURE 5-16d (Cont.). Monitoring and Maintenance Schedule – Fans and Motors

Supply Air Systems Monitoring and Maintenance Schedule								
Frequency Schedule[1]	D	W	BW	M	Q	SA	A	WR
Visual Inspection								
Inspect the differential pressure drop across the air handling unit filters		X		X				
Inspect the air handling unit filter media for clogs, dirt, rips and tears				X				
Replace the air handling unit filter media according to manufacturer's specifications				X	X		X	X
Inspect heating and cooling units (including piping, pumps and valves) for cleanliness, obstructions and damage				X	X			
Ensure all heating and cooling units are operating according to manufacturer's specifications				X	X			
Inspect humidification equipment (including piping, pumps and valves) for cleanliness, obstructions and damage				X	X			
Ensure humidification equipment is operating according to manufacturer's specifications (look for spray pattern, water pressure, water strainer clean, etc.)				X	X			
Inspect drain pan system (including the piping, pumps and valves) for cleanliness, obstructions and damage				X	X			
Ensure the drain pan system is operating according to manufacturer's specifications				X	X			

[1] Frequency Schedule: D = daily, W = weekly, BW = bi-weekly, M = monthly, Q = quarterly, SA = semi-annually, A = annually, and WR = when required

FIGURE 5-16e. Monitoring and Maintenance Schedule – Supply Air Systems

Ventilation System Part	Reason for Repair	Maintenance Performed	Date	Performed By

FIGURE 5-17. Sample ventilation system repair form

Ventilation System Audit Form					
Site:	Date:				
Perform audit for each industrial ventilation system					
System Number:	1	2	3	4	5
System Name:					
Technical Documentation – Proof of Performance					
Industrial ventilation systems, as built have (list drawing number and latest revision date).					
Isometric or schematic drawing(s) of the duct system?					
Design airflows and static pressures available?					
Airflow balancing devices (i.e., orifices or blast gates) sizes and locations listed?					
Air cleaning device and auxiliary devices specifications available?					
Exhaust fan specifications available (e.g., make, model, RPM and current draw)?					
Updated calculations available?					
Fan curve available?					
Logic and piping and instrumentation diagrams?					
Baseline Data:					
Dated airflow/static pressure table?					
Documentation that all branches are within baseline limits?					
Monitoring & maintenance using baseline data?					
Monitoring and Maintenance Program					
Written monitoring and maintenance plan or schedule?					
System owner for this system?					
Documentation that the system owner is qualified by training and/or experience?					
Clearly marked test points?					
Daily walkthrough and observations recorded?					
Prompt action taken and documented to correct problems?					
Use of database to document airflow and static pressure measurements?					
Trend tracking system is used to analyze data?					
System stays within baseline > 85% of time (as shown by trend tracking system)?					
Records of areas where major cleanout are noted?					
Scheduled maintenance is conducted and documented?					
System re-balancing conducted every 36 months or more frequently?					

FIGURE 5-18. Sample ventilation system audit form

Chapter 6
MONITORING AND MAINTENANCE – AIR CLEANING DEVICES

6.1   INTRODUCTION

This chapter provides the reader with insights into proper operation and maintenance issues with existing contaminant control hardware (air pollution control devices). Included are recommendations for maintenance intervals provided by individual manufacturers and other resources. However, it must be understood that these maintenance recommendations are conservatively based and should not supersede the recommendations and manuals provided by a vendor for their own equipment.

A note to all who use these data: they are biased to be more restrictive and will differ from manufacturer to manufacturer. The requirements of some control devices will differ significantly from others, even within a single type of device (i.e., baghouse, scrubber, etc.).

In addition, new technologies in sampling emissions devices (CEMs) can preclude or enhance some of the recommendations as set forth in this chapter. For example, a tribokinetic or triboelectric sensor positioned to indicate a broken bag in a baghouse may preclude the need for a daily visible emission reading done using USEPA Method 9.

Each section of this chapter defines a type of Control Device. This includes a brief description of how each device works. For the User or Operator of this equipment, this is included to help the reader understand where and how improper operation or maintenance will impact the efficiency of the device. (Design parameters for each type of collection device are included in *Industrial Ventilation: A Manual of Recommended Practice for Design*, Chapter 8.) This will be followed by a description of the parts of each device and how they function properly. Also, each section will include a table summarizing proper maintenance intervals for each control parameter within a particular control device.

6.2   FABRIC FILTERS

6.2.1 Introduction. Fabric filters, also known as baghouses, are some of the most common types of particulate collectors. These terms are all used interchangeably in this section.

Fabric filters are classified by:

1) methods used to clean the dust off the filter media; and

2) the types of media installed and used to filter the particulate from the air stream.

Fabric filters are normally used for the collection of dry and wet particulate. They are not effective for the control of vapors and gases, but some units with properly treated media can be used for gas control in some cases. Pulse-jet filters are the most common type of cleaning system, using high pressure compressed air to clean the bags. Pulse-jet filters have the largest variety of filter media shapes available (tubular/sock, cartridge, star, and envelope). Reverse air filters use low-pressure air from a filter-mounted blower to clean the bags. Both of these filters can be continuously cleaned while running although special cases can include off-line cleaning. Shaker type filters are cleaned by mechanical shaking or vibration when airflow is stopped; they must be cleaned off-line because of the design of the filter system and velocities involved. This gives them both advantages and disadvantages on certain types of particulate. Choosing the best fit among the three for your application is critical and can save you money and headaches.

6.2.2 Pulse-Jet Filter Systems. Pulse-jet cleaning baghouses are used as the primary example of Fabric Filters in this chapter. Examples of different filter bag shapes and alternate bag cleaning methods are provided later in this section.

Pulse-jet filters are highly efficient, self-cleaning dust or particulate filters. These filters provide the final function of dust control – the collection of airborne dust. Actual collection efficiencies are a function of the media efficiency and the effectiveness of the seal between the bag and the baghouse tube sheet. For certain types of dusts, efficiencies approaching that of HEPA filters have been shown with the use of special filter medias. Figure 6-1 shows a typical tubular bag pulse jet baghouse.

6.2.3 How Baghouses Work. As the dust-laden air enters the pulse-jet fabric filter hopper under the bags, the air velocity drops; allowing large particles to fall into the hopper. The hopper is designed to be a dropout box and must be kept empty for this dust dropout to occur. Particles with low aerodynamic diameters (like very fine dusts or fiber-like particulate) rise into the bag area. The air passes through the bag media, depositing the dust on the outside of the bag. Once filtered, the air continues through to the inside of the bag into the clean air plenum and then out of the collector. Since it is the dust cake at the surface of the bag that actually filters the air, a good layer of dust needs to be situated on the surface of the bags. In some cases, this may require seeding when the bag is newly installed to get the high dust collection efficiency needed to meet the environmental emission permit requirements. Refer to Section 6.10.4 (Biological Treatment System Operating Tips) for more information on startup conditions.

6.2.4 Removing Dust from Filter Hopper. With a pulse-jet collector, the collected dust must be continuously removed from the filter hopper to promote dust dropout as described above. Because the filter is under the highest negative pressure in the local exhaust ventilation system, an airlock valve is needed to remove the collected dust without significant ambient air leakage into the filter housing. Depending on the connected process, the collected dust could be recycled back into the process or it may have to be discarded. Allowing the filter hopper to run nearly full, like a surge bin, will cause operating problems and can crush cages and ruin bags. Refer to Sections 6.2.14 and 6.2.15 for more information on Hopper Operating strategy or Chapter 8, Figures 8-2 and 8-3 in *Industrial Ventilation: A Manual of Recommended Practice for Design*.

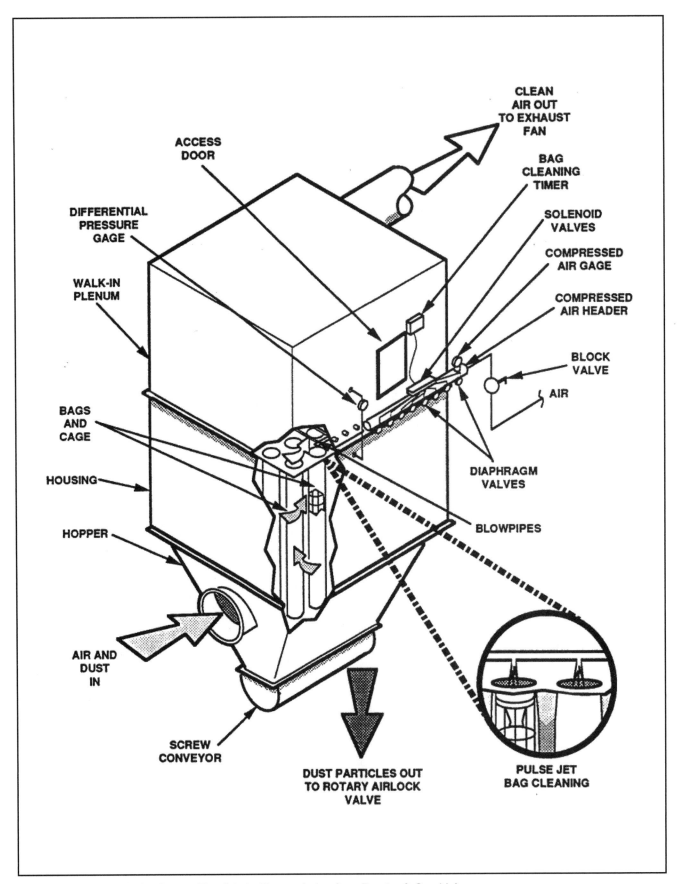

FIGURE 6-1. Pulse-Jet baghouse (Reprinted with permission from Procter & Gamble)

6.2.5 *Cleaning Dust Cake Off Filter Surface.* Depending on the dust loading to the filter, buildup of a dust cake on the bag surfaces can rapidly create a high pressure differential at the filter. This will add resistance to the local exhaust ventilation system and reduce exhaust airflows at the connected hoods and enclosures. The dust cake must be routinely removed from the bags to keep pressure differentials at expected values. As mentioned previously, three primary methods are used: pulse jet (compressed air), reverse air (low pressure air), and shaker (mechanical shaking).

6.2.6 *Baghouse Components Housing.* The housing is a dust-tight compartment that contains the filter bags and their assemblies. It usually has access doors to both the clean and dirty air plenums for easy servicing. Always lock out the system, obtain the proper confined space permit, and put on the proper safety gear before opening the access doors to the housing.

A key factor in housing design is access for changing bags. Top bag removal designs provide access to the top of the tube sheet and bags through either a walk-in clean air plenum or removable panels on top of the baghouse as shown below in Figure 6-2. Bottom bag removal designs, as shown in Figure 6-3, require an access platform inside the baghouse to reach all the bags from the dirty side housing of the baghouse.

Hopper

The hopper is an air plenum where a significant amount of dust settles out of the air, reducing the dust load on the filter bags. It also provides a distribution pattern of air to the bags and receives dust dislodged from the bags as they are cleaned. The hopper must be kept empty during operation of a pulse jet baghouse. If the hopper is trough-shaped, the hopper outlet usually feeds collected dust into a screw conveyor and airlock

valve as shown in Figure 6-4. For pyramid hopper designs an airlock valve can be all that is required. An airlock is not used for smaller filters when an airtight connection to a drum or other waste material receptacle is incorporated. The waste removal device must be absolutely airtight in order for the dust collector to work properly. Even a small air leak can encourage finer particulate back to the bag surface, causing an artificial challenge to the filter media and therefore high resistance (increased pressure drop).

6.2.7 *Filter Media Types.* Filter bags are available in a variety of shapes: tube, star, pleated, envelope/pillowcase, and cartridges (see Figure 6-5). Some of the bag shapes require rigid wire cages to support the bag and prevent its collapse from the differential pressure between the clean and dirty sides of the baghouse. Cartridges and some pleated filter bags do not require cages. The physical characteristics of the dust and process conditions are used to decide which shape to use.

Tubular/Sock Bag Filters

The most common filter bags are the tubular or sock-like bags, which are, in most cases, supported vertically within the housing by rigid wire cages. (Reverse-air and shaker-style filters often do not have cages to support the filters). Air passes through these filters and leaves dust trapped on the outer surface of the bags. The bag material is designed to operate at top efficiency with a coating of dust. This coat of dust partially fills the spaces in the mesh of the fabric and becomes part of the filtration process. Without this coating of dust on the bag surface, filtration efficiency is severely reduced.

When installing new filter bags in a baghouse, reference the "New Bag Startup Procedure" in Section 6.2.20. The clean startup procedure is also outlined in most filter vendor operation and maintenance manuals. Failure to follow the proper

FIGURE 6-2. Top access hatch, top bag removal design (Reprinted with permission from Procter & Gamble)

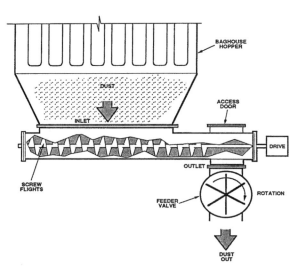

FIGURE 6-3. Side access, bottom bag removal design

FIGURE 6-4. Trough-shaped filter hopper with screw conveyor and rotary airlock valve (Reprinted with permission from Procter & Gamble)

procedure can cause premature blinding (clogging) of the filter bags and drastically shorten bag life. In addition, use replacement bags that meet the baghouse manufacturer's specifications. Poor quality bags and cages are the source of many baghouse operational failures. Proper filter media selection is key to efficiency as well as longevity of the materials. Specific media are available for most applications.

Filter failures come in two primary forms: high operating pressure drop and media material failure. The causes are varied, complex and often related.

Cartridge-Style Pulse-jet Filters

The use of pleated filters, such as cartridges has increased in popularity. Cartridge collectors are just another type of pulse-jet fabric filter (see Figure 6-6). They come in two types:

- Down-flow – where the air enters above the media, and

- Up-flow – similar to other fabric filters; has a "can" velocity and interstitial velocity.

The advantage of cartridges over conventional bags is the ability to fit much more media in the same sized housing. This advantage is most apparent in the application of extremely small spherical particulate, such as welding smoke or other metal fumes. Generally, items that cause problems with a standard filter will also subvert a cartridge. Dusts that are fibrous, hygroscopic, abrasive, hot, sticky, etc. are usually more difficult to handle in a cartridge collector. In addition, the nature of the cartridge media may put more restrictive temperature limits on the baghouse.

Cartridge filters generally have a more linear increase in pressure drop as opposed to the normal plateau of pressure drop experienced for the bulk of a bag filter's "lifetime." Cartridge life can be over two years with some applications. In addition, cartridge change-out does not usually require a restricted access permit and can be done in a bag-in/bag-out format. Cartridge change-out is usually accomplished in less

time when compared to a similarly-sized pulse-jet collector with bags.

Cartridges do not have a cage to support the fabric. They are typically made of cellulose, polyester or a blend of the two. Expanded Teflon® laminated filter media is available as well. Because of the large amount of media in a small package, very low air-to-media ratios (cubic feet per minute airflow divided by square feet of fabric area or penetration velocities) are possible, which gives an associated increase in filtration efficiency. Air-to-media ratios greater than 2:1 are rare and should not be exceeded without a written guarantee from the manufacturer.

6.2.8 Bag Cleaning System. Bag cleaning systems use high pressure compressed air (pulse-jet), low pressure air (reverse air), or mechanical shaking to remove the dust cake from the bags. Note that most, but not all, of the dust cake is removed from the media surface. A thin layer of dust on the bag surface is normal and necessary to achieve the filter collection efficiency needed to meet environmental emission permit requirements.

Pulse-Jet Cleaning

Accumulated dust on the exterior of a bag is periodically removed by directing a short pulse of compressed air. Airflow is from outside the bag to the inside and the bag is supported by an inner metal cage. The cage is usually made of steel suitable to the application (mild steel, galvanized or stainless). An aerodynamically designed venturi at the top of each bag causes the pulse of compressed air to induce a flow of clean air into the bag. A wave that temporarily expands the filter media is set up that travels down the bag and hits a solid plate at the bottom. The shock-wave momentarily pressurizes the bag, stops the flow of dust-laden air into it, and accelerates the fabric and dust cake away from the support cage.

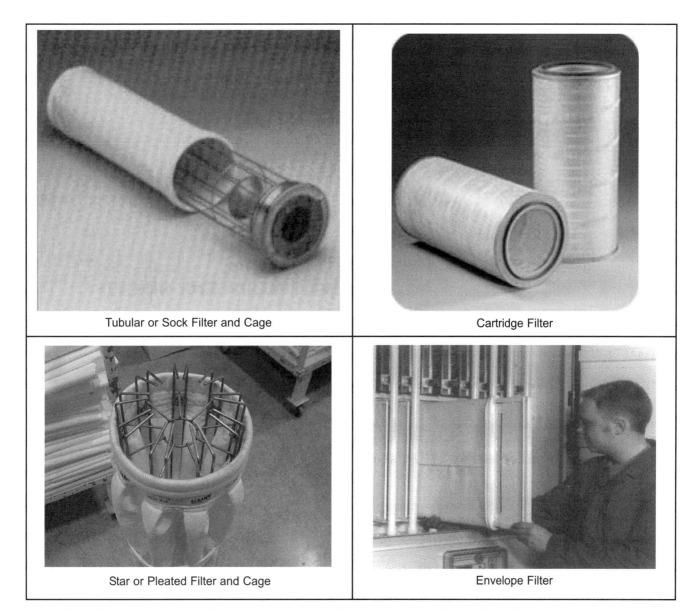

Tubular or Sock Filter and Cage	Cartridge Filter
Star or Pleated Filter and Cage	Envelope Filter

FIGURE 6-5. Examples of types of filter media (Reprinted with permission from Procter & Gamble)

The effect is enhanced by the plate at the bottom of the cage. Some dust falls off and drops into the hopper for discharge. Finer dust does not fall and returns to the surface of the bag. This action of fine dust returning to the bag surface is called re-entrainment. Particulate of low aerodynamic particle density (like feathers, or paper fines) are re-entrained in the upward movement of air between and below the bags bringing the fines back to the bag surface until they can form particles of such a size and density that they can fall to the bottom of the hopper. Any air leaks near the bottom of the hopper (worn rotary valve, etc.) significantly exacerbate this problem, causing high filter pressures and premature bag failure.

The instantaneous cleaning action progresses row-by-row while the flow of dust-laden air proceeds into the filter continuously. Each row being cleaned is off-stream for approximate-ly 1/10th to 1/15th of a second (100 to 150 milliseconds). This is the ideal time setting for pulse duration (often called "ON time"). More pulse time usually does not clean better, and can waste compressed air and energy. The entire fabric area of a pulse-jet filter is in virtually continuous operation. Most cartridge collectors and envelope-style collectors employ pulse-jet cleaning mechanisms.

Several components are used in the bag cleaning system. All components must be kept in good condition because failure of one part can cause baghouse performance problems. The cleaning system is illustrated in Figure 6-7. More detailed views are provided in Figures 6-8 and 6-9.

The pulse timer is the heart of the cleaning system. The steps of the bag cleaning sequence are started by the pulse timer which must be set for the length of the pulse of com-

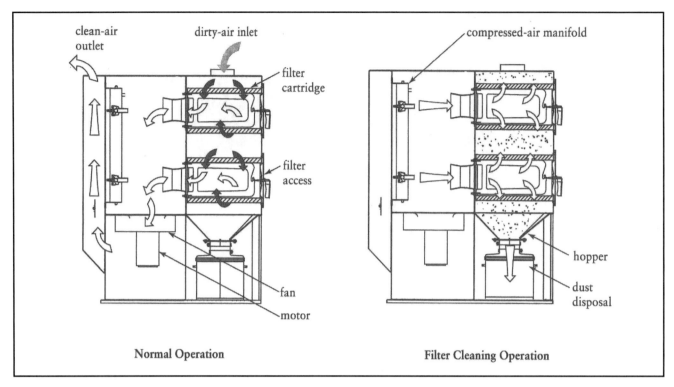

FIGURE 6-6. Cartridge collector operation

pressed air ("Duration" or "On Time") and the time before the next pulse is started for the next row of bags ("Interval" or "Off Time"), appropriate for the dust being filtered. The detailed cleaning sequence follows (see Figure 6-8):

- The timer signals the solenoid valve to open.

- Air is vented from one side of the diaphragm valve through the open solenoid valve.

- The diaphragm valve opens to vent the compressed air header to the blowpipe for a row of bags.

- Compressed air is released into the center of the venturi throat through holes drilled in the bottom of the blowpipe.

- The jet of compressed air and the venturi shape induces nearby air to also flow into the bag with the jet of compressed air.

- The entering air stops airflow briefly and sends a shock wave down the length of the bag. The shock wave continues upward by bouncing off the plate at the bottom of the bag cage.

- The shock wave accelerates the bag fabric away from the cage and knocks the dust layer off into the hopper below.

The cleaning system then sequences to the off position (see Figure 6-9).

- The timer signals the solenoid to close.

- Pressure can now build on the back side of the diaphragm, forcing the diaphragm against the blowpipe end and airflow to the blowpipe is stopped.

- The whole sequence takes approximately 1/10th of a second for one row of bags. As the bags in one row are being cleaned, the other rows continue to filter dust-laden air without interruption.

- The timer starts the sequence for the next row of bags.

- Each row of bags is cleaned in turn. Cycling through all rows of bags takes several minutes. See the vendor manual for the proper settings for your baghouse.

When the cleaning system's solenoid is closed, compressed air passes through a small bleed hole in the diaphragm or air bleed passage in the valve body, and is checked at the pilot valve by the solenoid armature. Pressure in the valve cover increases until it equals the pressure in the air header. Since the pressure is considerably lower in the blowpipe, the diaphragm seats tightly against the valve body (most valves use a spring to assist in seating the diaphragm). This is shown in Figure 6-8.

When a 100 millisecond (1/10th of a second) electrical pulse from the timer energizes the solenoid coil, the solenoid armature lifts off of its seat and allows compressed air to flow through the pilot valve to atmosphere. Pressure drops in the valve cover, and the higher pressure in the valve body moves the diaphragm into the open position. Air flows from the compressed air header through the blowpipe to clean the bags. At the conclusion of the 100 millisecond electrical pulse, the pilot

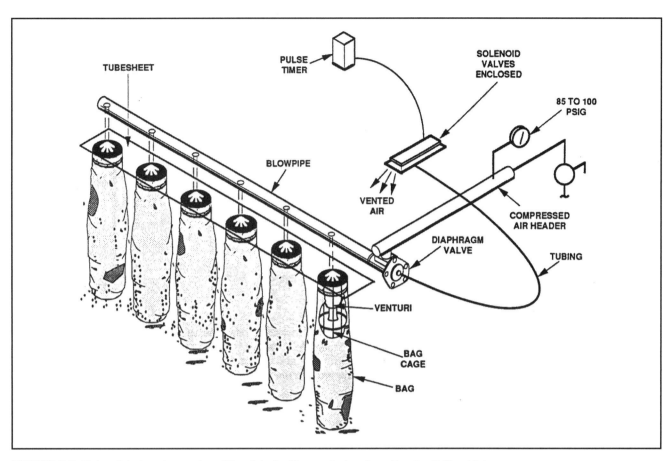

FIGURE 6-7. Pulse-Jet cleaning system (Reprinted with permission from Procter & Gamble)

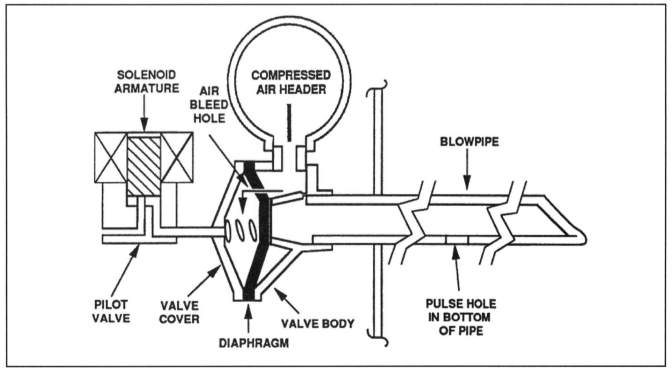

FIGURE 6-8. Normally closed solenoid valve (Reprinted with permission from Procter & Gamble)

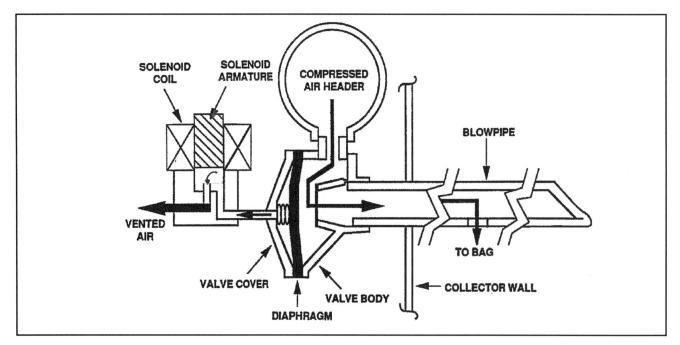

FIGURE 6-9. Solenoid valve – pulsing position (Reprinted with permission from Procter & Gamble)

valve closes and pressure rises again in the valve cover to return the diaphragm to the closed position (see Figure 6-9).

6.2.9 Establishing the Bag Cleaning System Set Points. The ON time (pulse duration) and OFF time (pulse interval) settings should be changed only with careful planning. The baghouse vendor has recommended settings for startup. Follow vendor procedures for adjusting timing to achieve a desired bag differential pressure. Too high of a bag cleaning frequency will lead to shortened bag life. Too low of a frequency will cause differential pressures higher than the desired design filter pressure drop. Keep records of when and why timer settings were changed and what results were achieved.

With a differential pressure (ΔP) sensor, such as a Photohelic® gauge, it is possible to set up the cleaning controls to start the cleaning cycle at a high ΔP set point and stop the cycle at a low ΔP set point. Specify a controller that remembers the last row cleaned. New cleaning controls offer features like digital pressure transducers with 4-20 mA outputs, digital high, low and alarm set points, offline cleaning and many other features.

6.2.10 Reverse Air Filters. Accumulated dust is removed by isolating one section or compartment of the baghouse from use long enough to send airflow from a smaller cleaning fan to the clean side (in a reverse direction) through the filter media. This dislodges the dust from the surface and the heavier particles fall to the hopper for final removal. Typically, collector design must take into account the fact that one compartment will be temporarily offline and air-to-media ratios must reflect such a consideration. Reverse air cleaning methods are gentler on bag media, which can add to bag longevity (see Figure 6-10).

6.2.11 Shaker-Style Filters. Accumulated dust is removed by shaking the entire bag assembly once the system fan is de-energized (see Figure 6-11). Shaker-style filters are therefore not continuous-duty and are typically used on processes where the local exhaust ventilation system can be turned off during production breaks and between shifts. Air typically moves from inside the bags to outside and therefore does not require a metal support cage. Filter pressure will steadily increase during use and will recover when the baghouse tubes are shaken. Extremely fine dust and fumes that do not agglomerate well and that do not fall well in an updraft style baghouse can do very well in shaker-style collectors. Therefore, re-entrainment is not an issue on shaker-style collectors.

6.2.12 Baghouse Indicators and Controls. Baghouses are a complex subsystem of a local exhaust ventilation system. They require indication of operating parameters such as pressure, alarms of problems like hopper high level, and controls for systems like bag cleaning. The Piping and Instrument Diagram (see Figure 6-12) shows most of the indicators and controls installed with a baghouse although all local exhaust ventilation systems do not require the use of all the devices shown.

6.2.13 Pressure Indication. Pressure is an important parameter for the normal operation of a fabric filter. It indicates whether airflow through the filter is at target or design values and whether the cleaning system pressure is adequate. Table 6-1 shows the common measurements needed and the sensor or devices used to provide the measurement.

Differential Pressure Gauge

Gauges should be mounted on baghouses to indicate differ-

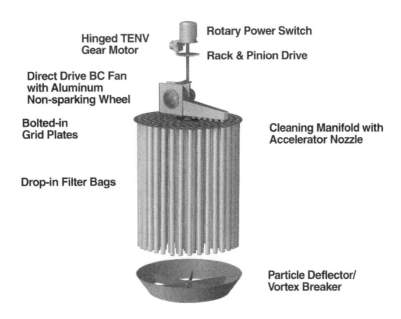

Hinged TENV Gear Motor

Rotary Power Switch

Rack & Pinion Drive

Direct Drive BC Fan with Aluminum Non-sparking Wheel

Bolted-in Grid Plates

Cleaning Manifold with Accelerator Nozzle

Drop-in Filter Bags

Particle Deflector/ Vortex Breaker

FIGURE 6-10. Reverse air dust collector

ential pressure (also called pressure drop or ΔP). Differential pressure can be measured across the media (filter ΔP) or across the whole collector (flange to flange), and is the difference in static pressure between points on the clean and dirty side of the baghouse. Because bags are filtering the dust from the air, they create a partial blockage of air within the baghouse. A pressure drop allowance is made during local exhaust ventilation design for this partial blockage. Remember that the system designer always designs for a MAXIMUM pressure drop during the design phase.

Pressure indication can be a dial indicating gauge or a U-tube manometer. Although a dial gauge is easier to read, the U-tube manometer is simple, has no mechanical parts to clean, and is a primary standard so it does not need calibration. Differential pressure between two and six inches of water is typical for local exhaust ventilation design. The pressure reading will bounce slightly when a row of bags is cleaned.

If a differential pressure gauge is mounted on the baghouse, ensure that the tubes connecting the gauge are free from blockage, particularly at the dirty side tap. Provide an easy way to clean out the dirty side tap as it can plug with dust. For instructions on how to calibrate the gauge, refer to the vendor's manual. If no differential pressure gauge exists for the baghouse, it is still possible to measure the pressure difference as a part of your routine system monitoring. Clean and dirty site pressure taps are a standard provision for baghouses. To take this measurement, open the taps and measure the static pressure at each point. The difference between the static pressures is the differential pressure. You can also connect each tap to a U-tube manometer and record the pressure difference (see Figure 6-

13). In either case, ensure that the taps are properly sealed when not in use.

Compressed Air Pressure Gauge

The pressure gauge on the baghouse compressed air header (see Figure 6-14) also provides important data for day to day operation. It is important that adequate pressure be available at the baghouse for cleaning the bags. Most baghouses need between 85 and 100 psig air and the baghouse maintenance manual should be consulted for manufacturer's recommendations. For dust with extremely high aerodynamic particle diameters and poor agglomerative properties, pulse pressures of less than 85 psig sometimes can provide better results, but review with collector vendor before making this adjustment.

Movement of the pressure gauge needle during the cleaning cycle will also indicate if the diaphragm valves are operating. When the diaphragm valve opens to clean a row of bags, the compressed air header pressure will normally drop by 10 to 20 psig for a short period and then rapidly recover to the starting pressure reading. If the drop in pressure differs from normal operations, it could indicate a diaphragm valve problem.

6.2.14 Dust Removal System. The dust removal system is a major part of larger fabric filters. Dust must be removed continuously for optimum filter operation in a pulse jet collector. Level sensors can be installed to indicate hopper backup. Because mechanical equipment is being used to remove the dust, the continuing rotation of that equipment and position of any installed diverters provide information to the logic control system to warn of failure of those components. The types of devices used to indicate Motion, Position, and Level are

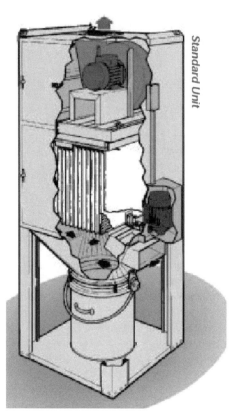

Standard Unit

FIGURE 6-11. Bag cleaning by shaking action with airflow stopped

described below, followed by a description of how the inputs are used by the logic control system.

Motion Indication

Motion switches are commonly used in local exhaust ventilation systems to electronically "prove" rotation of airlock valves and screw conveyors in the dust removal system. They are simple ON/OFF devices that send a signal to the logic control circuit whenever the absence of rotation is detected. They are used to give inputs to logic control circuits or sound alarms.

One of the many methods used to detect rotation is a combination of a metal tab on the shaft and a proximity switch. The L-shaped tab is fastened to the end of the shaft. A proximity switch, which can detect the presence of metal, is positioned on a bracket by the shaft. As the shaft turns, the L-shaped tab revolves, passing the end of the tab by the proximity switch. Electronic circuitry is programmed to time the interval between proximity switch detections of the tab. If the expected time interval is missed, the electronic circuit sends a signal to the logic control circuit.

Position Indication

These devices are used to indicate positions for a diverter valve or similar two-position damper. In a dust removal sys-

tem, the logic control circuit uses the signal to "prove" that material is flowing to the proper destination. One local exhaust ventilation application is a filter fines reclaim system; fines are sent either to the process to be recycled or to a container to be scrapped.

Either proximity switches or contact micro-switches are mounted at each valve position on the valve frame. A simple ON/OFF signal is sent to the logic control circuit when the valve mechanism activates the switch.

Level Indication

Level switches are used to detect the presence or absence of solid materials in process equipment. They are simple ON/OFF devices that send an electronic signal whenever a level is detected. The signal is used as input to a logic control circuit or to sound an alarm. Level switches in the hopper of a baghouse filter or in a chute are common applications. Some of the types of level sensors are described below.

VIBRATION – The level is sensed when the vibrations of the cylindrical probe are dampened (slowed) enough by the presence of material to activate the probe's electronic switch.

ROTARY PADDLE – The level is sensed when the rotation of a paddle, suspended on a shaft in a bin, is stopped by the presence of material and an electronic switch is activated.

ULTRASONIC – The level is sensed by sound waves reflected off the material, much like the SONAR used by submarines.

6.2.15 Typical Filter Dust Removal Control System. To put motion, position, and level components together into the control logic for the filter dust removal system shown in Figure 6-12 requires a number of different detectors to ensure continuous flow of dust out of the filter. The detectors are

TABLE 6-1. Common Baghouse Measurements

Measurement	Sensor or device
• Value of differential pressure (ΔP) between clean and dirty sides of baghouse (typically 2 to 6 "wg)	• Liquid filled U-tube manometer • Magnehelic® type dial gauge
• Set point for bag cleaning system to begin cleaning cycle (alternate to timer style controls)	• Photohelic® type dial/relay switch gauge • Digital differential pressure transmitter
• Alarm of high bag differential pressure	• Differential pressure transmitter
• Bag cleaning system compressed air pressure (typically 60 to 100 psi)	• Pressure gauge
• Dusty air pressure	• Magnehelic® type dial gauge • Pressure transmitter to control local exhaust ventilation fan damper

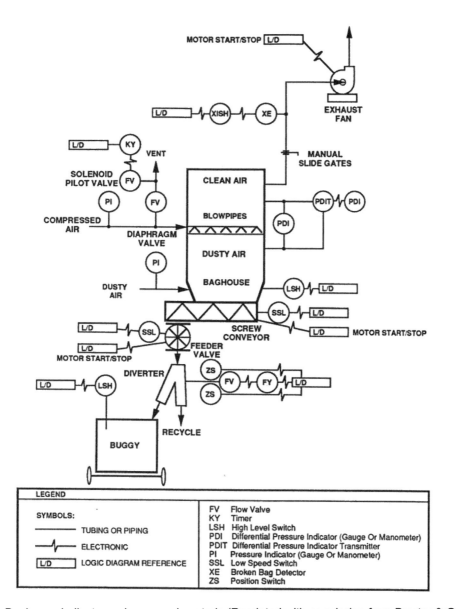

FIGURE 6-12. Baghouse indicators, alarms, and controls (Reprinted with permission from Procter & Gamble)

inputs to the logic control circuit for the local exhaust ventilation system.

- Buggy High Level (LSH): This level indicator alerts an operator when the buggy is full and must be emptied.

- Diverter Position (ZS): This indicator shows that the diverter is in position to allow product flow to the proper destination.

- Feeder Valve Low Speed (SSL): This motion sensor assures that the feeder valve is turning to discharge product. It does not warn of made up valve pockets or blockage above or below the valve.

- Screw Conveyor Low Speed (SSL): A motion sensor at this point indicates that the screw conveyor is also turn-

ing to discharge dust. It does not warn of made up screw flights or blockage above or below the valve.

- Filter Hopper High Level (LSH): This indicator shows the presence of dust in the filter hopper. High level can indicate:

  - Full dust removal container and chute,

  - Feeder valve malfunction,

  - Screw conveyor malfunction,

  - Bridging of dust in the bottom of the filter hopper.

6.2.16 Broken Bag Detectors. A probe, mounted in the clean air exhaust of a baghouse, detects the presence of dust. Most are simple ON/OFF devices that send an electronic signal whenever dust is detected. The signal is used as input to a logic control circuit or to sound an alarm. The instrument can indicate broken bags, slow leaks, or other problems.

A cylindrical probe in the air stream electronically senses the passage of low levels of dust. The probe is calibrated for that dust and sends an electronic signal when its set point is reached. See the plant control instrument specialist to learn what detection method is used at the plant.

In Figure 6-12, the bag break detector (XE, XISH) shows whether dust is present in the clean air exhaust of the baghouse and indicates that filter bags are missing or leaking. An example is shown in Figure 6-14.

6.2.17 Filter Cleaning Timer. The filter cleaning timer is normally provided by the baghouse manufacturer. It controls the cleaning air pulse DURATION and INTERVAL during the bag cleaning cycle. This system is described further in the Bag Cleaning section. The timer is an independent circuit and is not often tied into the plant logic control circuit.

Many baghouse vendors offer sophisticated controls that are more than timers. The bag break detector can be integrated so that the controller can note which row of bags was being cleaned in the event of a high dust emission reading.

6.2.18 Interlocks and Logic Control Circuits. Logic control circuits (LCC) establish a required sequence of events (also known as interlocks) to ensure that the equipment is operating as planned. For example when designing a local exhaust ventilation control system, the LCC can be designed to ensure the following startup sequence:

- Process will not run without local exhaust ventilation fan ON

- Local exhaust ventilation fan will not run without baghouse filter airlock valve ON

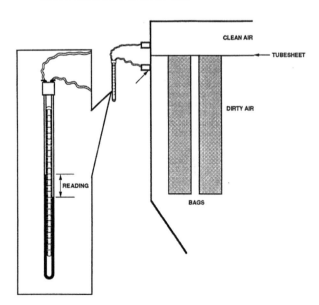

FIGURE 6-13. Bag differential pressure with U-Tube manometer (Reprinted with permission from Procter & Gamble)

- Baghouse filter airlock valve will not run without downstream dust removal system operating

Two types of LCCs used to set an interlock program are programmable logic controllers (PLCs) or hardwired electro-mechanical relays. Well-designed interlocks are needed to operate systems successfully. Modifications to the system interlocks should only be considered with the help of a qualified engineering resource and should be controlled as part of the plant Change Management System.

When indicators sense conditions and then transmit signals through the logic network to automatically initiate action, such as a local exhaust ventilation system shutdown, they have functioned as system interlocks.

6.2.19 Bag Replacement Issues. Under almost all circumstances it is best to change all the bags at the same time. If only a portion of the bags are replaced, the low resistance to flow of the relatively small number of new bags will overload their fabric with more than their share of air and dust. The higher air velocity on those bags will drive dust into the pores of the fabric that the bag cleaning system will not be able to remove.

When starting up with new bags, use the "New Bag Startup Procedure" described in Section 6.2.20. New bags have a very low resistance to airflow (usually less than 0.5 "wg). In the case of a cartridge collector, differential pressure on new cartridges before pre-coating can be less than 0.1 "wg. Since local exhaust ventilation design allows four to six inches of water column pressure drop for the bags, the new bags could be overloaded with high airflow as discussed. The New Bag Startup Procedure shows how to put a temporary resistance in the system so the total pressure drop across the baghouse is in the design range. This step is important for normal bag life. Failure to follow the New Bag Startup Procedures provided by the baghouse vendor can reduce bag life.

Always refer to the vendor instructions when changing the filter bags. Pay particular attention when installing new bags that require clamping to venturi or cage assemblies (no way to check for airtightness). Ensure that excess fabric is uniformly distributed around the cage. A single fold in one location will leak dust.

It is also recommended that all new clamps be used when changing bags in bottom removal bag designs. The worm gear mechanism that holds the clamp tight will not hold the bag as tightly in second and subsequent uses, possibly leading to dust leakage problems.

Safety Notes:

- Follow Lockout, Confined Space Entry, and Personal Protective Equipment Procedures

- Your lockout should include, at a minimum, the following preventive measures:

  - Screw conveyor/feeder valve OFF,

  - Baghouse exhaust fan OFF,

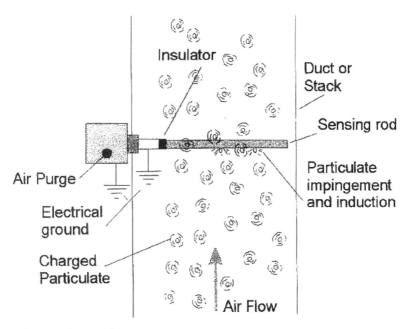

FIGURE 6-14. Broken bag detector (concept)

- Baghouse compressed air header block valve SHUT (Vent the air still in the header before the entry by allowing the pulse timer to run for a few minutes.)

Washing Filter Bags – Only a Short Term Fix

Washing or dry cleaning dirty filter bags does not restore them to "good as new" status. New bags, when properly conditioned as described in the Clean Bag Startup procedure, may have an effective life of three to five years. Washed bags usually only last a few months at best before their differential is unacceptably high again.

Washing bags diminishes their filtering effectiveness because:

1. Washing/dry cleaning does not remove all the dust particles from the bag, even water soluble dust like detergent. The residual material is stuck deep in the fabric and cannot be dislodged by the bag cleaning system.

2. Washing mats the fabric felt of the bag, creating large pore structures that get blocked and lead to a shorter effective life when returned to service.

3. Polyester felt fabric bags have a flame singed surface to remove the fine fibers for better dust cake release. After washing, the surface is more fuzzy, which causes the dust cake to adhere more tightly, requiring more compressed air consumption by the bag cleaning system with a greater bag cleaning frequency in an attempt to get the bag differential pressure down to acceptable limits.

4. Bag cleaning flexes the bag and causes filter fabric wear and dust migration through the fabric. Thus, there is a shorter time before the bag differential is unacceptably higher and local exhaust ventilation system total airflow decreases.

5. Some filter bags are still cotton and are not heat set. Shrinkage can render the bag useless for dust filtration.

6. Some filter bags have a surface coating on the polyester fabric to aid dust cake release. Washing damages the smooth coating and creates a fuzzy surface that more tightly holds the dust cake with the same bag cleaning problems as described in # 3 above.

With the amount of effort and downtime it takes to change bags, particularly in a large baghouse, using washed bags is a false economy. You will be changing bags again in a few months. Installing new bags that meet the Original Equipment Manufacturer's specification, followed by proper conditioning as described in the Clean Bag Startup procedure, gives the longest possible bag life and the lowest overall dust exposure in this high exposure job.

6.2.20 New Bag Startup Procedure. Use of proper procedures can provide longer bag life and reduced dust emissions (highest collection efficiency due to best bag pre-coat) for dependable baghouse operation. This assumes that moisture sources are controlled and a bag fabric compatible with the dust has been selected.

Improper new/cleaned bag startup leads to shorter bag life caused by bag blinding. This is seen as a high baghouse differential pressure and results in lower system airflows. One secret to longer bag life is maintaining the design air velocity through the clean bag fabric while its resistance to airflow is low; a new bag may have 0.5 "wg pressure drop where pressure drop for a properly conditioned bag is 2-6 "wg (see Figure 6-15).

Method: Temporary variable resistance (damper) between the baghouse and the fan is installed. This provides the necessary 3 to 6 "wg pressure drop to get the desired air velocity through the bag fabric. The procedures below describe how to measure airflow and set the damper to achieve desired air velocity. The system also should be balanced within 5 to 10% of design airflow. This assumes that the attached duct network is free of material buildup, has been balanced and can be operated at baseline flows and pressures.

Procedure: (see Figure 6-15)

1. After replacing all bags, record the date and the bag fabric used.

2. Install a damper at the baghouse outlet/fan inlet or the fan discharge.

3. Before introducing coating dust to the system, measure system total airflow and adjust the damper to reduce flow to within ± 10% of design or Baseline. The bag cleaning system should be turned off.

4. Allow dust to enter the system and coat the bags. Monitor both bag differential pressure and total system airflow; as differential pressure rises, airflow will drop.

Adjust the damper to keep total airflow within ± 10% of Baseline. When differential pressure rises to design amount (3 to 5 inches), activate the bag cleaning system.

5. Adjust the bag cleaning system to keep from over-cleaning the bags while building a good bag dust pre-coat. When baghouse differential pressure reaches its design value, fully open the damper. Lock it in the full open position.

NOTE: Do not replace a small percentage of bags at one time. The new bags will be quickly blinded by the very high airflow through their low resistance as compared to the older, pre-coated bags in the rest of the baghouse. The cleaning system will not be able to dislodge the particles driven into the fabric by the higher velocity. If 5 to 10% of the bags are leaking, it is better to block the bag cleaning venturis (with a tennis ball or wooden plug) for those bags until downtime to replace all bags can be scheduled. However, this may increase velocities through the remainder of bags to a high level also and should not be used except in emergency conditions.

6.2.21 Normal Startup Sequence. Manufacturer's recommendations for startup should always be followed. In the absence of documentation, a simple method for startup can be as follows (this assumes all safety controls and interlocks have been reviewed before activating the system and local exhaust

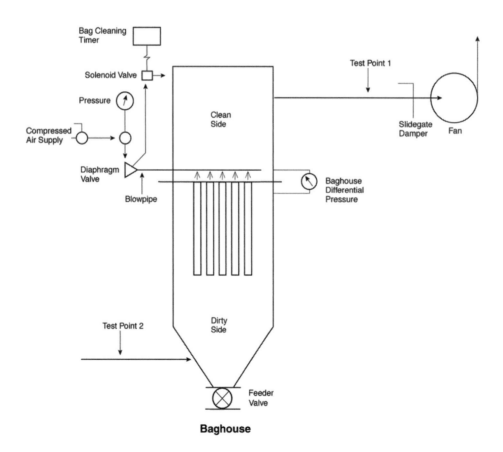

Baghouse

FIGURE 6-15. Controlling baghouse airflow with new bags (Reprinted with permission from Procter & Gamble)

ventilation baghouse):

1. Turn on the dust removal system (e.g., screw conveyors, feeder valves, or conveyor belts).

2. Turn on the fan.

3. Turn on the pulse cleaning system.

4. Turn on processes.

6.2.22 System Shutdown. To shut down the local exhaust ventilation system, reverse the order of the steps for a normal startup. Ensure that the people working in the area serviced by the local exhaust ventilation system know when a system will be turned off.

6.2.23 Recommended Monitoring and Maintenance. The keys to successful long-term operation of a baghouse is good inspection and monitoring of the bag cleaning system and baghouse differential pressure. It is also important to ensure proper operation of the dust removal system. Table 6-2 is a suggested schedule of Monitoring and Maintenance activities for starting up a new baghouse with 'normal' dust conditions. Special physical or chemical characteristics of the dust, the air stream or other factors may require more or less intervals. Experience with successful operation after several months without problems may also lead to a different scheduled frequency. Information is shown for a pulse-jet collector and can be adapted for reverse air and shaker collectors.

6.2.24 Checking for Proper Bag Cleaning System Operation. Weekly checks of this important sub-system are recommended to avoid operating problems that can affect local exhaust ventilation system airflow. To perform the suggested sequence below, two pressure indications that can be seen at the same time are required as follows:

- Compressed air pressure at the manifold (large pipe compressed air reservoir) under the diaphragm valves (suggest at the far end of the manifold from where the compressed air supply pipe enters); and

TABLE 6-2. Baghouse Inspection and Monitoring Frequency Schedules

DAILY	WEEKLY	OTHER

• Visual walk by inspections. Record and compare to log sheet action limits. Take action if beyond limits.
 	
  - Exhaust stack visible emissions or dust on roof?
 	
IMMEDIATE ACTION REQUIRED IF VISIBLE EMISSIONS FOUND – NOTIFY SITE ENVIRONMENTAL CONTACT
 	
  - Bag differential pressure (Does the reading "bounce" during bag cleaning? If not, check for dirty side tap plugging.)
 	
  - Adequate fluid in liquid filled manometer?
 	
  - Bag cleaning system compressed air pressure in recommended range.
 	
  - Static pressure at a strategic point in the duct network as a surrogate for system airflow.
 	
  - Broken bag detector output, if installed.
 	
  - Proper rotation of:
 	
  - rotary valve?
 	
  - screw conveyor?
 	
  - Dust fines flow?
 	
  - Access doors closed and leak free?
	• Inspect and record:
	
	  - Bag cleaning system operating properly? (See detailed description below.)
	
	  - Bag differential pressure sensing lines are not plugged.
	
	  - Compressed air pressure value.
		• Monthly:
		
		  - Clean and inspect differential pressure connections to baghouse
		
		• For the rotary airlock valve and the screw conveyor (if installed), conduct as per vendor manual and Preventive Maintenance Schedule:
		
		  - Lubricate bearings
		
		  - Inspect pulley belts and drive sprockets/chains for tension and wear and replace as necessary
		
		  - Change gearbox oil
		
		• Annual clean air plenum inspection:
		
		  - Blowpipes in place?
		
		  - Signs of leaking bags?
		
		• Annual instrument calibration:
		
		  - Compressed air pressure gauge
		
		  - Differential pressure instrument
		
		  - Broken bag detector (if installed)
		
		  - Secondary filter differential pressure alarm (if installed)
		
		• Changing bags:
		
		  - Replace all bags, not just a percentage.
		
		  - Record type of bag fabric and date in maintenance log.
		
		• Startup of new bags:
		
		  - Use clean bag startup procedure.

- Bag differential pressure (make sure the dirty side pressure tap is not blocked or you will get a false reading).

When standing by the bag cleaning valves, observe the following as each row of bags is cleaned:

- Check to see that the bag differential pressure reading bumps slightly.

- Observe drop in compressed air manifold pressure reading of approximately 10-20 psig and quick recovery to original reading.

- Hear the "snap" of the solenoid valve as it opens for 1/10th of a second to release the air off the diaphragm valve.

- If it is quiet enough in the area, you should be able to hear a distinctive "whump" of the air entering the filter via the venturis from the blowpipe. Listen carefully, as this is the best way to tell if a diaphragm valve is working properly.

- Get used to the normal sounds and sights; then differences will indicate which row(s) has a problem.

Signs of poor cleaning that show up are as follows:

- If the "snap" of the solenoid valve is not crisp, the solenoid valve may be sticking. Check for water or oil in the compressed air. Be ready to replace the valve (or replace the valve diaphragm) as directed by the manufacturer's maintenance manual.

- If the compressed air pressure gauge drops too far below normal, the diaphragm valve seat on that row may be wearing and admitting much more air than needed. Be ready to replace the rubber diaphragm in that valve as directed by the manufacturer's maintenance manual.

- If you hear a continuous airflow noise, one of the diaphragm valves is full open, probably due to solenoid valve failure. Be ready to repair both valves. *Hint: If the diaphragm valve is working properly, you can tell by removing the tube at the solenoid valve and capping it with your thumb. Covering the tube with your thumb will stop the compressed airflow through the diaphragm valve if the diaphragm valve is working properly. Pop the valve a couple of times by removing your thumb and recovering the top of the tube several times just to make sure that it works correctly.*

It is recommended to have some spare parts for diaphragm valves on hand. Repair kits with the common replacement items are available at a fraction of the cost of an entire diaphragm valve. Solenoid valves should be replaced in their entirety.

6.2.25 Troubleshooting the Baghouse. All baghouse manufacturers publish and furnish owner's manuals that include installation, operation, maintenance, and troubleshooting information. Troubleshooting issues are essentially the same for all pulse-jet cleaning baghouses. However, keep the vendor manuals at hand for each type of baghouse and review them for familiarity before any specific need arises. The most frequently encountered troubles are associated with the following:

- Bag installation or material selection

- Bag cleaning (including compressed air quality)

- Solenoid and diaphragm valve failure and timer operation

- Water intrusion into the filter

- Not continuously emptying the filter hopper

- Not using the Clean Startup Procedure for new bags when applicable

A well run local exhaust ventilation system can have bag life of about twice that of a poorly-maintained system. Short filter bag life is often a difficult problem to diagnose. If, after completing this troubleshooting list, problems continue, consult a qualified resource. There are several companies that can analyze used bags and determine what problems the bags were exposed to.

Local exhaust ventilation systems can be totally out of balance while the baghouse differential pressure looks to be within limits. It is important to consider how the baghouse and the duct network interact. As the Baghouse Differential Pressure Troubleshooting Guide shows, there are at least three major categories of causes for High Differential Pressure and two categories for Low Differential Pressure. Avoid focusing on just the baghouse; also get an understanding of what the rest of the system is doing!

6.2.26 Baghouse Troubleshooting Guide. As with previous sections, this section will focus on the pulse-jet collector (see Tables 6-3 and 6-4). Similar issues will exist for the reverse air and shaker collectors and the particular bag cleaning method can be substituted for compressed air cleaning issues.

6.2.27 Managing Baghouse Changes. When process changes, airflow increases or decreases, temperature changes or other revisions are made to a local exhaust ventilation system, this will obviously impact the operation of the baghouse since the original intent of the design is being changed. When a change is requested for a baghouse, there are two key considerations to address: 1) Will the airflow exceed recommended guidelines for your dust? and 2) Do the characteristics of the dust or air stream change in a way that hurts baghouse performance? Brief guidelines are listed below, followed by a detailed discussion of how to calculate "air-to-cloth ratio" and "interstitial velocity."

Increase local exhaust ventilation system airflow through baghouse

1) Do not exceed recommended air-to-cloth ratio

TABLE 6-3. Troubleshooting Guide (High Differential Pressure)

High	Differential Pressure
Possible Cause	Check these things

1. Bag blinding, bridging (System airflow < design?)	A. Check bag cleaning system
	• Compressed air supply:
	• Moisture (dryer failure)?
	• Pressure < design (85-100 psig)
	   • Pressure indicator okay?
	   • In-line air filter blockage?
	   • Valves positioned incorrectly?
	   • Air compressor problem?
	• Blowpipe loose, no air to venturis?
	• Control system:
	• Incorrect pulse timer settings?
	• Demand pulse not working?
	• Solenoid valve failure?
	• Diaphragm valve failure?
	B. Check dust removal system (filter hopper bridged?)
	• Outlet opening too small?
	• Rotary feeder valve failure?
	• Valve not rotating?
	• Valve rotating too slowly?
	• Valve pockets blocked?
	• Discharge chute blocked?
	C. Check process sources of moisture
	• Water getting in through leaks in baghouse housing?
	• High process moisture in dusty air?
	D. Check for static electricity cling in baghouse in low humidity climates (< 30% relative humidity)
	E. Air leaks in hopper
	• Rotary valve worn.
	• Screw worn or screw cover not sealed.
	• Interstitial velocity too high for the particulate.

2. High airflow through baghouse	A. Check fan speed – Belt pulley diameter? • Motor speed? B. Check fan damper at correct setting C. Duct inspection door open?
3. Bag fabric	A. Bag fabric meets baghouse vendor specification (surface treatment, size, tightness to cage, permeability, etc.)? B. Check correct fabric for service

TABLE 6-4. Troubleshooting Guide (Low Differential Pressure and Visible Emissions)

Low	Differential Pressure
Possible Cause	Check these things
1. Low bag resistance to airflow	A. Inadequate new bag precoat (bag conditioning)? B. Bags being cleaned too frequently? C. Missing bags due to incorrect installation?
2. Low system airflow	A. Major plugging of duct network? B. Fan performance? • Pulley diameter too small? • Belts slipping/loose? • Wrong motor? • Fan incorrect rotation (check motor hookup)? C. Baghouse clean side inspection door open?
Visible Dust in Baghouse Clean Air Side or Exhaust Stack	
Bags installed improperly	Bags sealed to baghouse tube sheet as per manufacturer instructions? Top removal bags seated in tube sheet mounting? Missing venturi gasket? Venturi not securely seated? Bottom removal bag clamps tight? (Replace worn clamps)
Torn or damaged bags	For < 10% of bags, plug those bag venturis until all bags can be replaced at once For > 10% of bags, replace all bags Check for rough or sharp spots on bag cage wearing holes in bag
Leakage between tube sheet and housing	Inspect tube sheet to filter housing joints for leakage and repair
General filter fabric failure	Correct fabric installed for service? Bags as per OEM specification? Too high bag cleaning frequency causing premature wear? Operating filter at design air to cloth ratio? Abrasive dust causing bag wear? Chemical attack of fibers in filter fabric from process operating conditions change?

2) Do not exceed recommended interstitial velocity (upward velocity between bags)

3) Do not allow new dusty air connections to filter to directly blast air onto the bags

Changing particulate that filter has to remove from dusty air or constituents of the air stream (moisture, pH, etc.)

1) Check impact of greater particulate mass loading of dust on filter:

   a. Dust removal system capacity adequate?

   b. Sufficient space between bags for new type of dust?

2) Check impact of greater percentage of finer dust particles:

   a. Lower air-to-cloth ratio to avoid blinding

3) Check impact of stickier dust:

   a. Lower air-to-cloth ratio?

   b. Change bag fabric to one with better dust release properties

4) Check impact of increasing moisture load on filter due to process condition change (see stickier dust list).

5) Check pH of incoming air stream:

   a. Effect on media type

   b. Effect on housing, tube sheet or cage materials

6.2.28 Air-to-Cloth Ratio. Air-to-cloth ratio refers to the volume of air passing through a square foot of filter medium. It is also known as filtration velocity or penetration velocity.

The ratio selected should be based on the "filter challenge," which is a compilation of physical properties of the dust, including particle size, hygroscopicity, aerodynamic particle diameter, concentration in the air to be filtered and other parameters. Experience is also a big factor in filter applications. Some consequences of exceeding a design ratio are reduced bag life (fabric blinding), poor cleaning (collected dust cannot drop into baghouse hopper below), and high pressure drop (system airflows are restricted with resulting loss in system performance).

EXAMPLE PROBLEM 1

Determine the baghouse cloth area needed to serve 20,000 cfm of air at an air-to-cloth ratio of 6:1.

$$\frac{20{,}000 \text{ ft}^3/\text{Min}}{6 \text{ ft/Min}} = 3330 \text{ sq ft Cloth Area}$$

EXAMPLE PROBLEM 2

An existing baghouse has a cloth area of 2000 ft². The maximum and design air-to-cloth ratio for the installation is set at 6:1. The original system airflow was 11,500 acfm. If total system airflow is increased by 20%, will the baghouse exceed an air-to-cloth ratio of 6:1?

$$\frac{11{,}500 \text{ ft}^3/\text{Min} \times 1.2}{2{,}000 \text{ ft}^2/\text{Min}} = 6.9 \text{ ft/min} = 6.9{:}1 \text{ (Greater than 6:1)}$$

The 6:1 ratio is an example and does not apply in all cases. Fine dust, for example, may require lower ratios to avoid the re-entrainment of dust on the bags. Higher dust loadings need a lower air-to-cloth ratio. The air-to-cloth ratio of a baghouse is engineered along with the other system engineering considerations; this ratio should be observed in all cases. For this reason there is no such thing as a "12,000 cfm baghouse." The baghouse is sized by the area of the cloth. When applying the correct air-to-cloth ratio, this provides the capacity of the baghouse itself.

Because filters represent an obstruction (resistance) to airflow in a local exhaust ventilation system, systems are designed to accommodate a specific bag resistance (pressure drop). Any change that might impact this resistance, such as a change in the type of filter fabric, increased airflow or dust loading, should be submitted for an engineering review.

6.2.29 Interstitial (Can) Velocity. Interstitial velocity refers to the upward air velocity in filter body between the filter bags. It has also been called "Tank Velocity" and "Can Velocity." Interstitial Velocity as a design parameter is only a consideration in pulse-jet collectors because reverse air and shaker-style collectors do not have an upward flow during the cleaning process. In addition, newer down-flow collectors reduce this problem significantly.

Depending on the particle size of the collected dust, too

high of an interstitial velocity will prevent the dust that is knocked off the bags by the cleaning system from falling down into the filter hopper for removal. Baghouses have been completely plugged with dust due to high interstitial velocities.

One way that vendors design around too high an interstitial velocity is to shorten bag length. Although tall, skinny baghouses might be desirable from an installation standpoint, interstitial velocities that are too high might dictate going with the next shorter bag length (and correspondingly larger baghouse "footprint" to keep from having filter operating problems). Always consider the interstitial velocity as it compares to the terminal settling velocity of a particular dust. Submicron-sized metal fumes as well as paper fines, textile dust and microscopic feather-like particulate are especially susceptible to this problem.

Baghouse designers set the target interstitial velocity based on the aerodynamic particle diameter, particle size and other dust particle properties. Here is the method to calculate a filter's interstitial velocity so one can determine if a proposed change (i.e., more airflow or longer bags) is close to the vendor's recommended velocity:

Given $Q = VA$ then $V = Q/A \rightarrow$ Equation 1.3 (Design Manual)

$$V_i = Q_t/A_i$$

$$V_i = Q_t/(A_f - A_b) \qquad [6.1]$$

where: V_i = interstitial velocity [fpm]
Q_t = Total airflow [acfm]
A_f = Filter housing cross-sectional area [ft²]
A_b = Total bag cross-section area [ft²]
A_i = interstitial area ($A_f - A_b$) [ft²]

EXAMPLE PROBLEM 3 (FROM FIGURE 6-16):

Q_t = 3000 acfm
A_f = 6' x 6' = 36 ft²
A_b = 49 bags at 0.1963 ft² or 9.62 ft²

$V_i = Q_t/(A_i)$; 3000/(36.0 − 9.62) = 3000/26.4 = 113.6 feet per minute

6.3 PARTICULATE SCRUBBERS

6.3.1 Introduction. Wet scrubbing is utilized where space is a concern, on high temperature or high humidity applications, for sticky dusts that do not dislodge easily from media collectors, and where fire or explosion concerns rule out other types of collection devices. All particulate scrubbers rely on the use of a liquid, usually water, to act as the collection medium for fugitive dust. The air, dust and water are intimately mixed, resulting in the dust particles being retained within the liquid, which can then be disposed of without the concern of generating a secondary dust source. However, scrubber discharge water is frequently treated in another process step to remove

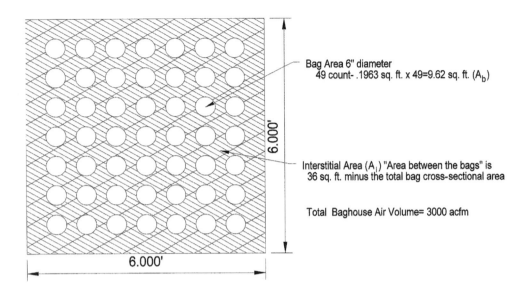

Bag Area 6" diameter
49 count- .1963 sq. ft. x 49=9.62 sq. ft. (A_b)

Interstitial Area (A_i) "Area between the bags" is
36 sq. ft. minus the total bag cross-sectional area

Total Baghouse Air Volume= 3000 acfm

FIGURE 6-16. Baghouse cross-sectional view to calculate interstitial velocity

solids before being discharged to a sewer. Scrubbers utilize three basic mechanisms for particulate capture:

- Impaction – the particle directly collides with a water droplet.

- Interception – the particle wants to follow the airflow path around a water droplet, but is close enough to be drawn to the water droplet by intermolecular attraction known as Van der Waals forces

- Diffusion – the random motion of the particle brings it into close enough contact with a water droplet to be captured by Van der Waals forces.

All wet particulate scrubbers are fractionally efficient; the efficiency of particulate capture is a function of the amount of energy utilized in this air, dust and water intermixing. Another way of saying this is that more energy must be utilized in the air, dust and water contact to achieve a given efficiency as the aerodynamic particulate size decreases; or, as the particle size decreases, greater scrubber energy, usually in the form of pressure drop, must be inputted in order to achieve the same efficiency as utilized for larger particulate capture.

Whether the energy is used to create more eddy currents (mixing) or produce greater quantities of smaller water droplets (for a given amount of water), does not seem to matter; either method creates a greater probability for dust and water interaction and thus increases efficiency. Note that the aerodynamic particle size, not the physical size, is important since many particles are not uniform in size and wet scrubbers are aerodynamic devices. Aerodynamic size is the equivalent

size of a round particle as it would behave in the airstream.

No matter how efficient a scrubber is in capturing particulate, it is useless without a way to remove the entrained water droplets. A good demisting section eliminates the water droplets created to capture the particulate, and keeps the dirty water from exiting from the stack. Fortunately, the water droplets generated in a scrubber readily agglomerate and lend themselves to simple mist elimination devices. Scrubbers usually employ chevron or baffle type demisters, centrifugal or cyclonic devices, to effect water droplet removal from the air stream. Mesh pads can also be used but are more sensitive to "plugging" from the entrained solids and must be "flushed" clean on a regular basis. The dust infused water is then either discharged for external treatment and reuse, discharged to sewer (laws permitting), or reused as is, with an internal means, such as built-in drag chains, for separating out the majority of suspended solids.

6.3.2 Types of Particulate Scrubbers. The most common particulate scrubbers can be categorized into four basics types: Centrifugal, Orifice, Venturi and Tray type. Each type is used for particular applications requiring efficiency, ease of cleaning, energy and other factors. Manufacturers of particular types of units should be consulted with regard to particulate efficiency, energy requirements and liquid usage.

6.3.3 Centrifugal Scrubbers. Centrifugal scrubbers such as wetted impeller and cyclonic types utilize centrifugal action to transport the heavier-than-air dust particle through the air stream and onto a thin film of water. The primary method of collection is by impaction, with some interception taking place. These types of scrubbers normally operate in the 3-8 "wg pressure drop range and provide efficiencies in the high 90% range for particulate 5 microns and larger. Water usage is usually in the 1-3 gpm/1000 cfm range. Mist removal is either inherent in the centrifugal action of the device or by external baffles or cyclonic separators. Typical inlet dust loadings to these types of scrubbers are less than 2 grains per cubic foot. However, depending upon particle size and outlet loading required this may increase.

6.3.4 *Orifice Scrubbers.* Orifice type scrubbers provide narrow "openings" that air travels through, aspirating water as it enters the "slot." The high velocity air shears the water into droplets and rapid changes in direction (tortuous path) "mix" the dirty air and water to induce particulate capture. A separate demisting section of chevrons or entrainment baffles will follow the scrubbing section. The primary method of particulate collection is interception, and includes some impaction and diffusion.

Pressure drop for these types of scrubbers is usually in the 5-12 "wg range, with efficiencies in the high 90% range for particulate sizes down to 1 micron. Water usage for the scrubbing action is usually in the 10-30 gpm/1000 cfm range, but is usually drawn from an integral sump within the scrubber, and is not the discharged amount going to sewer or treatment. Inlet dust loadings to these types of scrubbers can be as high as 10 grains per cubic foot, depending upon particle size and outlet loading required.

6.3.5 *Venturi Scrubbers.* Venturi scrubbers are probably the oldest design of wet scrubber, and can achieve efficiencies of 99+% on some submicron particulate if the pressure drop is high enough. These types of scrubbers can be designed for pressure drops as small as 5 "wg to as high as 200 "wg. Venturi Scrubbers operate by accelerating the air stream to high velocities via a converging section and injecting water into the throat area where the high velocity air shears the water into thousands of small droplets and causes them to mix with the particulate. A diverging section after the throat serves to regain some of the energy expended in the accelerating section.

A cyclonic separator or baffle type mist eliminator is typically used after the venturi for mist elimination. Water usage in venturi scrubbers will normally vary between 6 and 12 gpm/1000 saturated cfm, after which it is often sent to settling tanks/ponds and returned to the scrubber to minimize disposal costs. Inlet dust loadings as high as 10 grains per cubic foot can be tolerated by venturi scrubbers; outlet concentrations will depend upon pressure drop and particle size distribution.

6.3.6 *Tray Scrubbers.* Tray type scrubbers utilize perforated plates or trays on which water is distributed from either above or below, depending on the manufacturer's design. As the dirty air accelerates through the "holes" the water is sheared into droplets and a "froth" forms just above the plate. The water droplets and/or froth provide the surface area for the

dust particles to impact on and be intercepted. Some designs have "target plates" centered over the holes to cause increased turbulence for better mixing. Incorporating additional stages of plates in the vertical tower attains increased efficiency.

These types of scrubbers usually operate in the 2" – 15" pressure drop range, depending on the number of plates, and are typically used where both gas absorption and particulate capture is desired. Their particulate capture efficiency, as with other low to medium pressure drop scrubbers, is in the high 90% range for micron sizes of 5 and above. Water usage in tray scrubbers varies from 1.5 – 6 gpm/1000 saturated cfm. Demisting sections following the scrubbing section(s) are typically baffles or mesh pads. Inlet dust loading limits are subject to the size of the perforations and particulate characteristics; typical applications are for less than 2 grains per cubic foot.

6.3.7 *Issues for Improved Operation.*

Inlet Conditions

All scrubbers benefit from having proper inlet conditions. Ideally, a minimum of 5 inlet diameters of straight duct run should precede the scrubber inlet. This allows the inlet air and dust to "rebalance itself" after a disturbance and provide a uniform airflow and dust distribution pattern to the scrubber. Elbows, branch entries and other disturbances will provide poor air distribution. The entrained dust in these disturbed air patterns can cause uneven flow or overloading through a section of scrubber, resulting in poor operation and reduced removal efficiency.

Temperature Reduction

Where high inlet temperatures (greater than 300 F) are encountered, it is best to cool the air stream before it enters the scrubber. This will allow all of the scrubbing water to be utilized in particulate capture without sacrificing the scrubbing liquid for evaporative cooling. It also eliminates steaming of the water during the scrubbing process, which can cause disruptions or pockets of reduced water/air contact in the scrubbing zone. When cooling by water spray, the quality of the water can impact overall scrubbing efficiency. Although using recycled scrubbing water minimizes overall water usage, it can lead to a decrease in overall particulate removal efficiency. The suspended solids in the water will add to the inlet load to the scrubber, and once the cooling water is evaporated, the dissolved solids will increase the fraction of submicron particulate, which is the most difficult to remove. Therefore, it is beneficial to *use the cleanest water available for evaporative cooling.*

Water Flow Control

Different types of scrubbers require different methods of water control; consult manufacturer's specific recommendations regarding their requirements. The following general checklist can be applied to any scrubber.

a. Verify proper water pressure and flow at the scrubber.

Low pressure will not supply the proper water flow or develop the spray pattern for proper operation for those scrubbers employing sprays.

b. Verify spray patterns and full coverage of spray area. Clogged nozzles, worn nozzles or unequal coverage will permit dust bypass and result in dust removal inefficiency of the scrubber.

c. For scrubbers utilizing a sump for water supply, verify that the operating level of the water is maintained. In many cases, an external water level indicator will be employed; verify that it is operating properly and is not subject to external air leaks or blockage in connection piping.

Pressure Drop

As stated earlier, efficiency is directly related to the energy utilized. This is most often associated with the pressure drop across the scrubber. Decreases in pressure drop will result in decreased efficiency. Since most scrubbers are constant pressure drop devices, any change in pressure drop is an indication of a problem.

a. Verify proper airflow through the scrubber. Airflow will have a major impact on pressure drop.

b. Verify proper water flow and distribution. Improper distribution or inadequate water flow will impact the pressure drop.

c. Check for plugged orifices in the scrubber and demister. Blockage will increase pressure drop, but will decrease performance.

d. For those scrubbers aspirating water from a static sump, verify that the water level in the sump is adequate.

e. Check for plugged differential pressure sensing lines, which will give a false indication of pressure drop across the scrubber.

f. For those scrubbers with adjustable dampers, insure proper operation and set point of damper; adjust as necessary to attain desired pressure drop across the scrubber.

Demisters

Problems with the demisting section of scrubbers will result in decreased performance. Most problems with demisters will be associated with plugging or inadequate cleanliness.

a. Build up on mist eliminators not only impedes airflow but also serves to re-inject water droplets back into the air stream.

b. Improper orientation of removable mist eliminator baffles will result in water carryover. Chevron mist eliminators must have their "drip legs" pointing down.

Water Quality

The quality of water in the scrubber sump should be monitored and checked at least monthly. Too many total dissolved solids (TDS) or total suspended solids (TSS) in the scrubbing water can impact efficiency, lead to solids buildup within the scrubber and create corrosion and/or odor problems. The nature of the dissolved solids will determine the maximum concentration of dissolved solids. Calcium based and other compounds that lead to "hard water" will require more frequent maintenance or replacement of the scrubbing water. Suspended solids exceeding 5% will cause accelerated wear and will increase maintenance schedules for cleaning. Individual scrubbers may tolerate more or less TDS or TSS depending on their design and operational conditions; usually a schedule for maintenance or water changeover must be empirically determined since operating conditions, scrubbing water composition and scrubber design will vary from job site to job site.

Corrosion and Erosion

Deterioration of the internals of a scrubber from corrosion or erosion can allow bypass of dirty air, improper distribution of air or water, and leakage. Regular inspections and cleaning will detect these problems before they become major concerns. A weekly check of scrubbing water pH with litmus paper is a simple way to detect excessive corrosive conditions of the water. Draining and diluting with fresh make-up water is often sufficient to control pH; if a problem persists, soluble alkali or acid (depending on pH) can be added to bring the pH back to a neutral reading.

Controls

Scrubbers employ a variety of control devices to sense pressure drop, airflow, water level, etc. Since these devices are critical to the operation of the scrubber, it is imperative that they be kept in optimum operating condition. Material buildup on probes and floats will result in inaccurate water level control. Leaky connecting hoses and tubing will provide false pressure drop signals. Plugged water hoses or vacuum/pressure lines will affect water level control. In general, a regular preventative maintenance (PM) to insure clean, tight, unobstructed connections and instruments will eliminate the majority of concerns with control problems.

Location of instrumentation can result in improper readings. Instruments should be located above water level, and sensing lines should be routed so that they are completely self-draining back to the scrubber to prevent water accumulation in the instrument or in the sensing line.

6.3.8 Maintenance and Monitoring Schedule. Table 6-5 lists suggested maintenance and monitoring that will help insure proper operation of the air pollution control equipment. This table should be used for general reference only; manufacturers' specific requirements for individual scrubber designs should take precedence over the information provided herein.

Since some recommendations will be specific to only one type of scrubber, the following designators are used to indicate the type of scrubber affected:

C = Centrifugal; O = Orifice; V = Venturi; T = Tray

TABLE 6-5. Maintenance and Monitoring Schedule

Action	Scrubber Type (C = Centrifugal; O = Orifice; V = Venturi; T = Tray)	Comments
Record operating conditions – airflow, pressure drop across scrubber, water flow rate, water pressure	C, O, V, T	Initially at start-up; verify monthly or if operational problems arise.
Check/adjust pH of scrubbing water	C, O, V, T	Weekly or more frequently if variable or upset conditions present themselves, or acidic compounds are present in the air stream. Not required if once through water is utilized.
Inspect spray nozzle pattern	C, V	Monthly or if problems arise. Check for unusual wear and plugging.
Inspect air equalization hoses for leakage and blockage	O	Monthly or if problems arise.
Inspect instrument lines for deterioration or leakage	C, O, V, T	Quarterly or if readings are out of range.
Inspect scrubber internals for wear or blockage	C, O, V, T	Semi-annually
Clean instrument probes	C, O, V, T	Weekly or more/less frequently if experience dictates
Inspect demisters (clean as necessary) Chevron Cyclonic Mesh Pad	C, O, V, T	Monthly* Quarterly* Weekly* *more/less frequently if conditions dictate.
Blow down and replace recirculated water	C, O, V, T	Every two months or when dissolved solids concentration exceeds reasonable limits (see Operating Tip #5); when excessive odors emanate from scrubbing liquor.
Clean scrubber (internally)	C, O, V, T	Inspect monthly; frequency can be extended until proper cycle for a given application has been determined.

6.3.9 Troubleshooting. Table 6-6 indicates problems and potential causes that are applicable to all scrubber designs, but the manufacturer's operating manuals should be consulted for problem resolution exclusive to the individual manufacturer's scrubber design.

6.3.10 Managing Changes to Particulate Scrubber Operation. There are times when changes to the local exhaust ventilation system will be required. This includes changes to flow, chemicals in the dust or water systems, changes to dust loading, etc. This will directly impact the operation of an existing particulate scrubber. The following sections list several possible changes. Note that changes to the operation of the scrubber may also impact the resistance in the local exhaust ventilation system so other factors such as fan operation, motor horsepower and duct sizes may also be impacted. See Chapter 8 (Modifying Industrial Ventilation Systems) for more information.

Airflow Changes

Most scrubbers, including their demisters, have a range of airflows at which they can function effectively. This range will vary from manufacturer to manufacturer and among scrubber designs, but the range is usually somewhere between ± 10% to 25% of the median design capability. Needless to say, the actual amount of latitude one has in changing the air volume through a scrubber will be dependent on what the original design was and whether the equipment was sized around its maximum or minimum capability. Increasing/decreasing the air volume beyond the maximum/minimum capacity of a scrubber will result in decreased efficiency, water carryover and, in general, poor operation of the scrubber. *The following should be investigated prior to changing the airflow through a scrubber:*

a. Is the new air volume within the limits of the scrubber? Consult with the manufacturer before making any changes.

TABLE 6-6. Potential Problems and Sources (Particulate Scrubbers)

Problem	Possible Causes
Emission Problems(Reduced Dust Collection Efficiency)	Unbalanced air or water flow Plugged or worn nozzles (water supply) Increased dust inlet load Change in particulate size (reduced) Reduction in airflow below scrubber limits Deterioration of scrubber internals Orifice or Tray type scrubber not level Insufficient water supply Excessive water supply Surging – see below
Water Entrainment	Lack of drain or plugged drain in fan Excessive airflow through scrubber Incorrectly installed mist eliminator baffles Buildup on mist eliminator or scrubber internals Orifice or Tray type scrubber not level Plugged or leaking air equalization hose Plugged drains in scrubber Inadequately designed or functioning drain traps Excessive water flow to scrubber Surging – see below

Low Differential Pressure (across the scrubber)	Insufficient make-up air
	System pressure loss greater than designed
	Fan running backwards
	Fan belt loose or broken
	Damper in ducting closed
	Pluggage in duct
	Deterioration of scrubber internals
	Obstruction or leak in pressure sensing line
	Insufficient water supply to scrubber
	Low water level in scrubber (orifice type w/sump)
	   Drain open
	    Water supply not adequate
	    Faulty level control
	Air leak in ducting between scrubber and fan

High Differential Pressure(across the scrubber)	System pressure loss less than designed
	Damper in ducting opened more than required
	Obstruction in scrubber (pluggage/buildup)
	Obstruction or leak in pressure sensing line
	Excessive water supply to scrubber
	High water level in scrubber (orifice type w/sump)
	   Valve left open
	    Blockage in drain line
	    Faulty level control
	Air leak in ducting upstream of scrubber (fan downstream of scrubber)

TABLE 6-6 (cont). Potential Problems and Sources (Particulate Scrubbers)

Inadequate Airflow at Hoods	Addition of more exhaust points
	Insufficient make-up air
	System pressure loss greater than designed
	Fan running backwards
	Fan belt loose or broken
	Damper closed
	Air leaks through doors or joints
	Water level too high in scrubber
	Plugged drain in scrubber
	Leaky supply valve
	Air leak or plugging in vacuum hose
	Plugging in duct or scrubber
Surging	Uneven airflow at inlet
	Scrubber not level
	Fan operating in unstable range
	System static pressure fluctuating (loose damper)

b. Is the air mover (fan) capable of the increased/ decreased volume? Check with fan manufacturer for maximum rpm capabilities, operational point on the fan curve, hp requirement, etc.

c. Allow for duct changes to maintain dust transport velocities (reduced volume) or to minimize pressure loss (increased volume).

d. Water requirements, both supply and discharge, may have to be adjusted for the change in air volume in order to maintain the required liquid to gas ratio and solids content in the scrubbing water. Consult with manufacturer about new operational parameters.

e. Changes in airflow may also change the inlet dust loading; this must be taken into account if outlet emissions are not to be impacted. If the inlet dust load changes and the particle size distribution is the same, then the outlet loading will also change proportionally. See below for more detailed impacts of dust loading changes.

Changes in Inlet Dust Loading

Changes in dust loading can result from process changes, relocation of dust collectors or hooding, or airflow changes. Increasing/decreasing the dust load will increase/decrease the outlet emissions, all other things remaining constant. Because some scrubber designs have limits on inlet loading, increasing the dust load may overwhelm the scrubber whereby plugging occurs or a non-proportional increase in outlet emissions results. It is always advisable to consult with the equipment manufacturer before changing any of the operating parameters.

Changes to Dust Characteristics

The greatest impact will be seen by changes in particle size distribution because of the fractional efficiency of scrubbers. Any process change that reduces the particle size will invari-ably result in a higher emission rate. Other changes in the characteristics of dust that can potentially have a negative effect on performance include its ability to be "wetted," solubility, and particle shape.

Changes to Scrubber Water Supply

Water supply changes impact scrubber performance by changing dissolved and suspended solids and the pressure at which the water is delivered. Increases in either dissolved or suspended solids can increase the emission rate from a scrubber, cause increased scaling, and cause increased wear on the scrubber internals. Pressure changes can affect the water supply capacity as well as the spray patterns in those scrubbers employing nozzles or water jets; this will impact the scrubbing efficiency.

Changes to Scrubber Water Discharge

Although reducing water discharges is a desirable goal, it can cause unanticipated problems with scrubber systems. Reducing the scrubber water discharge increases the total dissolved and suspended solids. In addition to increasing emissions, causing buildup and eroding scrubber internals, it can also lead to obnoxious odors, and increase the corrosiveness of the water by lowering the pH. Where food products are being collected, there is an added concern for bacterial growth. All of these potential "negatives" should be considered and planned for before embarking on reductions in water discharge.

Changes to Local Exhaust Ventilation Duct System

System changes not previously discussed that affect scrubber performance may include any of the following:

a. relocating scrubbers

b. adding or deleting hood pickups

c. ducting changes

d. increasing production capacity

Any of these changes will require an examination of system pressure and volume impacts. Relocating scrubbers may entail redesigning ducting and changes in altitude, temperature or humidity that will affect the fan performance and therefore affect the airflow to the scrubber. Ignoring these impacts can result in poor scrubber performance. Increasing production capacity will often increase dust load or at least require additional air volume to control the fugitive emissions.

6.4   THERMAL AND CATALYTIC OXIDIZERS

6.4.1 Introduction. The purpose of a thermal or catalytic oxidizer is to reduce industrial air pollution emissions by treating polluted exhaust gas prior to discharge to the atmosphere. Oxidizer systems are effective on gaseous or particulate pollutants that can be neutralized by oxidation. Oxidation is a chemical reaction where the pollutants react with oxygen. Oxidizer systems are employed on a wide variety of industrial processes including printing, painting, drying and baking.

All oxidizers work on the same principle, they promote an oxidation reaction between the pollutant compound and available oxygen. In this reaction, the pollutant compound is consumed and several by-products are produced. For the most common Volatile Organic Compounds (VOCs), the by-products are carbon dioxide (CO_2), water vapor and heat. There are two basic classes of oxidizer – thermal and catalytic. They differ in the method used to cause the oxidation reaction.

6.4.2 Thermal Oxidizers. In a thermal oxidizer, the oxidation reaction is caused by heating the polluted gas to a temperature (referred to as the oxidation temperature) where the oxidation reaction occurs spontaneously. The gas is held at that temperature for a period of time (referred to as the oxidizer's residence time) to allow the reaction to be completed. The oxidation temperature is normally in the range of 1300 F to 1800 F and the residence time is between 1/2 and 2 seconds. The heating is accomplished by firing a gas or oil burner into the air stream as it flows through a combustion chamber. The residence time is determined by the size of the combustion chamber and volumetric flow rate of the polluted gas being processed.

There are three distinct types of thermal oxidizer:

- Afterburners (or Direct-Fired thermal oxidizers)
- Recuperative oxidizers
- Regenerative oxidizers

These are characterized by their primary heat recovery method. Primary heat recovery is defined as any type of heat recovery that takes heat from the hot clean gas (after the oxidation reaction is completed) and uses it to pre-heat the incoming polluted gas. Secondary heat recovery is any system for recovery of heat where it is used for something other than heating the incoming polluted gas. Examples of secondary heat recovery include process heating and comfort heating.

An important concept to understand is the thermal efficiency of the primary heat recovery system. In simplified terms, the thermal efficiency is the percentage of the heat that is recovered from the hot effluent gas and recycled. A very high thermal efficiency will correspond to a very low difference between the inlet and outlet gas temperature of the oxidizer. More importantly, higher thermal efficiency will result in lower fuel consumption for the burner. Heat recovery is a critical consideration in any thermal oxidizer because the ongoing operational costs are related directly to the thermal efficiency. The original capital cost of a thermal oxidizer can be a small fraction of the ongoing cost of heating a gas stream to 1500 F over the lifetime of the unit.

All of these types of oxidizers can be operated on the thermal principle. The catalytic principle can be employed as well, as long as the bed is protected from overheating and the contaminated gas stream will not cause chemical poisoning or foul the bed.

Thermal Oxidizers can also be differentiated by the nature of the gas stream and its contaminants. The amount of air in the gas stream and the amount of combustible contaminants impact the design approach selected.

6.4.3 Direct Fired Thermal Oxidizers. Direct-Fired Thermal Oxidizers (DFTOs), also known as Afterburners, are the simplest type of thermal oxidizer. They include no primary heat recovery. A typical afterburner system with a secondary heat recovery boiler is shown in Figure 6-17.

DFTOs are primarily used for applications where the chemical composition of the pollutants makes it impractical to use more fuel efficient oxidizer types. This includes pollutants with large quantities of halogenated VOCs that react and create acids in the oxidizer exhaust. If the concentration is great enough to present a regulatory and/or maintenance issue, the acid is frequently collected by a scrubber system located downstream from the afterburner. DFTOs (afterburners) are frequently combined with secondary heat recovery systems like boilers.

6.4.4 Recuperative Thermal Oxidizers. For contaminated air streams, a common design for heat recovery is preheating the air stream itself. Two types of heat recovery (preheat) methods can be provided. The first type is called recuperative heat recovery. These systems utilize plate-type or tubular heat exchangers. They can recover up to 70% of the heat liberated. Typical contaminated air preheat temperatures range between 600 F and 1100 F depending on the contaminant loading. Operation temperatures of typical thermal oxidizers are between 1200 F and 1600 F. A compact design recuperative oxidizer with a tube-type heat exchanger is shown in Figure 6-18. Recuperative systems are often used on paint bake ovens and printing presses.

6.4.5 Regenerative Thermal Oxidizers. A Regenerative Thermal Oxidizer (RTO) utilizes a regenerative system for primary heat recovery. A regenerative heat recovery system uses multiple beds of thermally stable (usually ceramic, either ran-

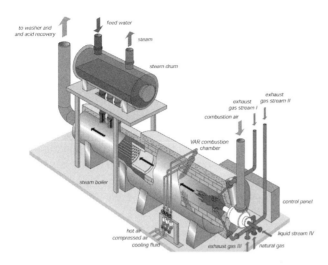

FIGURE 6-17. DFTO system with secondary heat recovery boiler

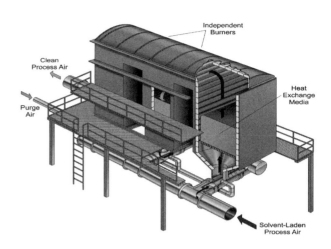

FIGURE 6-19. 3-Tower regenerative thermal oxidizer

domly packed or monolithic) media to store and recover heat from the process gas by direct contact.

This type of heat recovery works in a timed cycle. One bed of media is absorbing heat from the hot gas while another is giving up heat to the incoming process gas. Typical contaminated air inlet temperature ranges vary based on the temperature of the process gas. After a specified period of time, a series of dampers re-directs the gas flows so that the roles of each bed are reversed. Figure 6-19 shows a typical 3-tower RTO.

Rotary RTOs use a single valve to redirect the process gas to multiple ceramic media heat storage chambers within a single vessel with a common combustion chamber. The number of ceramic media heat storage chambers exposed to the process gas represents nominally one half of the total number of said chambers. This same valve is used to direct the hot gas to the other half of the chambers. The valve indexes periodically to change which chambers are on the process (or hot)

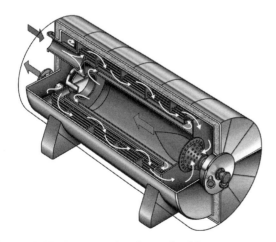

FIGURE 6-18. Recuperative thermal oxidizer

side. Figure 6-20 depicts a typical Rotary Regenerative Thermal Oxidizer.

RTOs can achieve thermal efficiency of 95% or higher, so that fuel consumption can be very low. In fact, is some cases, the heat by-product from the oxidation reaction is sufficient to operate the RTO and the burner can be shut down entirely. RTOs are used for a wide variety of applications including paint booths, chemical reactors, printing presses, wood dryers and paint bake ovens.

6.4.6 Catalytic Oxidizers. In a catalytic oxidizer, a catalyst is used to promote the oxidation reaction. A catalyst is a material that promotes the reaction without being consumed in the reaction. Catalysts will typically cause a given reaction to occur at a faster rate and at a lower temperature than it would occur without the catalyst.

A catalytic oxidizer operates much the same as a thermal oxidizer in that it uses a direct-fired burner to heat the polluted gas. Instead of heating the gas to a very high temperature and then holding that temperature for a set period of time, a catalytic oxidizer heats the gas to a lower temperature and exposes it to a catalyst. When catalysts are used, the operating temperature is in the range of 500 F to 1000 F. Catalysts can greatly reduce the fuel consumption of an oxidizer, however, they are vulnerable to de-activation by overheating, fouling and poisoning.

Overheating is caused by exposure of the catalyst to excessive temperature and results in the catalytic activity being permanently degraded. The only remedy for overheated catalyst is to replace it. Catalytic activity can also be degraded by fouling of the catalyst. Fouling is when the catalyst becomes coated with some material that does not allow the gaseous pollutants to interact with the catalyst surface. Fouling can sometimes be reversed by washing the catalyst or by exposing it to elevated temperatures for a period of time. When a catalyst is

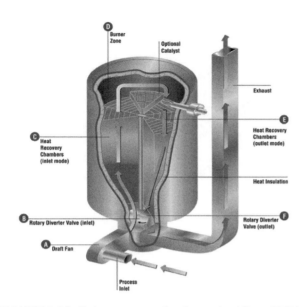

FIGURE 6-20. Rotary regenerative thermal oxidizer (RTO)

poisoned, it reacts chemically with some poison compound and becomes permanently deactivated. Some typical poisons are lead, mercury, sulfur and chlorine. The catalyst manufacturer can provide a detailed list of materials that are potential catalyst poisons, as well as guidelines to follow to avoid overheating and fouling.

Two types of catalysts are used in oxidizers for industrial air pollution control, precious metal and base metal. Precious metals catalysts use platinum (or other noble metal) as their primary active ingredient; they are similar to the catalytic muffler in an automobile. The platinum is dispersed in very fine granules embedded in the surface of a ceramic or metal honeycomb matrix. The matrix is encased in a stainless steel can and a series of these cans are mounted on a frame inside the oxidizer housing. Base metal catalysts are typically manganese dioxide with additives. The typical form for base metal catalyst is a rough extruded pellet, which is held in trays or bins inside the oxidizer shell.

6.4.7 Air Streams into Oxidizers.
Contaminated air streams are characterized by a composition of at least 18% Oxygen and Volatile Organic Compound (VOC) concentrations less than 25-30% of LEL (Lower Explosion Limit). Typical applications are Coating operations, Printing Lines, Paint Booths, and Packaging.

Contaminated Inert Gas Streams are characterized by a composition of less than 8% Oxygen and low concentrations of VOCs. Typical applications include inert (nitrogen blanket) drying, Kiln off-gases, and interim states of resin manufacturing. Rich Gas Streams are characterized by a composition of 3% oxygen or lower and a high concentration of VOCs. Typical applications can include Tank Vents, Reactor Exhaust Gases, Blast Furnace Gases, and Landfill Gas.

6.4.8 Contaminated Inert Gas Streams.
For contaminated inert gas streams, adding ambient air into the combustion chamber and employing preheat using a tubular heat exchanger (recuperative design) is common. Since the oxygen content of the inert gas stream is low, the preheat temperature and the tube metal temperature should be kept below the auto ignition temperature of the contaminants in order to prevent "cracking," fouling or carbon (soot) build-up on the heat transfer surface. A 600 F (approximate) temperature is most common for this type of waste stream. A heat recovery boiler, combustion air preheater, process gas heat exchanger, hot oil or asphalt heater, hot air heater and/or direct recycle of the Products of Combustion (POC) can also be added.

6.4.9 Rich Gas Streams.
For rich gas streams, the waste gas is used as its own fuel, and combustion air is introduced with the waste gas through a low BTU gas burner. A heat recovery boiler, a process gas heat exchanger, a hot oil heater and/or direct recycle of the products of combustion are the most common heat recovery options.

6.4.10 Advantages and Disadvantages of Different Types of Oxidizers.
Table 6-7 compares the advantages and disadvantages of the three different types of thermal oxidizers. Before final selection is made, the manufacturers of different makes must provide the final data needed to make a complete analysis. This information is for preliminary evaluation without benefit of the known quality and conditions of the inlet air stream.

6.4.11 Operation of Thermal Oxidizers.
Actual operation of Oxidizer systems is based on instructions and design intent of the manufacturer. There are some basic requirements for every type of unit, but since the units will generally include gas trains, electric controls and interlocks to meet NEC and local regulations as well as insurance rules, the manufacturer must be consulted before attempting any startup of equipment.

6.4.12 Startup of Oxidizer Units.
Almost all modern thermal oxidizers have an automatic startup sequence of some type. This sequence usually includes the following basic steps:

- Switching to and proving that the oxidizer has a clean air supply for startup (not polluted),
- Running the Thermal Oxidizer fan to purge the oxidizer and insure that no unburned fuel or pollutants are in the unit prior to burner ignition,
- Lighting the burner,
- Warming the unit up to operating temperature,
- For recuperative units:
  - Start the Heat Exchanger fan or pump,
  - Open the Heat Exchanger to secondary fluid flow (air, steam, process oil, etc.).

Depending on the type of unit, the warm up may range from 20 minutes to 4 hours or more. Each step in the startup sequence is important to the safety and reliability of the oxi-

TABLE 6-7. Comparison of Various Types of Thermal Oxidizer

Type	Advantages	Disadvantages	Size Range
Direct-Fired (DFTO)	• Simple, no moving parts • Able to handle corrosive pollutants, ***and some particulate*** • high destruction efficiency 99%+	• ***No recovery of heat*** • High fuel consumption at lower VOC loadings	1,000 scfm to over 100,000 scfm
Recuperative	• High destruction efficiency 99%+ • Improved energy efficiency vs. afterburner • Simple, no moving parts • ***Able to handle some level of corrosive pollutants, and some particulate***	• Limited flexibility • Vulnerable to overheating • Vulnerable to corrosion • Each on/off cycle causes thermal fatigue • Limited capacity • ***Moderate (50-70%) recovery of heat***	1,000 scfm to 25,000 scfm
Regenerative (RTO)	• Very high energy efficiency – ***up to 95% with no factor for fuel from VOCs*** • Versatile, can be customized for virtually any application • Virtually no limit on capacity	• More maintenance required than afterburner and recuperative because of moving parts • Generally lower destruction efficiency (***up to 99%***)	3,000 scfm to over 100,000 scfm

dizer and no attempt should be made to skip or accelerate any step.

6.4.13 Shutdown of Oxidizer Units. Most oxidizer systems go through an automatic shutdown sequence. This sequence normally includes the following basic steps:

• Switch to and prove that the oxidizer is running on fresh (pollution free) air,

• Shut off burner,

• Allow unit to cool to a pre-determined temperature,

• For recuperative units:

  • Shut down the Heat Exchanger fan or pump,

  • Isolate the Heat Exchanger from its secondary fluid flow (air, steam, process oil, etc.),

• Shut down Thermal Oxidizer fan.

As with the startup sequence, no attempt should be made to accelerate this sequence or the safety and reliability of the oxidizer may be compromised. In particular, it is important to allow the cool down period to run to completion before shutting down the fan. Shutting the fan off before the system has fully cooled down can lead to dramatically shortened lifespan for refractory insulation, heat recovery media and heat exchangers.

6.4.14 Idle versus Shutdown. Most processes that require thermal oxidizers do not run continuously. There are times when the process is not emitting pollution and the oxidizer is doing nothing except burning fuel and using electricity to clean already pollution-free air. Most oxidizers have a "fresh-air" mode that will allow the oxidizer to run at reduced air volume during these breaks and save significant energy. If these breaks in production are less than four hours, it is generally not advisable to shut any type of oxidizer down for the following reasons:

• The energy required to bring the oxidizer back up to operating temperature will probably exceed the energy saved by not running for the short period,

• Each startup and shutdown cycle causes some wear and tear on the oxidizer so excessive cycling can lead to premature failure,

• The greatest chance of failure occurs during startup, so the possibility of the oxidizer not being available and causing process down time is greatly increased.

One feature available on some oxidizers is a "set-back" mode that allows the oxidizer to idle at a reduced temperature during short production down times. In a set-back mode, the oxidizer operating temperature may be reduced from 1500 F to 1000 F. This temperature is high enough that the oxidizer can go back on line immediately and fatigue to the oxidizer's parts caused by thermal cycling will be minimal.

6.4.15 Monitoring Oxidizer Systems. It is a good practice to monitor the performance of the oxidizer system so that developing problems can be dealt with before they become a crisis. At a minimum, the oxidation temperature and pressure drop across the oxidizer should be monitored. If the oxidizer is a catalytic type, also monitor the temperature both before and after the catalyst. These parameters should be recorded on a daily basis. Note that the majority of oxidizer systems have chart recorders installed to record the combustion chamber temperature continuously. The recorder is often required by the environmental permit for the plant.

It is important that the monitoring be done in a consistent manner so that the data from one measurement to the next can be meaningfully compared. This can be problematic, because both temperature and pressure drop can vary depending on the process output and can fluctuate from minute to minute. If either parameter is varying from minute to minute (as is common for RTO systems), monitor it for a set time period (for example, 5 minutes) and record the minimum and maximum reading. Try to find a time period when the process is in some consistent condition from day to day. If this is not possible, record the process speed, output, etc. simultaneously with the oxidizer monitoring so the oxidizer parameters may be correlated to the process parameters.

Beyond merely taking the monitoring data, it is important to regularly review the data to see if other parameters have changed in the oxidizer. A plot of the data should be maintained and updated monthly, showing the combustion temperature and system pressure drop versus time. If working with a catalytic system, the temperature difference between the catalyst inlet and outlet should also be plotted. If any change or trend in the data is noted, it can be an indication that some corrective action is required (see Section 6.4.19).

Be aware that the operating permit for a facility may require regular source test monitoring of the pollution control efficiency of the thermal oxidizer. In order to satisfy an Air Quality Regulatory Agency, this testing should be done by a professional testing company. The plant environmental office will arrange this testing. It is critical to review the operating records well before this testing so that any developing problems can be corrected.

6.4.16 Routine Maintenance of Oxidizer Systems. Like any other system in the plant, the oxidizer must be regularly maintained to give the best performance and reliability. Generally, the manufacturer will provide detailed maintenance schedules for each component of the system. Table 6-8 gives the frequency of some typical tasks. The manufacturer's recommendations always supersede the information in Table 6-8 if provided.

6.4.17 Heat Exchanger Cleaning. Some systems require routine cleaning of the heat exchanger system in order to continue proper operation. The indicator that a system requires heat exchanger cleaning is that the system pressure drop has increased or that the system airflow capacity has been reduced. All of these cleaning procedures require some professional expertise, so contact the oxidizer supplier to either perform the task or provide training (see Table 6-9).

6.4.18 Oxidizer System Troubleshooting. A detailed troubleshooting guide should be included with the operating

TABLE 6-8. Table Indicating Maintenance Frequency – Oxidizer Systems

Frequency	Task
Weekly	"Walk-around" inspection; visual inspection of all physical components
	Observe damper sequence (RTO)
Monthly	Check combustion air filter
	Lubricate dampers (if on a tower-type RTO)
	Empty drain cocks on pressure signal piping
Quarterly	Check hydraulic/pneumatic pressure
	Inspect hydraulic/pneumatic hoses and replace if required
	Check fan, tighten bolts, lubricate as required
Annually	Check burner control motor/arm
	Clean/replace spark-plug and flame sensor
	Check combustion safeties
	Lubricate dampers (recuperative and afterburner)
	Internal inspection
	Touch up paint
	Vibration test of fan(s)

TABLE 6-9. Heat Exchanger Cleaning Methods – Oxidizer Systems

Oxidizer Type	Cleaning Type	Description
Recuperative	Tube Cleaning	The interior of the tubes is cleaned with a dry brush or rod to remove soot or dry particulate buildup (water or cleaning solvent may also be used). For Hot Oil/Asphalt systems, assure that the tube bank is purged of the secondary heated medium prior to opening for cleaning the interior. Compressed air and brushes can be used to clean the exterior of the tube bank.
RTO	Bake Out	An automated or semi-automated sequence is activated to bring high temperature air to the cold face of the heat exchange media. This burns off accumulated tar or resin.
RTO	Wash Out	The RTO is cooled down to ambient temperature and the heat transfer media is washed with water or mild cleaning solution. This removes particulate and soluble salt deposits.

instructions for your oxidizer. Manufacturers' recommendations always apply to each unit. Because Oxidizer systems include combustion or some other form of oxidizing reaction, special care must be taken so that all safety and health guidelines are followed when attempting to troubleshoot. Some common troubleshooting information is given in Table 6-10.

6.4.19 Managing Changes to Oxidation Systems. If changes are being considered to the thermal oxidizer system, it is very important to consider what effects, if any, the changes will have on the operating permit. Typically, a facility that has the potential to emit more than a certain amount of pollution will require a permit from an Air Quality Regulatory Agency in order to operate legally. Usually, the purchase and proper operation of the thermal oxidizer require that the operating permit be obtained. If changes are made to the oxidizer or to the process equipment it serves, the permit may be violated and the company may face possible legal consequences.

It is strongly advised that any planned changes in oxidizer operation be reviewed with the plant environmental office to make sure the changes do not violate the permit. If the plant does not have an environmental office, it is advisable to seek a consultant that specializes in permitting of the type of plant in the area. An environmental specialist can evaluate the proposed change and determine if the change will result in violation of the operating permit. In some cases, a change that is physically possible will not be allowed because of permit limitations. The discussion below assumes that any permit related issues can be resolved.

Changes to Air Volume

Different types of Oxidizers will react differently to changes in airflow to the unit. For Direct-Fired Thermal Oxidizer (DFTO) units such as an afterburner, the ability to increase air volume is primarily limited by the burner capacity because the burner load is directly proportional to the volume of air processed. The residence time in the combustion chamber will also be reduced in proportion to the increase in air volume. In some cases, the resulting loss in destruction efficiency (if any)

can be offset by increasing the combustion temperature. At some point, the velocity through the combustion chamber will become so high that either there will be mixing problems and full heating will not occur, or the insulation in the combustion chamber will start to break down. The manufacturer can provide guidelines for these limitations.

The excess capacity in the burner can be determined by comparing its peak measured fuel consumption (when in operation) to its rated fuel consumption. It is advisable to allow at least 20% burner capacity beyond the peak operating load to allow for warm-up and to allow the unit to ride through minor process variations.

Keep in mind that the burner output for any thermal oxidizer is not proportional to the position of the control system. In most cases, the automatic burner temperature control has a range from 0 to 100% output. This corresponds to the position of the control linkage, not fuel input or heat output. The reason for this is that the fuel flow is not a linear function of the linkage position. The fuel flow may be at 90% of the maximum when the linkage is at the 50% position. Contact the manufacturer if assistance is required in determining how much excess capacity the afterburner has.

Many DFTO (afterburner) systems are equipped with scrubbers to remove by-products of the oxidation like acid gases. These systems must be evaluated separately to determine if they can be run with additional airflow. The manufacturer of the scrubber should be consulted if any change in airflow is being considered.

Recuperative systems have a very limited capacity for increase in airflow. This is because the materials of construction of the heat exchanger place strict limits on the combustion temperature. This heat restriction prevents compensating for a loss in residence time by increasing combustion temperature to any great extent. Any significant increase in the combustion temperature will likely result in a reduction of the heat exchanger lifespan.

In cases where a slight loss in destruction efficiency can be

TABLE 6-10. Common Troubleshooting Issues – Oxidizer Systems

Problem	Cause	What to Do
Recuperative or RTO pressure drop has increased	Heat exchanger is fouled	1. Verify that the heat exchanger is fouled by inspection. 2. Clean heat exchanger (consult manufacturer for assistance).
Recuperative or RTO airflow has decreased	Heat exchanger is fouled	1. Verify that the heat exchanger is fouled by inspection. 2. Clean heat exchanger (consult manufacturer for assistance).
RTO Exhaust temperature has increased or decreased	Leaking or failed damper	1. External inspection of damper drives, verify that the dampers are traveling full stroke, verify proper sequence. 2. Internal inspection of damper to check seals. 3. Repair dampers as required.
Loss of combustion temperature	Burner problem	1. Check fuel supply and pressure. 2. Check fuel control valves and linkage. 3. Check temperature control system. 4. Inspect burner. 5. Repair as required.
Catalytic system, reduction of temperature difference between catalyst inlet and outlet	Fouled or poisoned catalyst	1. Check temperature control and monitoring system. 2. Verify that catalyst inlet temperature is within normal range. 3. Consult manufacturer for testing of catalyst. 4. Clean or replace catalyst as required.
Low pollutant destruction efficiency (recuperative)	Heat exchanger leak	1. Inspect heat exchanger. 2. Repair or replace as required.
Low pollutant destruction efficiency (RTO)	Damper leakage	1. External inspection of damper drives; verify that the dampers are traveling full stroke; verify proper sequence. 2. Internal inspection of damper to check seals. 3. Repair dampers as required.
Recurring burner flame out	Flame sensor fouling	1. More frequent routine cleaning or replacement of flame sensor. 2. Add compressed air purge to UV scanner.

tolerated, the airflow may be increased. Be aware that the burner capacity will need to increase more than proportionally to the airflow because the heat exchanger efficiency will drop as the airflow increases. Also, the static pressure drop across the oxidizer will increase approximately in proportion to the airflow squared. The fan that moves the air through the oxidizer may need to be upgraded or replaced to accommodate the additional load.

RTO systems are usually more forgiving than recuperative systems when increases in airflow are considered. The regenerative heat exchange system is composed of ceramic media that can sustain operating temperatures of 1700 F or greater. This means that, as with afterburners, a loss in destruction efficiency resulting from the lower residence time can often be offset by an increase in temperature.

As with recuperative systems, the fan and burner sub-systems may need to be upgraded to handle the additional load. For RTOs with random packing (saddle-type) heat transfer media, one popular method for increasing capacity is to replace the media with a honeycomb monolith block media. This media has lower pressure drop and higher thermal efficiency. In many cases, the capacity of an RTO system can be increased by 50% with no changes required to the burners or fan. The disadvantage is that, in some cases, this media may not be as thermally stable as the random packing and degradation of the media may be more rapid. On the positive side, if this type of media is installed in an RTO with no change in air volume, the fuel and electrical consumption can often be reduced by 30% or more.

Changes to Inlet Air Stream Pollutants

Any change in the type and quantity of pollutants should be reviewed by the plant environmental office to make sure it does not violate the plant operating permit. Assuming there is no problem with your permit, Table 6-11 gives some information about the effects of changes in the pollutants processed.

Changes to Required Destruction Efficiency

In some cases, a Thermal Oxidation unit can be altered to

increase efficiencies. This can be done to reduce emissions and meet new regulations. Limits are directly addressed by the manufacturer. In the case of a Direct-Fired Thermal Oxidizer (DFTO), the destruction efficiency of afterburners is typically very high (99% or greater) so there are few circumstances where the efficiency would need to be increased. The pollution destruction efficiency of an afterburner can sometimes be increased by increasing the combustion chamber temperature. The ability to do this is limited by the capacity of the burner, and possibly the temperature limitations of the oxidizer's own insulation.

As with afterburners, the destruction efficiency of a Recuperative Thermal Oxidizer in good repair can be 99% or greater. In some cases, the destruction efficiency can be increased by increasing the operating temperature, but the ability to do this is limited by the materials of construction of the heat exchanger. It is worth noting that if the destruction efficiency is significantly below 99% for this type of unit, there is probably a leak in the heat exchanger that is allowing incoming polluted gases to bypass the combustion chamber and exit the unit without being processed. If a recuperative system suffers from low destruction efficiency, it is worthwhile to perform a detailed inspection for leaks.

The destruction efficiency of an RTO is determined by three major factors: 1) destruction efficiency in the combustion chamber, 2) leakage through the damper system, and 3) bypass of residual gas in the heat exchanger media chambers. Depending on the design of the system, it may be possible to significantly improve the performance in one or more of these areas. The RTO manufacturer can provide detailed information about these possibilities.

6.5   ABSORBER SCRUBBER SYSTEMS

6.5.1 Introduction. Scrubbers for gas absorption are used to remove gaseous contaminants in an air stream that are hazardous, odorous or otherwise undesirable. Typically, water is the scrubbing medium, although specific chemicals are often added to enhance the scrubbing process; and in some very specialized applications the scrubbing medium may be a specific chemical. In all cases, the contaminant to be absorbed must be soluble in the scrubbing medium used. Since water is the most common substance used as a scrubbing medium, this discussion will focus on water-based systems although the principles can be applied to any system.

6.5.2 Method of Operation of Absorber Scrubbers. Gas absorption can be defined as the dissolution of a gas into a liquid. In order for this to take place, several conditions must be satisfied that take into account various physical and chemical characteristics of the gas being absorbed and the medium into which the gas is dissolved. Solubility, diffusivity, temperature, and pressure all affect the absorption of gas into liquid. Solubility can be expressed as the amount of gas that can actually be held by the liquid. Diffusivity is the ability of the gas molecules to equalize in concentration; or it is the rate at which gas molecules go from a higher concentration to a lower concentration. Temperature and pressure both have an effect on solubility and diffusivity.

Henry's Law states that the mass of a soluble gas that dissolves in a definite mass of a liquid, at a given temperature, is very nearly proportional to the partial pressure of that gas. This means that the amount of gas that can be absorbed into a liquid is limited by the concentration of that gas in the vapor above the liquid and that the higher the concentration of gas in the vapor phase, the more it can be absorbed into the liquid. The gas moves from a higher concentration (vapor phase) to a lower concentration (liquid phase). Since the object of absorption is to transfer gas molecules from the vapor phase to the liquid phase, a high rate of transfer of gas molecules (diffusivity) at the vapor-liquid boundary is desirable. Thus, the design

TABLE 6-11. Effects of Changes to Air Streams – Oxidation Systems

Change	Problem(s)	Solution
Solvent substitution	None if quantity and type are similar	
Increase in pollutant concentration	Possible overheating	Heat Exchanger Bypass (consult manufacturer)
Adding halogenated solvents (e.g., methylene chloride, freon)	Possible corrosion	Verify materials of construction are suitable
Add nitrogen compounds (e.g., amines, ammonia)	Increased NO$_x$ emissions	Consult environmental office
Increased organic particulate (e.g., tar, resin)	Heat exchanger fouling	Add "bake-out" feature to RTO (consult manufacturer)
	Reduction of destruction efficiency	Consult environmental office, may be unavoidable
Increased inorganic particulate (e.g., salt dust, wood ash, metal dust, sand)	Heat exchanger fouling	Possibly clean or wash heat exchanger (depends on particulate type, size and loading)

of a gas absorber must take into account good mixing of the gas to maintain a high concentration at the liquid interface, and it must also provide for low concentration of the gas in the liquid phase at the interface with the vapor.

Although the actual transfer of gas molecules at the vapor-liquid boundary is controlled by molecular diffusion, the gas molecules must get to the liquid boundary and thus maintain a uniform concentration in the bulk of the vapor phase. This is normally achieved by inducing eddy currents within the vapor phase. The turbulence created by water droplets passing through the vapor or the tortuous path that the vapor must take through the gas absorber, provides the means for mixing of the gas to maintain the uniform concentration of gas in the vapor phase.

Maintaining a low concentration of gas in the liquid phase is normally achieved by one or more of the following methods:

- having an excess amount of liquid for absorption
- continuously exposing new liquid at the boundary layer (turbulent mixing)
- providing a large surface area of liquid for contact with the vapor
- introducing a chemical reagent to neutralize or change the chemical characteristics of the absorbed gas so that the concentration of the "pure gas" in the liquid is zero

The "rate of transfer" mentioned above, indicates that there is a time factor involved in absorption. In any process, a sufficient amount of time is necessary in order for transfer to take place. Different gases absorb at different rates; different absorbers have different mass transfer characteristics and liquids and reagents react differently with different gases. Absorbers are designed to attempt to maximize contact time in order to maximize efficiency. A large surface area, turbulent mixing and maximized liquid rates all serve to achieve this goal.

Actual absorption efficiency is often characterized by the number of gas or liquid phase transfer stages (NOG or NLG) and height of gas or liquid phase units (HOG or HLG) required to achieve a given reduction of gas from the vapor phase. These values are derived from the specific absorber design and the equilibrium concentration of the gas in the vapor and liquid phases as well as from experimental data for the gas and liquid system involved. The number of transfer stages and height of transfer units take into account the solubility, diffusivity, temperature, pressure, residence time required and the characteristics of the individual absorber to achieve the desired removal efficiency of the problem gas.

6.5.3 *Types of Absorber Scrubbers.* The most common types of scrubbers used for absorption are Atomized Spray Scrubbers, Venturi Scrubbers, Tray Towers and Packed Towers, which include fixed and fluid beds.

6.5.4 *Atomized Spray Scrubbers.* Spray towers can be concurrent (gas and liquid travel in the same direction) or counter current (gas and liquid travel in opposite directions) design and utilize spray nozzles or spinning disks on which water is piped to generate a spray of droplets. Although the more typical design is counter-current with spray nozzles, this type of scrubber relies on the numerous water droplets generated to provide a large surface area for absorption and the height of the tower to provide sufficient contact time.

Often there are banks of spray nozzles at different heights in the tower to introduce fresh scrubbing liquid to maintain a low liquid side concentration of the absorbed gas. These devices operate at very high liquid to gas (L/G) ratios, some as high as 120 gal/1000 cfm in order to generate enough surface area and contact for absorption. Air velocities are normally between 400 and 800 feet per minute. If velocity is too slow, there is minimum turbulence; if it is too fast, contact time is adversely impacted.

Chevron or mesh pad mist eliminators are often used to eliminate liquid carryover. The advantage of this type of scrubber is usually the lower air side pressure drop, although high pump pressures may be required to supply the required flow rate and generate the droplet size required. The disadvantages of this type of scrubber are large physical size and high pump horsepower due to the quantity of liquid and the pressure required to deliver it.

6.5.5 *Venturi Absorber Scrubbers.* Venturi scrubbers generate liquid surface area by injecting liquid into the converging area of the scrubber where the high air velocity shears the liquid into thousands of droplets (see Section 6.3.5 for additional description of operation). Additionally, the turbulent interaction of the air and liquid serves to keep the air and water mixed to achieve good contact.

The advantage of this scrubber is that it is usually relatively compact and can collect particulate along with the absorption. The disadvantages are that it usually requires a larger air side pressure drop than other scrubbers and high efficiencies are only achieved on very soluble gases because of the relatively short contact time. It should be noted that eductor venturis (those that use a high pressure jet of liquid to induce airflow) are sometimes used to eliminate fans, but usually require a larger amount of liquid, and the fan horsepower saved is spent in pump horsepower.

6.5.6 *Tray Tower Absorber Scrubbers.* Tray scrubbers use perforated plates or trays, sometimes with "target plates" or "bubble caps" centered over the openings, and are supplied with liquid from either above or below the plate. As the air accelerates through the "holes" the water is sheared into droplets and a "froth" forms above the plate providing contact area and excellent mixing of the air and liquid (see Section 6.3.6 for additional description of operation). Contact time is increased by increasing the number of "plates."

The advantage of this scrubber type is that it handles particulate as well as absorbing the gas. The disadvantages can include high air side pressure drop and height required for a given efficiency.

6.5.7 Packed Tower Absorber Scrubbers. Packed tower scrubbers come in many variations. There are fixed bed and fluid or movable beds. However, they all utilize some form of packing or structure to mix the gas and liquid, provide a large surface area and "turn over" the liquid to expose fresh (low gas concentration) liquid to the gas stream. The scrubber may have vertical counter-current flow with the air drawn up and the liquid cascading down; or horizontal cross flow with the air traveling horizontally and the liquid coming down vertically.

The packing can consist of a structured framework or loose fill of various designs. Usually the packing is supported by grating and if the air velocity is high enough to displace the packing (loose fill) a hold-down net or grating is mounted on the top (vertical up flow scrubbers). Liquid is distributed over the top of the packing by means of sprays or overflow weirs. Fluid bed scrubbers usually incorporate a low density sphere and rely on the upper movement of air to constantly rotate the spheres within the supporting and retaining grids. The spheres can be fabricated like ping pong balls or made from closed cell foam. Some fluid bed scrubbers have a scrubbing zone and a recharging zone where fresh liquid (usually with a neutralizing reagent) can "coat" the spheres before being exposed to the gas in the air stream.

These types of scrubbers are usually the most efficient because they offer the most contact area in the smallest space, provide exceptional mixing of the air and liquid, continuously expose fresh liquid to the gas stream because the liquid is constantly flowing off one surface and onto another, and offer excellent contact time since the air travels a tortuous path through the packing. Mist elimination is accomplished with chevron type baffles, mesh pads or even an extra depth of packing. Air velocities and liquid rates vary considerably depending on the type of packing and the style of scrubber. It is important to stay below the flooding velocities (condition where the liquid is held up by the air pressure) when operating packed tower scrubbers.

The advantages of a packed tower scrubber over others is its higher efficiency, smaller space requirement (usually), low pumping requirements, and in many cases, a lower air side pressure drop. The main disadvantage of a packed tower scrubber is that it is sensitive to even small particulate loadings, which tend to foul or plug the packing. Newer, more open design packing can significantly improve the ability of the packing to handle some particulate loading.

6.5.8 Operating Issues for Absorber Scrubbers. Because these units do provide a chemical and physical reaction to control pollutants, the correct maintenance of all of the scrubber's parameters must be maintained within the design range of the unit. The following are issues and parameters that must be considered with absorber scrubbers.

Management of pH in the System

Most gases to be absorbed are either acidic or basic in nature. As they are absorbed into the liquid, they will change the pH of the solution, which will impact further absorption. To manage this, additives (reagents) are added to the scrubbing liquid to keep the solution at a pH favorable to absorption. It is often advantageous to add the reagent at the scrubber pump intake to insure good mixing and to provide the scrubber with the best concentration of neutralizing reagent. If pH is monitored where the spent scrubbing liquid is discharged from the packing and reagent is metered in to maximize its effectiveness, the discharge liquid will not have excess reagent and scrubbing will be optimized.

Scrubber Cleanliness

Keeping a scrubber clean is imperative for absorber effectiveness. Fouling will severely impact a packed bed scrubber by reducing surface area, increasing air velocity, and causing poor distribution of liquid flow; it can also cause poor distribution in tray towers, plug liquid nozzles, and impact the liquid quantity and distribution. In addition, it can reduce the effectiveness of mist eliminators. Solids build-up in the scrubber sump or discolored scrubbing liquid is an early sign of potential fouling. Scrubbers should be inspected regularly and cleaned when these conditions present themselves. Over time, even what is considered particulate free air, will deposit materials, bad water quality can produce scaling, and chemical reactions with reagents can precipitate solids.

Presaturation

Presaturation of the air stream with the scrubbing liquid is necessary in order for the liquid to be fully available for absorption. If the scrubber design does not allow for this, then a portion of the scrubbing liquid and depth of the scrubber (and so the contact time) is spent bringing the air stream to saturation. If presaturation is not considered in the overall design it will result in less than expected performance.

Water Distribution/Redistribution

The initial liquid distribution is essential to getting full benefit of the surface area and contact time designed into the scrubber. Initial introduction of liquid must be evenly distributed across the cross-section of the scrubber, or residence time and absorption area will be under-utilized. It is also important that the liquid maintain contact with the air stream throughout its path through the scrubber. In tall scrubbers and where the air velocity is in the high operating range, the liquid will tend to channel to the walls of the scrubber, rather than remain in the gas path. A good design will take this into account and have distribution baffles or other means to redistribute the liquid back into the air stream. The use of baffles around the inside perimeter of a packed tower accomplishes this. In addition, using several banks of sprays in spray towers or levels of trays in tray towers with individual liquid distributors will generally solve this problem.

Air Distribution

As with initial water distribution, initial air distribution is critical. If not accounted for, the air can channel through the scrubber without the full benefit of the cross-sectional area. This can cause increased velocity, reduced contact with the liquid and reduced residence time. The entrance of the scrubber should be designed to take this into account with either sufficient room for the air to distribute or include distribution vanes or baffles. Elbows or other disturbances closer than 5 or 6 inlet duct diameters to the entrance of the scrubber can also cause poor distribution of air and should be avoided.

Mist Eliminators

Problems with the demisting section of scrubbers will result in decreased performance. Most problems with demisters will be associated with plugging or inadequate cleanliness.

  a. Buildup on mist eliminators not only impedes airflow, but also serves to re-inject water droplets back into the air stream.

  b. Improper orientation of removable mist eliminator baffles will result in water carryover. Chevron mist eliminators must have their "drip legs" pointing down.

Pump Strainers

It is recommended that all pumps have inlet strainers to prevent damage to the pump and minimize the potential for plugging and fouling of the scrubber internal parts.

6.5.9 Maintenance and Monitoring of Absorber Scrubber Systems. Table 6-12 lists suggested maintenance and monitoring that will help insure proper operation of the air pollution control equipment. This table should be used for general reference only; manufacturer's specific requirements for individual scrubber designs should take precedence over the information provided herein. Since some "recommendations" will be specific to only one type of scrubber, the following designators are used to indicate the type of scrubber affected:

S = Spray Tower; T = Tray Tower; P = Packed Tower; V = Venturi

6.5.10 Troubleshooting of Absorber Scrubber Systems. Table 6-13 lists common problems and potential causes for Absorber Scrubber Systems. It is applicable to almost all scrubber designs, but the manufacturer's operating manuals should be consulted for problem resolution exclusive to the individual manufacturer's scrubber design.

6.5.11 Managing Changes to Absorber Scrubber Systems.

Airflow Changes

Most Scrubbers, including their demisters, have a range of airflows at which they can function effectively. This range will vary from manufacturer to manufacturer and among scrubber designs, but the range is usually somewhere between ± 10% to 25% of the median design capability. The actual amount of latitude one has in changing the air volume through a scrubber will depend on what the original design was and whether the equipment was sized around its maximum or minimum capability.

Increasing/decreasing the air volume beyond the maximum/minimum capacity of a scrubber will result in decreased efficiency, water carryover and in general, poor operation of the scrubber. *The following should be investigated prior to changing the airflow through a scrubber:*

  a. Is the new air volume within the limits of the scrubber? Consult with the manufacturer before making any changes.

  b. Is the air mover (fan) capable of the increased/decreased volume and Static Pressure? Check with fan manufacturer for maximum rpm capabilities, operational point on the fan curve, hp requirement, etc.

  c. Allow for duct changes to minimize pressure loss (increased volume).

  d. Liquid requirements, both supply and discharge may have to be adjusted for the change in air volume in order to maintain the required liquid to gas ratio and reagent in the scrubbing water. Consult with manufacturer about new operational parameters.

  e. Changes in airflow may also change the inlet gas concentration; this must be taken into account if outlet emissions are not to be impacted. If the inlet concentration changes, the outlet concentration will be affected. Consult with manufacturer about new operational parameters.

Inlet Gas Concentration

Changes in gas concentration can result from process changes or relocation of hooding. Increasing/decreasing the inlet gas concentration will affect the outlet emissions, all other things remaining constant. It is always advisable to consult with the equipment manufacturer before changing any of the operating parameters.

Inlet Gas Composition/Characteristics

Changes in inlet gas characteristics will cause a change in scrubber performance. Any process change that changes the inlet gas parameters will invariably have an effect on the outlet emissions. Consult with the manufacturer for impacts from changing inlet gas composition.

Scrubber Liquid Supply

Liquid supply changes impact scrubber performance by changing the chemistry, flow rate and possibly the liquid distribution. Any change from the original design should be re-evaluated for possible negative impacts on scrubber performance. Consult with the manufacturer before making changes.

Packing Changes

Changing the size or style of packing will affect pressure drop, airflow, and absorption efficiency. This sort of change

TABLE 6-12. Suggested Maintenance and Monitoring Table for Absorber Scrubber Systems

Action	Absorber Type S = Spray Tower; T = Tray Tower; P = Packed Tower; V = Venturi				Comments
Record operating conditions – airflow, pressure drop across scrubber, water flow rate, water pressure	S	T	P	V	Initially at start-up, verify monthly or if operational problem
Check/adjust pH of scrubbing water	S	T	P	V	Continuous monitoring and control is suggested, unless once through liquid is utilized.
Inspect spray nozzle pattern	S	T	P	V	Monthly or if problems arise. Check for unusual wear and pluggage.
Clean pump strainer	S	T	P	V	Monthly or if problems arise.
Inspect instrument lines for deterioration or leakage	S	T	P	V	Quarterly or if readings are out of range
Inspect scrubber internals for wear or blockage	S	T	P	V	Semi-annually
Clean instrument probes	S	T	P	V	Weekly or more/less frequently if experience dictates
Inspect demisters (clean as necessary) Chevron Packing Mesh Pad	S	T	P	V	Monthly* *more/less frequently if conditions dictate.
Blow down and replace recirculated water	S	T	P	V	Whenever solids build up is noticed in recirculated water
Clean scrubber (internally)	S	T	P	V	Inspect monthly; frequency can be extended until proper cycle for a given application has been determined.

should not be undertaken without consulting both the packing manufacturer and scrubber designer, who will offer insights into how the system will be affected.

System Changes

System changes not previously discussed that affect scrubber performance may include any of the following:

a. relocating scrubbers

b. adding or deleting hood pickups

c. ducting changes

d. increasing production capacity

Any of these changes will require an examination of system pressure and volume impacts. Relocating scrubbers may entail redesigning ducting, changes in altitude, temperature or humidity that will affect the fan performance and therefore affect the airflow to the scrubber, as well as affecting the mass transfer parameters in the scrubbing process. Ignoring these impacts can result in poor scrubber performance. Increasing production capacity will often increase air volume to control the fugitive gaseous emissions, and may even increase the gaseous emissions.

6.6   VAPOR ADSORPTION SYSTEMS

6.6.1 Introduction. The most common approaches to vapor adsorption include Rotor Concentrator and Fixed Bed systems. Other technology such as Fluidized Bed, Vacuum Regeneration or Pressure Swing Adsorption will not be dis-

cussed. The technology is used to adsorb organic and inorganic compounds in relatively low concentrations from air streams. Vapor Adsorption Technology (VAT) is used to remove organics (alcohols, aliphatics, aromatics, esters and ketones) as well as some inorganics from air streams.

These are used in applications such as paint finishing and coating, semiconductor and electronics, expanded polystyrene, fiberglass and composites, soil remediation, oil and gas, petrochemical, chemical, investment casting, printing and packaging, pharmaceutical and others. Typical motivation to employ VATs is environmental regulatory requirements, odor control, corporate environmental policies or product recovery. These systems generally provide greater than 95% destruction and removal efficiency. Low operating cost is the primary benefit of this technology compared to other systems.

In order for these technologies to be applied there is some preliminary work that must be done to characterize the particular air stream. This information will determine the physical size, capacity and performance of the eventual technology selected. A typical application will have the following parameters; <120 F, <100% RH and <500 ppm(v) organic concentration. Table 6-14 includes a partial list of Volatile Organic Compounds (VOCs) that can be controlled using VATs. Those materials with a low adsorption potential include methanol, methylene chloride, formaldehyde and any solvent whose boiling point is lower than the temperature of the process air.

Adsorption can be defined as the concentration of gases, liquids or dissolved substances (adsorbate) on a solid (adsorbent).

TABLE 6-13. Troubleshooting Guide – Absorber Scrubber Systems

Problem	Possible Causes
Emission Problems (Reduced Absorption Efficiency)	Unbalanced air or water flow
	Control malfunction/pH change/metering pump malfunction
	Change in liquid rate/pump problem
	Reduction/increase in airflow below scrubber limits
	Deterioration of scrubber internals/Plugging or Fouling
	Scrubber or packing not level
	Channeling
	Settling of packing
Water Entrainment	Lack of drain or plugged drain in fan
	Excessive airflow through scrubber
	Incorrectly installed mist eliminator baffles
	Buildup on mist eliminator or scrubber internals
	Orifice or Tray type scrubber not level
	Channeling
	Packing used as demister uneven or "blown" out
	Condensation in outlet
Low Differential Pressure (Across the scrubber)	System pressure loss greater than designed
	Fan running backwards
	Fan belt loose or broken
	Damper in ducting closed
	Plugging of duct
	Deterioration of scrubber internals
	Settling of packing (cross flow packed scrubber)
	Insufficient liquid supply to scrubber
	Pump malfunction
	Air leak in ducting between scrubber and fan
High Differential Pressure(Across the scrubber)	System pressure loss less than designed
	Damper in ducting opened more than required
	Obstruction in scrubber (plugging/buildup)
	Obstruction or leak in pressure sensing line
	Excessive liquid supply to scrubber
	Settling of packing (vertical packed scrubber)
	Air leak in ducting upstream of scrubber (fan downstream of scrubber)
Inadequate Airflow at Hoods	Addition of more exhaust points
	Insufficient make-up air
	System pressure loss greater than designed
	Fan running backwards
	Fan belt loose or broken
	Damper closed
	Air leaks through doors or joints
	Plugging of duct or scrubber
	Excessive liquid supply to scrubber
	Settling of packing (vertical packed scrubber)
	Deterioration of scrubber internals/Plugging or Fouling

Physical adsorption is the process taking place to remove the organics. This type of process is exothermic and reversible. The most commonly used adsorbents are hydrophobic zeolite and activated carbon. Polymeric adsorbents are also used but are less common.

The ideal properties of an adsorbent used include high internal surface area, uniform pore structure, non-flammable, strong and stable, capable of operating under high temperatures, fully regenerable and good performance in high humidity conditions. Adsorption capacity for all adsorbents is affected by vapor pressure, temperature, humidity and organic characteristics. In fixed bed systems without regeneration, this is the only process step that takes place. Once the capacity of the system is used up, the adsorbent will require replacement.

The desorption process is needed to remove the collected materials from the media. Energy addition is required to liberate the organics from the adsorbent. This energy addition to the adsorbent is typically in the form of a low volume heated air stream. This heated air leaves the adsorbent at a lower temperature and contains the organics that were in the adsorbent. Other methods of energy addition (i.e., steam) can be used if organic recovery is desired. This is the low volume high concentration air stream after desorption is complete. The concentrate can be ducted to an oxidation device for final treatment. Thermal Oxidation, Regenerative Thermal Oxidation or Catalytic Oxidation can be used. If recovery is desired it may be ducted to a condensation system for product recovery.

6.6.2 Types of Adsorption Systems. There are two main types of adsorption systems: Rotor Concentrator Systems and Fixed Bed Adsorption Systems. Each type is considered separately with regard to issues of maintenance and monitoring. As with all collection devices, the manufacturer's recommendations for Operation, Maintenance and Monitoring should be followed in all cases.

6.6.3 Rotor Concentrator Systems – Hydrophobic Zeolite and Activated Carbon. In these systems, solvent laden air is drawn through the rotor where organics and inorganics are removed from the air by adsorption onto the hydrophobic zeolite or activated carbon. The cleaned air passes through the rotor and is discharged to the atmosphere. The rotor turns at a speed of one to six revolutions per hour, continuously transporting adsorbed VOCs into a desorption sector, and returning regenerated media to the process air stream. In the desorption sector, the adsorbed compounds are removed from the media with a small stream of heated air. Figure 6-21 and 6-22 show typical arrangements of these systems.

As the rotor exits the desorption sector, it is cooled with a small portion of process air. This air stream, referred to as the cooling air, is captured in an isolated plenum, heated, and returned to the rotor's desorption sector to remove the adsorbed compounds. The concentrate is sent to an oxidizer, where the compounds are converted to water vapor and CO_2. The energy content of the compounds contributes to the oxidation process, thereby reducing the fuel requirement.

TABLE 6-14. Chemicals with Potential for Adsorption System Control

Alcohols	Aromatics	Ketones
Methanol	Benzene	Acetone
Ethanol	Toluene	Methyl ethyl ketone
Propanol	Xylene	Methyl isobutyl ketone
Butanol	Ethyl benzene	Methyl amyl ketone
	Styrene	
	Naphtha	
Hydrocarbons Aliphatic	**Chlorinated Compounds**	**Aldehydes**
Hexane	Trichloroethylene	Formaldehyde
Heptane	Perchloroethylene	
Cyclohexanone	Methylene chloride	
Naphthas		
Mineral spirits		
Acetates	**Glycols**	
Ethyl acetate	Glycol ethers	
Propyl acetates	Glycol ether acetates	
Butyl acetates		
Amyl acetates		

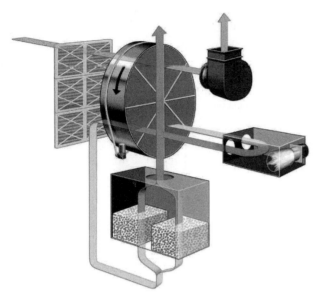

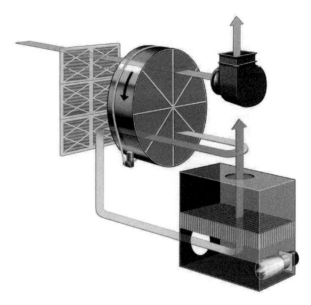

FIGURE 6-21. Rotor concentrator with regenerative thermal oxidizer

FIGURE 6-22. Rotor concentrator with catalytic oxidizer

The oxidizer is equipped with heat exchanger(s) to reduce fuel consumption by preheating the concentrate stream entering the oxidizer and providing the necessary energy for desorbing the rotor. Natural gas or other suitable fuel is supplied to reach the necessary oxidation temperature.

6.6.4 Monitoring of Rotor Concentrator Systems. There are general operating parameters that are monitored and include inlet pressure, rotor differential pressures, particulate filter differential pressure, oxidizer pressure differentials, and inlet temperature, desorption temperatures, concentrate temperatures, outlet temperature, oxidizer temperatures, etc. These systems can be furnished with a range of controls from basic to very elaborate control and monitoring.

6.6.5 Maintenance of Vapor Adsorption Systems (see Figure 6-23). As with other facility equipment this equipment requires maintenance. Detailed maintenance requirements would be provided with the individual equipment. See Section 6.4 for the associated oxidation equipment.

In general, the monitoring of the system should occur on a minimum schedule as follows:

- Weekly – Complete a walk around the equipment and observe temperatures and pressures and compare to start-up conditions.

- Monthly – Insure compliance with lubrication requirements and make visual inspection of particulate filters.

- Quarterly – Inspect the rotor drive assembly, lubrication and particulate filters. Drain pressure sensing lines.

- Annually – Inspect all electrical and electronic controls, rotor seals and fans. Perform an overall internal inspection of all equipment. Drain and refill gear

reducer on rotor drive assembly.

6.6.6 Vapor Adsorption System Troubleshooting. Table 6-15 provides a source of common causes and possible solutions for operations of the systems. As with all equipment of this type, consult manufacturer's published information and manuals for particular data for each unit.

6.6.7 Fixed Bed Adsorption Systems – Activated Carbon. Activated carbon systems are the most common although other adsorbents may be selected depending on the application. Solvent laden air is drawn through the media where organics and inorganics are removed from the air by adsorption into the activated carbon. An example is shown in Figures 6-23 and 6-24. The cleaned air passes through the media and is discharged to the atmosphere. This process will continue as long as there are available adsorption sites. These systems can be combined with a regeneration system for continuous operation. This is typically accomplished with the addition of an offline adsorption bed and an oxidation device.

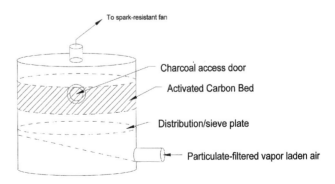

FIGURE 6-23. Vapor adsorption system

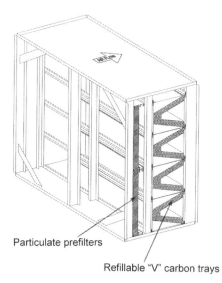

Particulate prefilters

Refillable "V" carbon trays

FIGURE 6-24. Carbon bed adsorption system

6.6.8 Fixed Bed Adsorption System Startup and Shutdown. Manufacturer's manual and information should be used before any startup procedure. Before startup, the adsorbent bed should be inspected to be sure that any opportunity for channeling (bypass) is eliminated. Care must be taken when shutting these systems down as the adsorption process creates an exothermic reaction that is normally cooled by the process airflow. The safest method is to continuously ventilate the adsorption system. Depending on the application, a shutdown is typically feasible with bed temperature monitoring or other safety measures. There are cases where the system can be placed in standby mode rather than shut down with proper procedures. Check manufacturer's recommendations.

6.6.9 Monitoring Fixed Bed Adsorption Systems. There are general operating parameters that are monitored that can include inlet pressure, adsorbent differential pressures, particulate filter differential pressure, inlet temperature, adsorption bed temperatures, outlet temperature, etc. These systems can have basic controls to very elaborate controls and monitoring, depending on the needs of the application and user. An online emissions monitor may be required. This device continuously records what is leaving the adsorption system and may have alarms or other set points. This can aid in determining when to change the adsorbent.

6.6.10 Maintenance of Carbon Bed Adsorption Systems. These systems require periodic sampling of the adsorbent to monitor remaining life expectancy. An online emissions monitor or other device may require frequent maintenance.

6.6.11 System Troubleshooting. Manufacturer's installation manuals and provided data will normally be used for troubleshooting these systems. Table 6-16 shows some basic problems and solutions.

6.6.12 Process Changes. In the event that process changes are required, it is very important that the equipment manufac-

turer be involved. A list of process changes should be recorded including temperature, humidity, air volume and organic concentrations. A system may also require adjustments in order to properly treat the new process conditions.

6.7   FIBER BED FILTRATION

6.7.1 Introduction. Fiber bed filter mist collector systems are used to remove liquid mist and droplets, and soluble particulates from a process air or gas stream. They may also be used to collect insoluble solids. Removal of this particulate may be required for a number of reasons, including:

- Preventing contamination of a subsequent process
- Preventing corrosion or damage to downstream equipment
- Eliminating an undesirable atmospheric emission
- Recovering a useful product

Fiber bed filter elements are typically constructed in annular cylindrical form (candle-style filters) with an outer and inner screen and the fiber bed filter material placed between the two screens. Particle laden gas passes in a horizontal direction perpendicular to one side of the fiber bed and cleaned gas exits from the opposite side.

The fiber bed filter elements rest on (sitting filters) or are suspended from (hanging filters) a tube sheet inside a closed filter vessel. Gas flow can be from outside the filter face to the inside or the reverse. Clusters of filter elements are used to clean large volumes of gas.

Fiber bed filters remove particulate from an air or gas stream using mechanical collection by the fibers. Fiber bed filters work using three basic theories of particle collection: Impaction, Interception, and Brownian Diffusion. In a process air stream, particles flow in the same direction as the fluid in which they are contained. The fluid will flow around any obstacles that appear in its path, but large particles (>3 microns) with sufficient momentum will not. Instead, inertia of the large particles causes them to continue along the fluid's original path until they strike (impact) the obstruction (a filter fiber), and are collected through Impaction. Smaller particles, whose lower inertia allows them to be carried by the fluid around a filter's fibers can be collected through Interception. This occurs when particles graze the surfaces of the obstacles. Very small particles (<1 micron) oscillate randomly along the flow path of a gas as they are jostled by the molecules of the gas. This is called Brownian Diffusion. The smaller the particles the larger are the oscillations. Although the small particles flow around the filter fibers with the gas stream, their oscillating motion, perpendicular to the direction of flow, brings them into contact with the fiber surfaces and they are collected. Because of the nature of Brownian Diffusion, turndown is unlimited. Collection efficiencies of sub-micron particles are affected by the depth and density of the fiber bed. Once collected, liquid particles coalesce into larger droplets,

TABLE 6-15. Troubleshooting Chart – Vapor Adsorption Systems

MESSAGE	POTENTIAL CAUSES	POSSIBLE SOLUTIONS
1. ROTOR VFD FAULT	The VFD controls the speed at which the rotor turns. If the VFD fails, the concentrator(s) will not rotate. This could be caused by: 1. VFD has error message. 2. Loose or damaged wiring. 3. Power loss. 4. Faulty motor/gear reducer.	1. Consult VFD manual. 2. Check wiring and repair if necessary. 3. Reset fault. 4. Check motor/gear reducer.
2. WHEEL ROTATION FAULT	A limit switch is opened and closed by hitting cams as the wheel rotates. If the switch is not opened/closed once every 10 minutes, the PLC (PLC01) will sense a fault. 1. Faulty or loose drive belt. 2. Faulty motor/gear assembly. 3. Limit switch misaligned or cams faulty.	1. Tighten/check drive belt. 2. Inspect motor/gear assembly. 3. Check or adjust limit switch.
3. DESORPTION HIGH TEMP. FAULT	Fault occurs if desorb temperature reaches 410 F (normal set point ~360 F). Excessive temp. could be caused by: 1. Faulty control actuator on Desorb damper 2. Faulty thermocouple/temperature control.	1. Check wiring actuator linkage and wiring. 2. Check thermocouple and wiring.
4. DESORPTION LOW TEMP. WARNING	Warning occurs if desorb temp declines below 300 F (normal set point ~360 F). Low temp. could be caused by: 1. Faulty control actuator on Desorb damper. 2. Faulty thermocouple/temperature control.	1. Check desorb actuator and wiring. 2. Check thermocouple and wiring.
5. DESORPTION LOW TEMP FAULT	Fault occurs if desorb temp remains below 300 F for 30 minutes (normal set point ~360 F). Low temp. could be caused by: 1. Faulty control actuator on Desorb damper. 2. Faulty thermocouple/temperature control.	1. Check desorb actuator and wiring. 2. Check thermocouple and wiring.
6. SYSTEM PURGE AIR ACTUATOR FAULT	Actuator controls position of purge damper. Failure could be caused by: 1. Loose or damaged wiring. 2. Actuator motor failure. 3. Damper binding. 4. Faulty end (limit) switch. 5. Damper not in necessary proximity to end switch. 6. Faulty PLC (PLC01) input. 7. Loss of pneumatic air (if applicable).	1. Check wiring and repair if necessary. 2. Inspect motor and repair/replace if necessary. 3. Inspect damper and repair/replace if necessary. 4. Check end switches repair/replace if necessary. 5. Adjust damper travel to make sure switches are made. 6. Check pneumatic supply (if applicable).

TABLE 6-15 (Cont.). Troubleshooting Chart – Vapor Adsorption Systems

7. PROCESS INLET DAMPER FAULT	The Process Inlet damper. Failure could be caused by: 1. Loose or damaged wiring. 2. Actuator motor failure. 3. Damper binding. 4. Faulty end (limit) switch. 5. Damper not in necessary proximity to end switch. 6. Faulty PLC input. 7. Loss of pneumatic air (if applicable).	1. Check wiring and repair if necessary. 2. Inspect motor and repair/replace if necessary. 3. Inspect damper and repair/replace if necessary. 4. Check end switches repair/replace if necessary. 5. Adjust damper travel to make sure switches are made. 6. Check pneumatic supply (if applicable).
8. OXIDIZER FAN, COMBUSTION FAN, OR PROCESS FAN	The motor overload has tripped. This is caused by: 1. Loose or faulty drive belts. 2. Faulty motor component.	1. Check drive belts and all fan components. 2. Check motor. 3. Check incoming power supply.
9. MOTOR OVERLOAD FAULT	1. Power supply problems.	1. Reset overload.
10. PROCESS BYPASS DAMPER FAULT	The Process Bypass damper. Failure could be caused by: 1. Loose or damaged wiring. 2. Actuator motor failure. 3. Damper binding. 4. Faulty end (limit) switch. 5. Damper not in necessary proximity to end switch. 6. Faulty PLC (PLC01) input. 7. Loss of pneumatic air.	1. Check wiring and repair if necessary. 2. Inspect motor and repair/replace if necessary. 3. Inspect damper and repair/replace if necessary. 4. Check end switches repair/replace if necessary. 5. Adjust damper travel to make sure switches are made. 6. Check pneumatic supply (if applicable).
11. COMBUSTION BACKFLOW DAMPER NOT OPEN	The Combustion Back-flow Damper must be open prior to Main Flame ignition. This could be caused by: 1. Loose or damaged wiring. 2. Actuator motor failure. 3. Valve binding. 4. Faulty end (limit) switch. 5. Damper not in necessary proximity to end switch. 6. Faulty PLC (PLC01) input. 7. Loss of power to the actuator.	1. Check wiring and repair if necessary. 2. Inspect motor and repair/ replace if necessary. 3. Inspect valve and repair/ replace if necessary. 4. Check switches and repair/ replace if necessary. 5. Adjust valve actuator travel to make sure switches are made. 6. Check PLC input card. 7. Check power to actuator.

TABLE 6-16. Troubleshooting Carbon Adsorption Systems

MESSAGE	POTENTIAL CAUSES	POSSIBLE SOLUTIONS
1. Low airflow.	• Adsorbent bed increased pressure drop. • High particulate filter differential pressure.	• Measure differential and analyze. If significant it may require replacing. • Check particulate filters and change if required. • Inspect the fan.
2. Reduced removal efficiency.	• Adsorbent is reaching capacity and breakthrough is increasing. • A change in process conditions.	• Obtain an adsorbent sample for testing. • Compare current operating parameters with startup.

and drain by gravity from the filter element (see Figure 6-25).

One of the main advantages of fiber bed filters is their very high efficiency in the removal of fine aerosols, achieving particulate collection efficiencies of up to 99.9% wt. Fiber bed filter systems generally require little maintenance, and in a liquid mist collection system with a low solid particulate content, the continuous drainage characteristics of a fiber bed filter typically result in extended periods of steady state operation.

Fiber bed filter systems are commonly used in industrial processing operations where hot organic compounds, acids, and corrosive chemicals are ventilated. Some specific industries that utilize this technology extensively include Sulfuric Acid, Chemical Processing, Nitric Acid, Phosphoric Acid, Pulp and Paper, Chlorine and Hydrogen Production, Asphalt Roofing Products, Asphalt Storage Tank Vents, Acid Storage Tank Vents, Machine Tool Coolants, Plasticizer, Urethane, Styrene, Compressed Air and Gases, Platinum Recovery, Oil Refining and Distribution, Oil Mist, Power Generation, Semiconductor, Solder Leveling, Food Processing, and Chemical Weapon Destruction.

6.7.2 Fiber Bed System Components. The main components of a fiber bed filter mist collector system typically include a filter vessel or housing and fiber bed filter elements (see Figure 6-26), a fan, differential pressure gauges, and a drain system to drain the liquid that will collect within the filter elements and in the filter vessel. Various other components that may be part of a fiber bed filter mist collector system include a pre-filter, temperature gauge, internal spray wash or filter irrigation system, and cooling coils or some other method of cooling the process air stream prior to the fiber bed filter.

6.7.3   Fiber Bed Filter Elements. Typical fiber bed filter elements (also known as candles) are installed vertically in a filter vessel, and are available in a variety of sizes, ranging in height typically from about 2' to 20'. The fiber bed materials are available in various grades of Glass, PTFE, Polypropylene, and Polyester. A wide range of corrosion resistant support structure materials including steels, alloys, plastics, and fiberglass are used. The type of fiber material, the diameter of the fibers, and the materials packing density determine the operating parameters of the filter (such as pressure drop, collection rate, gas through-put, etc.). At the top and bottom ends of the

filter elements, plates and flanges are attached to permit a variety of mounting and draining methods. Some filter elements, designed to provide more filter area within a given filter housing volume, are of a concentric cylinder design, where the process gas passes from the gap between two concentric filters to the outer face of the outer filter, and to the inner face of the inner filter.

6.7.4 Fiber Bed Drain System. The design and maintenance of a proper drain system may be the most overlooked and important detail of a fiber bed filter system installation. Liquid that is collected in the fiber bed must be drained both from the individual filter elements and from the filter vessel. For a sitting filter element installation, the collected liquid will gravity drain naturally from the fiber bed onto the top of the tube sheet on the down stream side of the filter, or the liquid will drain into the vessel sump through the upstream side of the filter. For a hanging filter installation, however, collected liquid will gravity drain from the fiber bed, and accumulate inside the filter element on the bottom endplate, unless a drain line through the bottom endplate is provided. The filter vessel may require draining from one or more different locations. These may include the vessel sump, pre-filter section, or drainage may be required from on top of the filter element tube sheet.

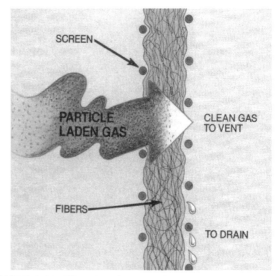

FIGURE 6-25. Fiber bed filter section

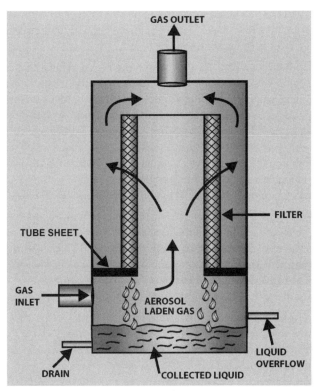

FIGURE 6-26. Typical fiber bed filter unit

When designing a drain system, it is important to consider the differences in the static pressures between the points within the filter system from which the draining will occur, and the points outside the filter system to which the collected liquid will be drained. The drain system must be designed in such a way that the filter system remains closed with respect to the process airflow. Therefore, while the drain must allow the flow of collected liquid out of the system, it also must be sealed or trapped so that there is no outside airflow into the system, no process airflow out of the system, and no process air by-pass of the filter elements within the system, which can occur because of the static pressure differentials that exist between these points in the drain lines.

These drain line seals are typically achieved through the proper design and maintenance of either J-tube type pipe traps or seal cups, which allow collected liquid to gravity drain from or within the various parts of the filter system as discussed above. A seal cup is designed to function using the same basic principles of hydrostatics as the J-tube, but includes only a single vertical dip tube pipe leg attached to a cup, which is sized to provide the necessary volume of liquid required to maintain a seal in the drain/dip tube pipe. Both of these devices – the J-tube and the seal cup – require a minimum drop in elevation from the drain point within the system, to the bottom of the seal trap. This generally requires that the filter system is installed in an elevated position, or that a drain pit or trench is available along side the filter vessel.

A pump or pump-out system is another option for removing collected liquid from a fiber bed filter system, and can be used in conjunction with, or instead of a piped seal trap or dip tube. Positive displacement pumps such as air diaphragm pumps have an internal check valve mechanism, which prevents flow into or out of the system, unless the pump is in operation.

6.7.5 Monitoring Temperature for Process Cooling. Temperature monitoring of the process gas may be required (particularly if the process temperature can rise above about 120 F), and a temperature gauge, installed in the filter vessel sidewall at a point where the process gas temperature can be measured, is a common accessory.

Fiber bed mist collectors are commonly applied in situations where a liquid aerosol has been, or would be, generated by the condensation of a vapor in a warm saturated gas stream. The greater the amount of cooling in this process stream, the greater is the amount of condensed (and therefore filtered out) vapor, and less chance that a visible exhaust will result when the process stream is subsequently exhausted to the atmosphere, where it is likely to undergo further cooling. If necessary, process cooling before the fiber bed filter system can be achieved by bleeding in dilution air to the process stream, or by passing the process stream through cooling coils, which have been designed integral to the filter vessel.

It is important to ensure that the process stream has been sufficiently cooled prior to entering the Filter System. This cooling causes the vapor in the process stream to condense so that it can be captured by the filter elements. If the process stream is not sufficiently cooled, gaseous vapor will pass through the filters and may condense as it is exhausted, resulting in an opaque or semi-opaque exhaust stream.

6.7.6 Treatment of Fiber Bed System Air Streams and Filters. Fiber bed mist collector systems are commonly equipped with a pre-filter. Two main functions of the pre-filter are to provide some protection to the more costly fiber bed filters from solid particulate and other debris that might be carried by the process stream, and to knock down heavy liquid loadings, which might cause the fiber bed to become oversaturated. Pre-filters are commonly of the form of relatively coarse panel filters (typically 30-40% ASHRAE or about MERV 8 efficiency), which tend to be much less expensive and easier to maintain than the fiber bed filters.

A spray wash system, intended to result in the application of a liquid wash stream to the fiber bed, can be useful in applications where solids, particularly soluble solids, are being deposited by the process stream on and into the fiber bed. Over time, solids will build up on and in the fiber bed and result in shortening the life of the filter element.

Spray wash systems generally consist of a number of spray nozzles and the required internal piping to deliver the wash stream to the system. In applications where the solid contaminates are light, and relatively soluble, the spray wash system might be as uncomplicated as a single, fine, solvent spray delivered at the inlet to the filter system such that the spray is dispersed and carried by the process stream to the contaminated fiber bed. In more severe applications, a single or a series of spray nozzles can be installed to apply a wash stream directly to the fiber bed by being positioned at the process stream inlet to the individual filter element. Alternatively, spray nozzles can be made integral to the filter element by mounting them in the filter endplate.

Spray wash systems can be designed for manual operation, to be applied only when differential pressure readings indicate solids build up. Alternatively, they can be set up to operate automatically by timer or by filter pressure drop. Spray nozzles, particularly those meant to deliver a fine spray, are prone to clogging, and a fine liquid filtering device should be included in the spray wash delivery system. It is also wise to include a flow meter so that flow through the spray nozzles can be easily verified.

6.7.7 Fiber Bed Installation Issues.

Location. A suitable location for the Filter System is required so that the unit can work correctly. The location must adequately accommodate the size and weight of the system, provide level support, and allow room for installation and future maintenance of the filter elements. Leveling the Vessel Base is very important to ensure proper drainage and operation of the filter vessel. Fiber bed filter systems generally use high pressure fans, which can be quite noisy. The noise level should be taken into consideration when determining the location for the installation and the need for sound attenuation. The need for freeze protection should also be considered, particularly with respect to drain lines, for all outdoor installations.

Drains. Sufficient space, and provisions for a receptacle must be made to collect the fluid that will gravity drain or be pumped from the tube sheet and sump drain ports of the Filter Vessel. When a filter system is designed to utilize multiple liquid drains, there is a tendency to want to simplify the drain system by combining the drain lines. This is possible only after first seal trapping each line separately before combining with other drain lines.

Filter Elements. Proper handling and installation of the fiber bed filter elements are extremely important in ensuring the effective operation of the fiber bed filter system. Care should be taken not to damage the fiber bed of the filter elements. If the elements are to be laid horizontally at any time, care should be taken to avoid bending them. It is essential that a good, secure connection is made when fastening the mounting flange of each filter element to the vessel tube sheet, and that a gasket is used at this connection, and is adequately compressed to prevent bypass of the process air stream.

Inlet Duct. Some fiber bed applications are prone to a buildup of sticky fluid in the inlet duct. This material can create maintenance issues and possibly a fire hazard. When sizing a fan for the installation, one should consider allowing enough pressure loss to provide for a high flow velocity in the inlet duct (>3800 ft/min). Some applications on especially viscous condensates have found velocities of up to 5500 fpm necessary to keep ducts clean.

6.7.8 Fiber Bed System Maintenance.
Individual manufacturer's manuals for the fan, gauges, and various other filter system components should be consulted for further maintenance recommendations. Typical Maintenance intervals are shown in Table 6-17. One of the advantages of fiber bed filter systems is that they tend to be relatively low maintenance air pollution control devices. However, it is important to regularly monitor and record the parameters of operation in order to maintain proper operation and to identify operation failures or upsets as soon as they occur.

One of the most important and basic operating parameters is the pressure drop across both the fiber bed filters and the pre-filter. The pressure drop should increase slowly over time to the recommended maximums for the given systems, at which point a filter element change-out should be performed.

NOTE: It is advisable to shut down the filter system whenever possible during a process shutdown. Operation of the filter system in the absence of a process load may result in evaporation of collected fluid within the filter elements and lead to solids deposits, which can reduce the useful operating life of the filter elements.

As the pressure drop across the filter elements changes, the process flow volume will change unless adjustments to the fan speed or damper positions are made. The process flow rate should be monitored and adjusted as necessary to maintain the rated flow. Fan motor current and damper positions should be noted and recorded at regular intervals. A qualitative observation of drainage flow rates should be made regularly on each drain line. The vessel drains should be checked and cleaned as necessary during each system shutdown. At every fiber bed filter change-out, the filter vessel tube sheet, and the sump and pre-filter sections should be checked for buildup, and cleaned as necessary.

6.7.9 Washing Fiber Bed Filter Elements.
The fiber bed filter elements, as well as most types of pre-filter elements, may be washed to remove soluble and insoluble substances from the filter media. The washing solution should be compatible with the materials of construction of the filter. Water, mild acids, detergents, and alkalis have all been used as washing compounds.

NOTE: One should contact the fiber bed manufacturer for exact washing instructions and other system specific considerations.

Care must be taken when removing filters for the purpose of washing. Filters absorb a large amount of liquid during normal operation and are usually heavy and full of liquid immediately after operation ceases. If the filters are to be removed from the containing vessel before they have had time to fully drain, extreme care should be taken, as the filters may be heavy and dripping with liquid. It is advisable to wait until the

TABLE 6-17. Maintenance Intervals – Fiber Bed Filter Systems

Record Operating Parameter / Perform Maintenance Task	Monitoring Frequency when process conditions are likely to change on a daily basis	Monitoring Frequency when process conditions are NOT likely to change on a daily basis
Fiber bed filter pressure drop	Daily	Weekly
Pre-filter pressure drop	Weekly	Weekly
Exhaust opacity (eye ball)	Daily	Daily
Process temperature	Daily	Weekly
Process flow rate	Daily	Weekly
Fan motor amps	Daily	Weekly
Drain Flow	Daily	Daily
Check operation of gauges	Weekly	
Filter Change-out	At recommended maximum DP	
Inspect and clean vessel interior as necessary	At filter change-out	
Inspect and clean drain lines as necessary	At all system shutdowns	

rate of liquid dripping from the filters decreases or stops altogether before removing them.

Care must also be taken when handling the filters so as not to damage the fiber bed. If they are to be placed horizontally, they should be handled very carefully to make certain that they are not bent.

Water is a good solvent for many materials. However, care should be taken if water is used as a washing medium when the filter is in strong acid service. If the filter is hanging and does not have a bottom drain, all water must be drained from the filter prior to starting the process. This is to insure that a dilute acid is not formed. The dilute acid will quickly corrode stainless steel and other metals. If alkalis are used, make sure that the filter media and hardware are not sensitive to alkali attack. Organic solvents, acids, and other materials should be used with caution if the filter assembly cage is made from plastic material. Certain cleaning solutions may affect the filter media. Use only compatible materials.

When washing the filter elements, use a gentle spray. Do not exceed 10 psig at the face of the wash nozzle, and keep the nozzle at least one foot from the filter media surface. The pre-filter panels will be somewhat more durable than the main filter elements, and can tolerate a stronger spray wash. Nonetheless, care should be taken to avoid damaging the filter panels with excessive force while using a spray wash.

Filters may also be washed by total immersion in a washing solution. The immersion may take place with the filter in the vertical or horizontal position. After washing, the filters must be handled with extreme care. They are very heavy and must be lifted so that bending is minimized. It is suggested that the washed filters be allowed to drain before replacing them into the filter vessel.

6.7.10 Troubleshooting Fiber Bed Filter Systems. Pressure drop across the filters is the primary indicator of filter condition. Conditions encountered could include:

Increased Pressure Drop: Increases in pressure drop can be due to an increase in the liquid loading in the process stream, collection of insoluble particulate on the filter media, or drying of soluble particulate. If an increased liquid loading is the cause of the high pressure drop, the pressure drop will (gradually) return to normal when the process exhaust returns to normal (lower liquid level) conditions. If collection of solid particulate is the cause, media replacement or washing is required.

As solid materials build up on and in the filters, pressure drop will increase. Large particles (>3 microns) tend to be captured in the filter's outer layer, where they have little effect on filter performance. While this may cause an increase in pressure drop (because the gas must pass through a restrictive layer to enter the filter), filter efficiency is relatively unaffected. Fine particles (<0.5 microns, typically blue haze), however, can penetrate deeply into the filter's interior. The resulting decrease in open area increases the gas velocity through the filter, increasing the pressure drop and eventually degrading performance.

If a large pressure drop is accompanied by an increase in opacity (a visible plume other than water vapor), check that the filter drain is clear and there is no build up of collected fluid within the system. If the drain becomes plugged, liquid can build up in the filter assembly, leading to increased pressure drop, re-entrainment of the collected mist, and an opacity increase in the exhaust stream.

Filter replacement or washing is required either when the pressure drop exceeds acceptable levels (usually determined by the limitation of the blower moving the process air through the system), or when opacity returns to the exhaust stream. A log of system operating parameters, process conditions, etc. helps in accurately planning maintenance requirements.

Decreased Pressure Drop: Decreases in pressure drop may be caused by physical damage to the filter assembly, empty or broken seal cups/legs, or corrosion of some part of the filter assembly by components of the process exhaust. If there is a sudden decrease in pressure drop, system components should be visually inspected.

Plugged Filters: When new fiber bed filters are placed into service they are clean and dry. Operation of the upstream process will result in the filters being exposed to an environment sometimes laden with mist, soluble particulate, and insoluble particulate. The filters are manufactured to achieve the required collection efficiency at a particular flow rate and liquid mist loading. If the liquid mist loading is very low (<2 mg/acf) it will take hours or days of operation to achieve equilibrium of operating pressure drop. If the liquid loading is high, equilibrium can be achieved in a few hours. If solid particles are present, they can cause the pressure drop to rise after liquid mist equilibrium is reached. The rise in pressure drop is related to the amount of solids present. If the solids are soluble or semi-soluble they may be washed from the filter surface during operation with the use of an internal irrigation system (if the unit has been so equipped). Insoluble particles usually will not be fully removed by irrigation.

When pressure drops reach extreme levels, the filters will have to be more thoroughly washed. There is no assurance that the operating pressure drop of the system will be restored to its initial level after washing the filter elements, but it should be significantly lower then the operating pressure drop of the dirty filter elements.

6.7.11 Startup, Shutdown and Operation of Fiber Bed Systems.

Startup: Before equipment startup, inspect the duct between the Process Takeoff and the Filter Vessel. The duct should be clear of debris, and all duct vents and dampers should be placed in their proper operating positions. Make sure that all seal legs, which have been incorporated in any drain piping, are filled with an appropriate process fluid. The filter system is started by simply starting the system fan. If the system fan is controlled using an AC Drive, start the fan according to the operating guidelines provided with the AC Drive unit.

NOTE: In general, the Mist Collector System should be started by slowly ramping up the process flow volume so that any drain trap seal legs are not sucked empty by a sudden increase in negative pressure.

Adjust the process flow through the System using a VFD to control the Fan motor speed, or by use of mechanical dampers.

The flow volume should be regulated to provide the desired level of ventilation at the process take-off, and also to provide the required level of dilution air, if necessary, to cool the process to the required operating temperature. Once the desired process flow rate is attained, begin tracking the pressure drops across the pre-filter and the fiber bed filter sections of the system, as indicated by the differential pressure gauges. Monitor the process temperature within the vessel, as indicated on the temperature dial. Record all relevant operating parameters, including the fan motor RPMs.

The initial pressure drop readings will be for a clean, dry system. As mist collects within the filters, the pressure drop readings will rise and stabilize at the clean, wet, operating conditions. Tracking this information will help detect if any non-soluble solids are being deposited into the filters. Track the effluent air for visible emissions.

The pressure drop across the fiber bed filter section should be monitored every half hour for the first three hours of normal operation, then once per day for the following two weeks. The pressure drop should then be recorded once per week for the remainder of the life of the filter elements. Should an upset occur, the pressure drop monitoring schedule of the initial startup should be repeated. As the Filter Elements load up, the pressure drops will increase, and Fan motor speed will need to be increased, or damper positions adjusted in order to maintain the desired process flow rate.

Shutdown: When shutting down the system, take into account the length of time the system will be shut down, and the properties of the fluid that has been collected. If the fluid will have time to dry out and leave a solid or highly viscous residue; if the fluid could freeze; or if the fluid could become rancid, then drain and/or clean the system as required. To shut down the fiber bed system, simply shut down the fan.

If the process output stream becomes shut down for any extended period of time, the Filter System should also be shut down. Running the Filter System in the absence of an aerosol stream can result in residual fluid within the filter elements becoming overcooled and deposited through evaporation or hardening within the filter media, resulting in a shortened filter element life.

Draining the Vessel: If the Filter System is to be drained periodically by pump-out, rather than continuously drained by gravity through piped seal legs, the frequency requirements for this pump out must be determined after Startup based on the rate of liquid accumulation within the system. *NOTE: Never allow the collected liquid within the vessel to accumulate to a depth that could result in an obstruction to the flow of the process stream, or to a depth that results in any part of the filter element being submerged in collected liquid.*

6.8   ELECTROSTATIC PRECIPITATION

6.8.1 Introduction. When extremely small particles such as smoke are to be collected, an Electrostatic Precipitator (ESP) can be used. Electrostatic precipitators utilize a high potential electric field of as high as 20,000 volts of electricity in order to charge the dust particle and "accelerate" the particle of dust to an oppositely charged plate for collection. In practice, ESPs are used in two general fashions: First, as an ambient air cleaner and secondly, for locally exhausted (close capture) applications. There are several advantages and disadvantages of this type of particulate removal system. They include:

Advantages

- Very low pressure drop – Since the precipitator is essentially just a section of wires followed by a section of parallel plates in the direction of airflow, pressure drops in excess of 1 "wg are rare. Other than the current required by the fan motor, the only other current required is the flow of electrons from the ionizing electrode to the collection plates. This is termed the corona current and it is usually small. ESPs are, in fact, highly energy efficient in the removal of small particles.

- Highly efficient on very fine particulate – ESPs retain high capture efficiencies even as the particle size decreases to less than 1 micron in diameter.

Disadvantages

- Limited to low inlet concentrations – Large amounts of particles cause problems for positive corona, also called "Penney-type" or "two stage" ESPs. A buildup of about ½" to 1" on the plates will cause a complete failure of the affected field of the ESP.

- Limited to lower inlet temperatures – temperatures in excess of 175 F cause problems for the Positive Corona Penney-style collector. Other types of ESPs can operate at temperatures up to 800 F.

- In some applications of ESPs the pollutant is organic in nature and will combust. The internal part of an ESP is subject to continuous sparks and is a place where fires can easily start. Check local codes, installation and operational manuals, and the Fire Marshall or insurance carrier for guidance as to whether a fire suppression system is required. Addition of a fire suppression system may reduce or prevent the possibility of internal ESP fires. If the unit is a local exhaust system, consider fire suppression in the ducts leading to the ESP unit as well.

6.8.2 Types of Electrostatic Precipitators. ESPs can be divided into three basic types. These include:

Low Voltage Precipitator (Penney-style) or two-stage precipitator

This type of precipitator is characterized by the sharp differentiation of the collector into two different sections. The ionizing section (positively charged corona up to approximately 10,000 volts) is located upstream from the collecting cell (neutral charge or negatively charged to as much as 5,000 volts). It is operated in positive polarity and at a lower voltage in order to reduce the formation of ozone.

Units are usually characterized by their use on finely divided particulate aerosols, such as smokes or mists and are most frequently used in local exhaust ventilation applications. The most widely used application for low voltage ESPs is on tobacco smoke, followed by its use as filtration for oil mists on a variety of metalworking processes that use oil as a lubricant.

There are limitations for the use of ESPs. For example, metal oxides that do not conduct electricity (i.e., aluminum welding smoke) cause significant problems with buildup of material on the collection cell. The captured aluminum oxide smoke (a ceramic material) makes a perfect insulator on the surface of the collection cell halting further buildup. Additionally, large amounts of material, bulk materials, etc., do not fit well with the application to an ESP.

High Voltage Precipitator (Cottrell type) or single stage precipitator

This type of precipitator is typically characterized by negatively charged corona wires suspended between the plates. Collector voltages of as high as 100,000 volts are not uncommon. This type of collector is typically applied to large (greater than 50,000 acfm) sources of dry particulate.

Wet Electrostatic Precipitator

Either of the above precipitator types can be operated with a continuous or intermittent wash of water or other liquid across the collection plates in a fashion that prohibits the particle from attaching directly to the collection plate. The disadvantage of this type of precipitator is the complexity of the water wash as well as the need for an ancillary wastewater treatment system. Wet electrostatic precipitators are further described in Section 6.9.

6.8.3 How Low-Voltage Electrostatic Precipitators Work. Electrostatic forces are forces of attraction and repulsion between charged ions that tend to force particles toward a collector of opposite charge. The collection plate spacing affects the maximum voltages that can be achieved. Extra ionizing/collection fields can be added in series to improve efficiency. In addition, sometimes several ionizer/collection cells can be set up in parallel to treat larger air volumes.

The forces of attraction/repulsion are used in a precipitator much like magnetic forces. With extremely small particles the electrostatic forces that occur in nature become much more important than the forces of inertia or gravity. For example, a particle of cigarette smoke will take over 24 hours to fall from a height of 6 feet. Yet cigarette smoke in a room will generally disperse in a relatively short while. The smoke collects anywhere there is a large surface area, especially in porous fabric that may carry an electrostatic charge (like hair or clothing), or any surface that is well grounded. All particles carry a definite charge, some much more than others. In an ESP, we set up an area (called a field) where we provide the optimum amount of electrostatic attraction and repulsion forces. The charge is given to an incoming particle and then it is accelerated toward a collection electrode (plate) where it resides until removed or drained off (see Figure 6-27).

The five steps in the process are as follows:

• Gas ions are formed by means of high-voltage corona discharge,

• The solid or liquid particles are charged by bombardment by the gaseous ions,

• The electrostatic field causes the charged particles to migrate to a collecting electrode that is electrically grounded,

• The charge on a particle must be neutralized or removed by the collecting electrode (plate),

• Removal of the dust or liquid from the collecting surface by gravity (dripping), mechanical shaking (rapping), in-place water washing or by removing the collection plates for cleaning.

6.8.4 Components of an ESP.

Prefilter section

This section is especially important, as large particles such as hair or bulk materials are very detrimental to the continuous functioning of an ESP. The prefilter section typically is very efficient on particulate larger than 10 microns (larger than talcum powder). As the filter loads with dust, the resistance "back pressure" will increase and the flow through the ESP will reduce.

Corona section

The charging of the dust particles takes place in the Corona section. The discharge electrode has a small cross sectional area (such as a wire or a piece of metal flat stock) and is charged to a critical voltage that causes a "corona" field to be generated around the electrode. A corona is a sustained electrical discharge that creates electrically charged ions from gas molecules. The spacing between the electrodes is critical so

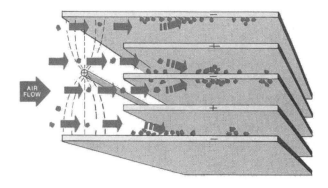

Principle of Operation

FIGURE 6-27. Electrostatic precipitation process

that all particles are forced through a corona area. Ionization of gases takes place and the charged ions attach to the particles giving the particle a very high static electrical charge.

Collection cell section

In the collection cell section the charged particles are attracted to the electrically grounded plates. Excessive material buildup of any kind will build a "bridge" between the charging electrode and the housing, causing an electric short to ground.

Fan section

Typically, a forward-curved "squirrel cage" fan is used to minimize fan noise. Forward-curved fans are susceptible to material buildup and, therefore, must receive periodic service. Check the individual blades for buildup and clean as necessary. Sometimes an axial "propeller" type fan is used (see *Industrial Ventilation: A Manual of Recommended Practice for Design*, Chapter 7 for Fan information).

Odor removal section

In some cases, a charcoal adsorbent section is added after the fan in order to remove odors that remain (odor causing gases are not collected by ESPs). This is most common in tobacco smoke removal units.

Power pack

This area is one of the most important because the power pack is susceptible to failure when a continuous short circuit happens between the ionizing section and the collection plates. Most units include an operation light and a voltmeter on the control panel. If the proper high voltage exists between the ionizing wire and the collection plates, then the unit will collect particles as designed. When the voltage difference is too low, the unit will not work properly. Monitoring and recording the operating voltage (set by the manufacturer) will ensure continued service. If the power pack has trouble maintaining the manufacturer's prescribed voltage differential or has intermittent trips or dropouts, there can be a short circuit between the current loop that feeds the ionizing wires and the cabinet or the collection cells. The source of this problem may be the voltage isolators. Any buildup on these ceramic isolators can cause a spark to jump across the gap and cause a short in the unit. Sometimes an isolator can become cracked. Annual inspections should include a review of the voltage contacts and isolators to insure proper functioning.

Water-wash systems

In applications where a large amount of particulate/aerosols is in the air stream, some manufacturers incorporate intermittent water wash systems complete with a spray distribution tree. These are used to periodically wash down the collection cells. This system acts similarly to a dishwasher system and must receive regular maintenance. The field being washed is usually turned off for the short time that the electrodes are being cleaned.

6.8.5 Recommended Operation and Maintenance of ESPs. Manufacturer's manuals and data should always be consulted for a Maintenance and Monitoring plan of an ESP installation. As mentioned previously, these units can be susceptible to fires and electric shorts if not properly maintained. A minimum recommended Maintenance schedule is shown in Table 6-18.

6.8.6 ESP Operation Issues and Troubleshooting Guide. There are several key elements required for proper operation and long life of an ESP. These include:

Non-uniform velocity – Uniform distribution

In order for an ESP to perform properly, the airflow through the unit should be uniformly divided. If the air in the unit has areas of higher and lower velocity it will not perform as well as it is designed to perform. The typical cause of this problem is an improper inlet condition like an elbow or a restriction at the inlet. One possible solution to better distribute the airflow is the addition of a perforated plate (sometimes termed "sieve plate") or other distribution mechanism at the unit inlet.

Insulating process particulate

In order to work properly, all of the internal components containing high voltage must be insulated from the housing. Over time, all internal components become coated with dust or wet residue or a lacquer from sticky aerosols or tobacco smoke. This must be removed on a periodic basis with a solvent cleaner or a strong detergent or the charge will short-circuit to the housing. In applications where heavy loading of smoke is expected, consider an alternate collection/ionizer set so that one can be cleaned as the other is operating. Often, leaving a collection cell in some degreaser/detergent water overnight allows for easier cleaning the following day.

Controlled sparking rate or short circuiting

Short-circuiting of the electrical power applied to the discharge electrodes can reduce the operating voltage of a field below the level needed to sustain a corona discharge. When this happens the particles passing through the ESP are not electrically charged and collected. Short-circuiting occurs when moisture and/or electrically conductive dusts coat the surfaces of the electrical insulators used to separate the electrically charged ionizing wires and the electrically grounded collection surfaces. Cleaning or replacing the insulators is often needed when short-circuiting occurs. Frequent severe sparking and/or intermittent severe arcing can be caused by poor alignment of the ionizer wires and the grounded collection plates. Correcting the spacing between the ionizer wires and the plates can usually solve this problem.

Sometimes, when visible emissions are noted by operators due to heavy sparking/arcing, the operators will reduce the voltage potential between the corona section and the collection cell plates. This tendency should be resisted, as this reduces the overall efficiency of the collector. The unit should be shut down at the next immediate maintenance interval and physically cleaned. Input changes should be made to the maintenance schedule to adjust the maintenance frequency to keep this from happening again.

Erosion of Corona Wire or Blade

Over a period of time, the corona wire or blade will degrade. The wire can become flimsy and lose tension. Corona wires should be inspected regularly. In some cases, a saw-tooth or scalloped blade can be used instead of a wire. However, these devices also need inspection and maintenance.

Low particulate matter resistivity

Captured solids that conduct electricity too easily cause low particulate matter resistivity. The static charge on the particles is conducted through the particles to the grounded collection surfaces. Once the static charge is released, the particle is not held to the side of the vertical collection surface and can be easily re-entrained. Low particulate matter resistivity is common in particles that have a high carbon or metal content.

6.8.7 Managing Changes to ESP Systems.

Increase in Airflow – Increasing the airflow is typically not recommended but can be accomplished by increasing the fan speed. However, this increases the velocity through the collection cells. The velocity through the collection cells is a very important design consideration and the unit will become less efficient for capturing particles if velocity through the precipitator is significantly increased. This can sometimes be remedied by the addition of a second collection/ionizer section. Consult the ESP Manufacturer before making such a change.

Problem inlet conditions – When filtering ambient room air, this should not be a problem. However, in ducted applications, especially on those with elbows at the inlet to the ESP, air can be forced (due to inertia) to one side of the unit causing irregular distribution. Turning vanes or an added distribution plate (sieve plate) will help relieve this problem.

Visible emissions – Visible emissions are primarily caused by lack of maintenance. A flickering of the power pack light indicates an electrical short. For every flicker, some pollutant is getting through the unit. The cure for this problem is to clean the unit more often or more thoroughly. In addition, make sure that the collection cells seat properly in the tracks of the unit so that air cannot bypass around the cells.

6.9   WET ELECTROSTATIC PRECIPITATORS

6.9.1 Introduction. A Wet Electrostatic Precipitator (WESP) is a device for high efficiency removal of effluent from exhaust gas streams. WESPs are typically used as a "polishing" control device on sub-micron particulate, fumes and mists to which other forms of collectors may not be applied. This is usually a result of air streams that contain contaminants that are corrosive, tacky, very fine, or a combination of these conditions.

Contaminant particles are electrically charged as a result of passing near high voltage electrodes, as the gas stream travels

TABLE 6-18. Maintenance Schedule for ESP Systems

Each Shift or Daily	Weekly or Monthly	Quarterly or Annually
<u>Visual walk-by inspections</u> • Exhaust stack visible emissions (opacity) or dust on roof? ***IMMEDIATE ACTION REQUIRED IF VISIBLE EMISSIONS FOUND – NOTIFY SITE ENVIRONMENTAL LEADER.*** • Noticeable signs of electrical arcing (popcorn sound inside the field). • Record Voltage readout on Indicator on Power Pack(s). • Record pressure drop across prefilter(s).	<u>Record and compare to log sheet action limits. Take action if out of limits:</u> • Differential pressures across prefilter and entire assembly. • Collected contaminant removal system functioning. • Check that ionizer wires/blades are not broken and have the proper tension and alignment. • Check to see that the power contactor is in the correct position and does, in fact, transfer voltage to the cells inside the unit. • If the unit has an automatic wash system, inspect thoroughly and observe one proper cycle of cleaning. • If the unit has a prefilter, this will need the most maintenance in most circumstances – wash or replace, as necessary. • Remove each collection cell and wash with water and/or detergent. Smaller cells can sometimes be run through a dishwasher cycle for cleaning. **Take care in handling the ionizer/collection cells – wires can break and plates will bend easily rendering the ESP inoperable.** • In wet applications make sure that the drain system is not plugged and that liquid will drain. • If the unit has afterfilters wash with water and detergent or replace. • Check to make sure that insulators and all other internal components do not have a material buildup which will cause arcing.	<u>Annual instrument calibration</u> • Differential pressure gauges and alarms. • Volt and amp meters. • High voltage circuitry – check the voltage across the collection cell to assure that design voltage is present. <u>Scheduled inspections</u> Semi-Annually: • Check for material buildup or differential pressure on pre-filter elements. Annually: • Inspect all access door gaskets for leaks. • Clean contaminant collecting system. • Measure and record total airflow through unit. • Check the collection cell for bent or damaged plates (use a pair of pliers to make adjustments). • Zero and check differential pressure gauges with a second gauge.

through grounded tubes or by grounded plates (see Section 6.8 – ESPs). The charged contaminant is then attracted towards the grounded walls. A continuous film of cascading water is applied to these grounded walls. The contaminant is attracted to the grounded walls' surfaces and entrained in the water film. This film of water cascading continually over the collection surface keeps the contaminant from attaching to the metal surface. Instead it is carried away by the water film. The water film containing the contaminants is drained from the WESP, thus removing them from the gas stream. Figure 6-28 depicts the WESP concept.

The high voltage electricity is supplied by a Transformer/Rectifier (T/R) set and control panel. Inside the WESP, voltage electrodes are centered in each of the collection plate grids or tubes and supported by the high voltage grid. The high voltage grid is isolated from the grounded WESP casing by support insulators. The insulators are separated from the gas stream in insulator compartments. An Insulator Compartment Ventilating System (ICVS) supplies a flow of warm, dry air to the insulator compartments, to keep the insulators dry and dust free.

Typically, spray nozzle systems are provided to the WESP. A conditioning nozzle system continuously sprays a small amount of finely atomized water. These small water drops are electrically charged and then attracted to the grounded walls near the top of the walls. The water then forms a falling film, which keeps the collection walls clean and carries the collected particulate to the bottom of the WESP. The flush nozzle system sprays intermittently to provide a secondary cleaning for the collection walls and to flush particulate from other parts of the WESP. A mist eliminator in the outlet plenum collects large water droplets, which can pass through the unit during flushing, thus ensuring there is no droplet carryover into downstream ducts. A bottom drain allows water to flow out of

the WESP, and an emergency overflow is provided in case of bottom drain plugging.

The air in the WESP is saturated to 100% humidity, so some WESP designs use lower temperature "ambient" water to condense this water film on the grounded wall surface; other designs use lower temperature "ambient" air to accomplish the same function.

There are several types of WESPs, each employing different types of technology, depending on its age and manufacturer (see Figures 6-29 and 6-30). These are classified by:

- Grounded Wall Shape
- Electrode Design
- Flow Direction
- Grounded Wall Wetting

Before the gas enters the WESP, it should be saturated to 100% relative humidity. Locally available plant water is usually used for saturation. If necessary, pumps boost the water pressure to the level required. A water pressure regulator is usually located downstream of the pumps to ensure constant water pressure. An inlet strainer or filter upstream of the pumps may be necessary to eliminate larger impurities that may clog the nozzles.

Some designs use compressed air atomization nozzles. Main compressed air supply is usually from available plant air supply. A pressure switch is usually located at the nozzle and will provide an alarm signal to the Programmable Logic Controller (PLC) if the compressed air pressure falls below the pressure switch set point.

Gas enters the WESP through an inlet plenum, which contains two perforated gas distribution plates. Plate type WESPs typically use one at the inlet and outlet. Size of holes, percent open area and location of the plates is usually modeled to pro-

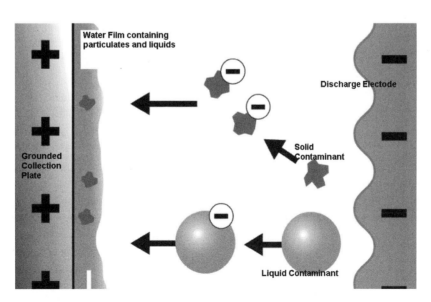

FIGURE 6-28. Liquid and particulate collection in a WESP

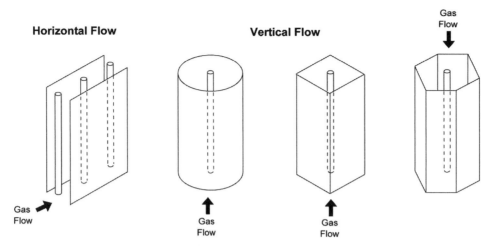

FIGURE 6-29. WESP collection wall and flow options

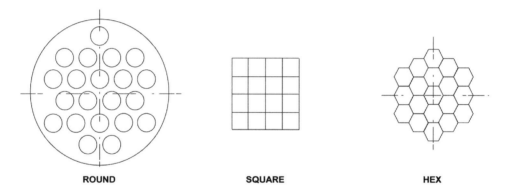

FIGURE 6-30. WESP footprint options

vide smooth gas flow through the WESP as well as minimal pressure loss.

6.9.2 Components of a WESP.

- High Voltage Grid: The high-voltage support grid is supported by support insulators. The grid hangs above the collecting tubes/plates and supports the rigid/weighted wire electrodes. Proper electrode alignment is essential to the performance of any WESP.

- Insulator Compartment Ventilating System (ICVS): Most modern WESPs have positive pressure systems to protect the insulators. The ICVS provides a continuous supply of warm, dry air to the insulator compartments, to ensure that the insulators stay clean and dry. Fans draw ambient air in through filters and blow it into the ICVS ducts with sufficient static pressure to overcome both ICVS duct losses and positive static pressure inside the WESP vessels.

- Temperature Control: Typically, the ICVS is sufficient to protect the insulators. WESPs can have a temperature control system and heaters to maintain a specific

minimum compartment temperature. Typical alarm features of the system include sensors and/or alarms that monitor compartment temperature.

Flow – A flow switch is often provided for each fan. The flow switch will provide an alarm signal if airflow delivered by the fan falls below the flow switch set point.

High Temperature Cut-out – Temperature switches can be mounted in a heater enclosure. The temperature switch will provide an alarm signal if the temperature set point is exceeded.

Temperature Control – A temperature controller that has an alarm can be used. It is activated if the system cannot maintain temperature at the thermocouple.

- Flush Nozzle Control System: For those WESPs equipped with an intermittent flush system, the flush cycle is either automatic or manual and can be operator adjustable in frequency and duration. In automatic, the controls activate the automatic valve, such that the flushing spray system for each WESP is turned on for a preset duration at preset intervals. A magnetic flow meter is usually used to measure flow of the flushing water supply to the WESP units. A control valve downstream of the magnetic flow meter can be used to adjust the flow to the pre-determined set point when a flush cycle is in operation.

- Flush Nozzle Water Supply: Available plant water can be used for the flushing nozzle system. The flush nozzle pump boosts the plant water pressure to the level required at the inlet to the flush nozzle controls. An inlet strainer can be located upstream of the pumps to eliminate larger impurities. The pump only operates during flushing cycles.

- Grounded Wall/Collecting Surface: The collecting surface consists of a series of collecting tubes/plates for the WESP. The design of the collecting surfaces usually utilizes both sides of the walls as collecting surfaces, except when using round tubular units.

- Outlet Plenum: In some WESPs, the cleaned gas leaves the collecting zone and then enters a special outlet plenum. For tubular units, this outlet plenum can have an internal "bell" and "elbow" configuration that reverses the gas flow direction to exit the WESP. Other tubular design WESPs have been known to use mesh pads or chevron mist eliminator devices. The cleaned gas then exits the WESP.

- High Voltage Power Supply (T/R Sets): The transformer/rectifier is typically a complete unit in one tank with bolted cover and consists of a high voltage supply transformer, a full wave bridge silicon rectifier, and a choke coil in each High Voltage Direct Current (HVDC) outlet lead to suppress High Frequency (HF) current surge.

- Gas Bypass System: On some systems, dampers are provided to allow gas to bypass the WESP system for maintenance and repair purposes. Operation of the dampers is usually operator initiated.

6.9.3 Operation Characteristics of a WESP. Each unit and unit manufacturer has unique features and methodologies for startup and shutdown. This section is a generic treatment of those procedures. Refer to the operating manual supplied by the original supplier of the WESP for exact procedures. All operating personnel should become familiar with the correct procedures prior to startup, shutdown or starting maintenance work.

Prior to startup or energizing any component or piece of equipment in the WESP, check to be sure that all personnel are out of the WESP, and that all doors/access ports are properly bolted and secured. A mechanical interlock system should be required in order to prevent the energizing of the high voltage system while personnel are inside the WESP or if the access doors/panels have not been installed properly.

The sequence below is for a typical WESP. Execute the following sequence to prepare to energize the high voltage system:

- Bolt and lock all access panels and inspection doors on the WESP.

- Activate any interlock devices that may be designed to interrupt current flow to the WESP when the access panels or inspection doors are open.

  At this time, the key interlock system will permit the high voltage system to be energized.

Electro-Mechanical Sequence for Shutdown:

> **WARNING!**
> **DO NOT APPROACH OR ATTEMPT TO ENTER THE WESP UNLESS: (1) INTERNALS ARE GROUNDED; (2) GAS FLOW IS STOPPED; (3) WATER SUPPLY HAS BEEN SHUT OFF; (4) ALL MANWAY DOORS HAVE BEEN SECURED OPEN; (5) OUTSIDE AIR IS BEING DRAWN THROUGH WESP; (6) ANY OZONE HAS BEEN FLUSHED FROM THE WESP. ONLY AFTER THESE CONDITIONS HAVE BEEN MET SHOULD AN ATTEMPT BE MADE TO ENTER THE WESP.**

Execute the following sequence to prepare to shutdown the high voltage system:

1) De-energize the power to TR sets,

2) Shut down the main fan(s) serving the WESP to purge the vessel,

3) Shut down/valve off the water supply,

4) Allow adequate time for the unit to drain,

5) Activate any power interlocks at the access and inspection doors,

6) Unbolt and remove the access/inspection doors.

> **DO NOT REACH INTO THE WESP UNIT AT THIS TIME.**
> **DO NOT ENTER THE WESP UNIT WITHOUT FIRST GROUNDING THE WESP INTERNALS.**
> **DO NOT ACCEPT VERBAL CONFIRMATION OF DE-ENERGIZATION.**

7) Most WESPs are supplied with portable grounding sticks. Locate the nearest portable ground stick.

8) Insert the portable ground stick into the WESP or

Insulator Compartment and gently rub any internal hardware that is part of the high voltage network (i.e., High Voltage Support Grid, Electrodes). The ground stick will discharge any existing static charge.

The WESP is NOW properly de-energized and should be safe to enter.

6.9.4 Startup Procedure for a WESP. Prior to startup or energizing any component or piece of equipment in the WESP, check to be sure that:

1) no personnel are inside WESP,

2) all doors/access ports are properly bolted and secured,

3) water is available at pump suction,

4) compressed air (if required) is available at main compressed air valve,

5) power is available,

6) dampers are adjusted for normal operation,

7) damper seal air fan is operating.

Prior to energizing any component or piece of equipment, check to be sure that no one is inside the WESP and that all doors/access ports are properly bolted and secured with an Interlock System.

1) Check the plant main power feed for available power,

2) Activate any slurry pump system,

3) Turn purge-air blower on,

4) Turn purge-air heater on,

5) Check, adjust and/or program the insulator compartment purge air temperature controller for the temperature setting and programming. Also check and/or adjust the balancing dampers and confirm airflow,

6) Activate the flush system,

7) Check and/or adjust the flushing timer duration and frequency cycle time settings,

8) Verify viability of electrical system safety interlocks,

9) Energize the T/R power feed,

10) Close all disconnect switches,

11) The WESP T/R is now energized and in the ready,

12) Turn on the WESP saturation system,

    a) ensure there is compressed air pressure (if required) and fresh water pressure available at the control assemblies,

    b) open the compressed air ball valve, if compressed air is used,

    c) open the fresh water ball valve,

    d) adjust any manual controls as necessary to achieve operating set points.

13) Open any dampers that may be used to isolate the

WESP during Shutdown,

    a) open inlet and outlet dampers,

    b) close any bypass damper(s).

6.9.5 Shutdown Procedure for a WESP. All recommendations for manufacturer's equipment must be followed for the shutdown of a WESP unit.

To shutdown the WESP, execute the following procedure:

1) Open any bypass dampers,

2) Close any inlet and outlet damper,

3) Turn off WESP saturation nozzle by de-energizing the pump and shutting the valve on the main water line. Then shut the valve on the main compressed air line (if used),

4) De-energize the high voltage system at the T/R control panel,

5) Cut the T/R power feed by disengaging the high voltage control panel disconnect switch. The high voltage panel is now de-energized.

    Note: If vessel entry is required then remaining equipment should be shut down.

6) Manually activate the flushing system. Flush for at least 5 minutes to ensure that the internals will be clean prior to entering the WESP unit,

7) Wait approximately 5 minutes after flushing cycle is complete for excess liquid to drain,

8) Shut down the flushing system,

9) Turn the purge air heater off, if used,

10) Turn the purge air fan off.

6.9.6 Changes in WESP System Operating Settings. The operating settings have been determined during initial startup/commissioning of each system. Operation of the WESP may be modified to meet changing demands imposed by regulations or varied process conditions. It is recommended that the manufacturer be contacted before any significant changes are made in system operation. Any adjustment to the WESP settings is also to be submitted to the manufacturer in order to update their archives.

6.9.7 Recommended Maintenance of WESP Systems. Wet Electrostatic Precipitators (WESPs) are designed and engineered to provide reliable operation with minimum service requirements. As with any mechanical device, regular maintenance is required to ensure continued operation at the required performance level.

A WESP, like all other operating equipment, needs routine cleaning and adjustments that are important to maintain its performance. It is recommended that a competent engineer or operator be responsible for the operation and maintenance of the precipitator. Recommended minimum maintenance frequencies are shown in Table 6-19.

6.9.8 Troubleshooting Components of WESP Systems. If design flows cannot be achieved within the normal range in operating parameters or if normal operating parameters begin to diverge from past experience; then check the following items:

- Saturation Nozzles (see Table 6-20)
- WESP Tube/Plate Bundle (see Table 6-21)

6.9.9 ESP Troubleshooting Checklist. Once the characteristics of the problem have been determined, the following can be utilized to locate the problem.

1) Manually flush the WESP. It is possible that collected material has built up on the high voltage network. By manually flushing the unit, discharge of the build-up of collected material should occur.

2) Determine the location of the sparking. Sparking should occur within the WESP, not in the pipe and guard between the T/R bank and the WESP insulator compartment.

3) If sparking has been detected within the pipe and guard, then the internal pipe is not centered. Shutdown the system as outlined in Section 6.9.5 of this Manual and inspect bud duct.

4) If excessive sparking has been detected within the WESP, shut down the system as outlined in Section 6.9.5 of this Manual and inspect the unit (use manufacturer's shutdown procedures).

5) A properly aligned mast or wire discharge electrode will be centered at the top and at the bottom with respect to the collector walls.

6) If the above procedures do not relate to or solve the problem, then contact the manufacturer.

6.9.10 Managing Changes to WESP Systems. Any time changes are being considered on the WESP system, it is very important to consider what effects, if any, the changes will have on the operating permit. Typically, a facility that has the potential to emit more than a certain amount of pollution will require a permit from a governmental agency in order to legally operate. Usually the purchase and proper operation of the WESP is a requirement of this permit. If changes are made to the WESP or to the process equipment it serves, the permit may be violated with possible legal consequences.

It is strongly advised that any planned changes in WESP operation be reviewed with the plant environmental office to make sure the permit is not violated. If the plant does not have an environmental office, it is advisable to seek a consultant that specializes in permit requirements of this type of plant in your area. An environmental specialist can evaluate the proposed change and determine whether the change will result in violation of the operating permit. In some cases, a change that is physically possible will not be allowed because of permit limitations. The discussion below assumes that any issues related to permits can be resolved.

Increased Airflow

Any significant change in airflow can impact the

- inlet air saturation system: an increase in flow can tax the saturation system to the extent that it fails to reach 100% humidity in the WESP. This will have an undesirable effect, in that the burden will be shifted to the grounded wall water film system.

- grounded wall water film system: the burden to saturate the air assumed by this system can mean that the water film is interrupted, exposing dry grounded wall areas to the contaminant. This defeats the purpose of utilizing a WESP as opposed to a dry ESP.

- tube bundle/plate flushing system: duration and overall effectiveness of flushing can be affected due to the increase in velocity of air through the WESP.

- contaminant migration to the grounded wall: Duration and overall effectiveness of flushing can be affected due to the increase in velocity of air through the WESP.

- outlet plenum mist elimination: If the increase in velocity is too great, the mist will "carry over" the eliminators. Free moisture will be found in the outlet duct/stack. This will result in higher outlet contamination readings, and a potential for corrosion.

Increased airflow increases air velocity. If the velocity is too great, the contaminant will not have enough time to be attracted all the way to the wetted grounded wall. WESP collection efficiency will suffer.

Decreased Airflow

Generally, the WESP will be much more tolerant to lower airflows, and air velocities, than an increase in airflow. However, if the flow is dropped too low, the effectiveness of the mist elimination section can be radically diminished. "Carry over" can occur at low flows as well as high flows.

Pollutants

Any change in the type and quantity of pollutants should be reviewed by the plant environmental office to make sure it does not violate the plant operating permit. Assuming there is no problem with the permit, the sections below give some information about the effects of changes in the pollutants processed.

Contaminant Loading

WESPs are typically polishing devices. Low loadings to most other types of devices are high to a WESP. Any significant increase in loading will affect outlet contamination readings. This will also require an evaluation of the Flush Water Cycle to determine if the cycle duration needs to be extended and/or cycle timing needs to be compressed. Lowering the WESP inlet loading will conversely decrease outlet emissions. The Flush Water Cycle may be evaluated to determine if its

TABLE 6-19. Maintenance Intervals for WESPs

Frequency	Task
Daily	Check the WESP operating settings to ensure that they are as installed at start up, or otherwise documented,
	Take T/R control panel readings at least once per shift,
	Check that the flushing system is working properly,
	Check that WESP inlet conditioning nozzle water pressure and flow rate are maintained as well as the compressed air,
	Ensure that the insulator compartment vent system is operating properly,
	Remove dust and foreign matter from electrical equipment.
Monthly	Check the insulator compartment heat and vent system inlet filter, and change if necessary.
Quarterly	Clean the insulators in the insulator compartments as well as all other insulators. All insulators must be cleaned at regular intervals to remove accumulation of solid particles, acid or moisture using the following procedure:
	a) Wipe the insulators with a dry, clean cloth to remove all foreign matter,
	b) To remove acid, clean with ammonia and polish with a clean, dry cloth,
	c) Replace any broken insulators. Breakage may be caused by mechanical stress or electrical flash-over.
	Thoroughly inspect the interior of the unit. Any necessary adjustments or repairs should be made immediately. Particular attention should be given to the high voltage discharge electrodes, mast or wire, each of which should be in the exact center of the grounded wall surfaces. Misalignment of even a single electrode results in a serious reduction of collecting efficiency.
	Check the WESP shell casing inside and outside for corrosion, damage, etc.
Annually	Weighted Wire Electrodes should be inspected to insure proper alignment and integrity.
	Rigid mast electrodes should be inspected for alignment or damage.
	Any damaged electrode should be disconnected and removed. The tube/plate with the missing electrode should be sealed until the deficiency is corrected.
	The insulator compartment heating and purging system:
	a) Check the heater and the thermostats to ensure proper functioning,
	b) The purge blower and motor bearings should be checked for vibration; a periodic lubrication schedule should be implemented,
	c) The air filter should be cleaned regularly and replaced as necessary,
	d) The high voltage insulator compartment heating system should be kept in operation at all times, even during shutdown periods where the hazard of condensation can take place,
	e) The purge blower should be operating at all times even when the WESP runs under positive pressure. A blower failure would immediately allow dust and moisture to be blown into the insulator compartment.
	The transformer-rectifier sets:
	The temperature of the oil should never exceed 185 F. High oil temperatures indicate one of the following problems:
	a) Overloading of the transformer,
	b) Short circuit in the system,
	c) Heat transfer from the surrounding areas or surfaces,
	d) High ambient temperatures exceeding 104 F
	e) A defective transformer.
	For items a) and b), an electrician should examine the system and correct the cause.
	For items c) and d), steps must be taken to insulate or to cool the transformer enclosure sufficiently to reduce the oil temperature.
	For item e), the transformer manufacturer should be contacted and arrangements made to forward the defective transformer to them for inspection and repair.

TABLE 6-20. Saturation Nozzle Troubleshooting Guide

Problem	Cause	What to Do
Improper Compressed Air (if used) usage	Excessively high usage	Check all lines for air or water leakage.
		Check liquid lines for plugging.
		Check liquid lines for closed or over-throttled valves.
		Check atomizing nozzle and its feed lines for plugging.
	Excessively low usage	Check main compressed air feed line for plugging.
		Check compressed air lines for closed or over-throttled valves.
		Check the compressed air supply line, ensuring a minimum of 60 psig. If minimum pressure cannot be achieved, check the supply lines for restrictions and/or check compressor operation.
	Flows cannot be achieved	Check the atomizing nozzle compressed air lines for plugging.
		Check the control valve for plugging, maintain/repair as required.
	Flow is erratic	Purge any compressed air lines of any water buildup.
		Check the condition of oil and water traps/filters, if any.
		Maintain/repair/replace as required.
Conditioning Liquid Flows not per design	Restrictions in the system	Check isolating ball valves at the nozzle elevation. All ball valves should be fully open.
		Check the liquid flow control valve, ensuring that it is fully open and/or readjust the valve to maximum open position.
		Check the liquid supply pump, ensuring isolation valves are fully open.
		Check the nozzle liquid feed lines for plugging.
		Check the liquid supply line and ensure no restrictions exist in this line.
		Reduce the total airflow to the nozzles.
		Check if the liquid supply pump can deliver the required water pressure to the water control assembly.

TABLE 6-21. WESP Tube/Plate Bundle

Problem	Cause	What to Do
Low Voltage, High Current (steady)	Ground/shorts in High Voltage system	Check for… Grounded Electrode – can be traced visibly during internal inspection Cracked Inlet Bushing – can be difficult to detect, as it does not always show up with a 500 volt meggar Cracked support insulator – normally readily visible during inspection of insulator compartment Short caused by buildup of particulate between HV system and Collecting system
Low Voltage, High Current (cycling)	Discharge Electrode mis-alignment	Check for… Swinging mast or wire electrode
High Voltage, Minimal Current	Open Circuits or dirty/broken discharge electrodes	Check for… Faulty rectifier (open) Broken or corroded flex braid Bus open Uniform excessive buildup of particulate on mast or wire electrode Snapped wire electrode Open transformer primary
Low Voltage, Low Current	Open circuit	Check for… Opening in DC reactor circuit Loose or poor wiring connection Defective control

cycle duration can be compressed and/or the cycle timing extended.

Contaminant Type

The effectiveness of the WESP is dependent upon, among other things, the resistivity of the material being removed. Changes in the resistivity of the contaminant being introduced to the WESP will change its efficiency. Contact the unit manufacturer if significant changes in contaminant type occur.

6.10 BIOSCRUBBERS AND BIOFILTERS

6.10.1 Introduction. Oxidation of odors and volatile organic compounds (VOCs) is the process of converting hydrocarbons and partially degraded organic molecules to carbon dioxide and water vapor. This is accomplished by several different processes in air pollution control equipment. In thermal oxidation (see Section 6.4) an elevated temperature of around 1500 F is maintained to combust the solvents and odorous compounds. In catalytic oxidation, a catalyst metal is combined with heat to facilitate the chemical conversion. In activated carbon systems, the organics are simply captured in the charcoal matrix, and then burned during the regeneration process. In bio-oxidation systems, commonly referred to as biofilters, bioscrubbers, or bioreactors, microbes such as bacteria and fungi consume the organic pollutants as a food source, converting the organic air pollutants to carbon dioxide and water vapor.

Traditional biofilters have been very large, single-layer units that rely on a thick bed of organic media to control conditions for treatment. This chapter focuses on engineered bio-oxidation systems, which use a variety of advances to increase their efficiency of treatment and reduce their size. First, the contaminated air stream is conditioned to maintain temperature and humidity levels ideal for the metabolism of the microbes. Second, the compost or other media that supports the microbes is structured to increase the effective surface area and allow treatment throughout the depth of the beds.

As the contaminated air stream passes through the filter media the volatile organic compounds (VOCs) are captured into the water or slime layer where the microorganisms can effectively metabolize the organic molecules as a food source, releasing more environmentally friendly by-products such as carbon dioxide and water vapor.

Bio-oxidation systems can effectively treat a wide variety of airborne organic compounds. Generally, those organics that are water-soluble or can be captured into a water layer with the help of biological surfactants are good candidates for treatment. Gases and extremely volatile materials may be difficult to capture, extremely large molecules may tend to coat the media rather than be effectively degraded, and certain compounds may be toxic to the organisms or result in undesirable by-products. Each air stream with its unique mixture of organics should be specifically evaluated for suitability to be treated biologically.

The organic compounds in the air stream must be captured within the treatment system in such a way that they become biologically available to the microbes. More soluble compounds, such as alcohols, ketones, and acetates, are primarily captured into the water phase, either within the recirculating sump water of a bioscrubber, or into the water/slime layer on the surface of the biofilter media. Less soluble compounds, such as petroleum distillates and oils, are typically captured

due to their affinity to organics in the support media or with the assistance of biosurfactants. Many microbes secrete biosurfactants that act like a soap and allow the less soluble compounds to be captured into the water or slime layer on the surface of the biological media. Compounds that cannot be effectively captured will simply pass through the system untreated.

The VOCs, odorous compounds, and other organics are biologically converted to carbon dioxide, water vapor, and biomass. Certain compounds have other by-products that must be considered, such as the sulfuric acid formed from degrading H_2S. Removal efficiencies, or the percentage of the incoming contaminants that are eliminated, are generally in the range of 80% to greater than 90%, but vary with the types of contaminants and designs of the treatment systems. The bioscrubber or biofilter system must be specifically designed to achieve the required removal efficiency for the target compounds. Removal or recycling of biomass growth is largely accomplished by natural recycling within the filter, although a portion of biomass and secondary by-products must be removed from the system through the sump water blow down process. Uneven or excessive biomass accumulation can cause localized plugging or other problems.

Compounds Generally Suitable for Biological Treatment:

Alcohols

Ketones

Benzene, Toluene, Ethylbenzene, Xylenes

Petroleum distillates – lighter ends such as gasoline

Formaldehyde

Hydrogen sulfide, reduced sulfur compounds

Acetates

Glycol ethers

Styrene

Ammonia and amines

Organic odor compounds, organic acids, etc.

Most organic solvents and compounds containing primarily carbon and hydrogen

Compounds Generally Not Suitable for Treatment or requiring specialized design:

Extremely light compounds – Methane, Butane, Propane, Hexane, etc.

Extremely heavy compounds – asphalts, PAHs, etc.

Inorganics or oxidized compounds with little energy available – SO_2, etc.

Chlorinated and halogenated compounds

Biocides and compounds containing heavy metals

Plasticizers and materials that may polymerize and coat the biofilter media

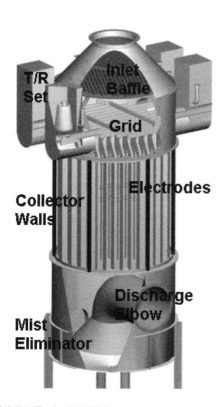

FIGURE 6-31. Typical WESP showing key components

Advantages of bio-oxidation systems include being a sustainable technology with low energy consumption and less production of secondary contaminants such as nitrogen oxides and greenhouse gases. Biofilters can also handle wet or moist air streams more readily than many other approaches. Capital costs are slightly less than most other technologies, and operating costs are usually significantly less. When pricing different technologies, a life cycle analysis is a useful evaluation tool.

Disadvantages are generally related to challenges in maintaining a productive ecosystem within the biofilter. Air stream characteristics such as extremely hot or cold temperatures, heavy particulate, the presence of toxic or untreatable compounds, compounds that cause significant pH swings, etc., can be challenges for cost-effective treatment. Biological systems require water for humidification and produce a relatively small quantity of wastewater. Locations with water challenges or where industrial discharges may be restricted can pose additional challenges.

Industries where commercial and pilot bio-oxidation technologies have been successfully applied include:

Paint and coatings manufacturing – solvents, VOCs, and odors,

Wood product manufacturing – methanol, formaldehyde, and total VOCs,

Paint application/paint booths – solvents, VOCs, and odors,

Pulp and paper – VOCs, odors, H_2S, reduced sulfur compounds,

Industrial vents and emissions – solvents, alcohols, odors, wide range of organics,

Rendering/food processing – odors, ammonia, complex organics,

Municipal sewage collection/treatment – odors, H_2S, VOCs, amines,

Die casting operations – oil mist control,

Remediation – gasoline vapors from soil vapor extraction and air stripping,

Mixed wastes/rag dryers/still bottoms – solvents, styrene, etc., for waste reduction,

Aerosol puncturing/recycling – treatment of paint solvents and recycling of cans.

6.10.2 Preconditioning of the Air Stream.
Bio-oxidation systems are ecosystems in a box, and as such, the proper conditions must be maintained. Preconditioning of the air stream is needed to assure proper physical, moisture, and temperature conditions to promote proper metabolism by the microorganisms. Particulate removal is necessary to prevent plugging or uneven airflow, smothering of the media surface, or accumulation in sump water where parameters such as pH are affect-ed. Temperature adjustment may be necessary to maintain the desired range of 80 F to 100 F.

Hot inlet air streams can be quenched by evaporative cooling during humidification, although heat exchangers to recover or waste the excess heat are sometimes necessary. For cool air streams, or where seasonal cold temperatures demand additional heat, the energy can be provided by adding heat to either the air stream or the sump water of the humidification process. Humidity is adjusted to near saturation, which is the desirable condition for the microbial populations within the treatment system.

6.10.3 Biofiltration System Components.

Blower or Fan Air Mover

Induced draft systems have the fan or blower located at the system outlet, resulting in the air stream being drawn through the entire treatment system under negative pressure. The pressure differentials in biological treatment systems are generally less than 16 to 20 "wg. The negative pressure throughout the system provides some advantages. First, any leaks in the system will draw in ambient air rather than allow contaminated air or water to be pushed out. This reduces the likelihood of fugitive emissions or system losses that would otherwise undermine the removal efficiency of the treatment system. This also eliminates drips of organically rich water that would grow slime and algae. Second, in many designs the induced draft configuration favors a more even draw of the air stream through the biofilter media beds, resulting in more even distribution of the food source and less tendency for localized biomass accumulation.

Forced draft systems have the fan or blower located early in the treatment system, or may rely on the process exhaust pressure for movement of the air stream. However, most axial fans, such as those common in paint booths, are not designed to handle the increased backpressure of the treatment system. Supplemental fans or blowers will be required in most situations. Forced draft systems must be built with extra care in joints and seals to avoid leakage of contaminated air and water.

All fan systems must be evaluated and designed so that they are adapted to the paint booth or industrial process and so that changes in pressure and airflow do not negatively affect the process or compliance with other requirements. For example, a bakery oven is very sensitive to changes in airflow, pressure, and temperature; and a treatment system would have to be either isolated or adjustable so that the treatment system does not upset normal oven conditions and affect product quality. Another example is for a paint booth where the booth face velocity must remain adequate to meet OSHA requirements for worker exposure, regardless of changes in backpressure for the treatment system.

Bioscrubber or Biotrickling Filter

A bioscrubber or biotrickling filter may be used as a stand-alone treatment unit or as the initial stage of a combined treatment system. A bioscrubber provides treatment primarily in the water phase. Biologically active water is recirculated over an inert media that provides a large surface area to maximize the air-water contact. Soluble contaminants, such as H_2S, alcohols, and ketones, are transferred into the water where the microbes can metabolize them, as is done in a sewage treatment process. Some biological growth and treatment may occur on the media surface, but that is secondary to the treatment occurring in the active sump water. Figure 6-32 illustrates the parts and functions of a simple bioscrubber.

The recirculation pump system and overhead spray nozzles must be designed to handle biological growth in the sump water without clogging or being a major maintenance concern. Automatic water level controls are necessary to assure replacement of the water that evaporates into the air stream, and to prevent overfilling or flooding of the system. As water evaporates into the air stream, the salts from the fresh water are concentrated into the sump over time. Regular or automated blow down (removal of a portion) of the sump water is necessary to remove the accumulating salts and maintain the chemistry balance necessary for the health of the biological system. The amount of blow down needed is primarily a function of the salt content of the fresh water supply, the relative humidity of the inlet air stream, and any treatment by-products that may accumulate in the water – such as sulfuric acid from the breakdown of H_2S.

Biofilter or Bio-Oxidation Unit

A biofilter works on principles similar to those of a bioscrubber, but the primary mechanism for removal of the contaminants is adsorption and/or capture directly from the air

stream into the active biological media beds. Figure 6-33 illustrates an engineered bioscrubber-biofilter combination.

The inlet air stream is conditioned by bubbling up through the sump water or through massive water contact in the bioscrubber or biotrickling filter. The goal of conditioning is to bring the humidity of the air stream up to near saturation and allow for adjustment of temperature if necessary. The conditioning step also provides some protection against upsets such as a temperature spike or a slug of particulate in the inlet air stream.

The biofilter media beds typically consist of an organic material such as compost or bark chips that serve as an appropriate support material for the community of microorganisms necessary to treat the air stream contaminants. Some designs use an inert material with a biofilm on the surface. Regardless of the specific design, the biofilter beds are an environment where moisture and temperature conditions are maintained to favor the capture and destruction of air stream contaminants. Air stream conditioning provides the majority of the moisture, but supplemental water is normally added to the media as needed through a direct spray system. This moisturizing spray may be from sump water or fresh water, depending on the specific system design.

Sump water from the biofiltration beds is nutrient rich and biologically active. In a combined system it is normally recirculated between the bioscrubber and biofilter. The biofilter sump must also have a regular blow down cycle to remove accumulating salts and maintain system chemistry. The blow down water is similar in character to raw sewage, and is normally handled through discharge to the sanitary sewer system. Some jurisdictions may require pretreatment and discharge to industrial wastewater treatment.

6.10.4 Biological Treatment System Operating Tips.

Normal Startup Sequence

For system startup, make sure electrical and mechanical systems are connected and functioning properly. Test for correct direction of rotation for pumps and fans. The biofilter media and/or bioscrubber media should be installed uniformly and moistened. Turn on recirculation pumps followed by airflow. Observe the system for normal operating conditions and verify that automated processes, such as fresh water supply, media watering, and sump blow down, are properly programmed or scheduled.

System Shutdown

For very short-term shutdown (a few hours), all processes can be stopped simultaneously. Normal startup should restore the entire system to normal performance with little loss in treatment efficiency.

For medium-term shutdowns (a few days), care must be taken to assure oxygen and moisture are available to the biological systems. As a minimum, there should be a very gentle air movement through the system to provide oxygen, and the

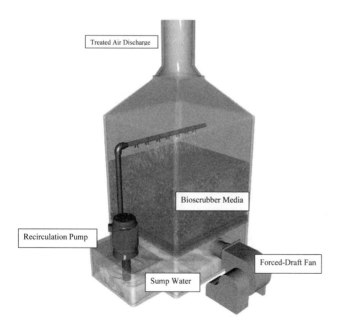

FIGURE 6-32. Bioscrubber system schematic

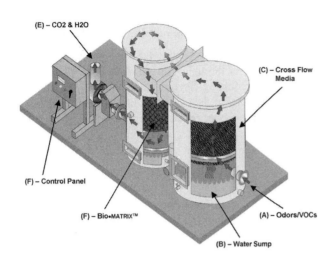

FIGURE 6-33. Engineered bioscrubber-biofilter treatment system

media should be watered periodically to prevent drying out. The sump water also should be aerated during the shutdown. The risks from medium-term shutdown are that the biological systems would lose oxygen and/or moisture, resulting in a longer re-acclimation process for the microorganisms and slower return to effective treatment once the system is again in operation. Avoid high airflows without air stream humidification, as drying conditions will result in rapid stress to the biological system. Most systems can tolerate shutdowns of several days without a food source, and still return quickly to effective treatment. Follow the system manufacturer's guidance on appropriate actions for the length of shutdown needed.

For long-term shutdowns (a few weeks), the same concerns apply as for medium-term shutdowns. However, in addition to preserving moisture and oxygen availability, supplemental feeding will be necessary to maintain the populations of organisms. Solvents or contaminants typical to the air stream can be fed into the sump water and/or the minimal air stream. Consult the system manufacturer for guidance on supplemental feeding requirements for the particular situation.

For extremely long-term shutdowns (a few months or longer), consult the system manufacturer for guidance. It may be appropriate to remove the biological media, drain the sumps and piping, and fully "mothball" the systems, realizing that the media may need to be replaced and the biological community restored at the time of future startup.

Maintaining Consistent Operations

Bioscrubber and biofilter systems are active ecosystems that must be maintained. Short-term changes or conditions that stress or unbalance the operation of the ecosystem should be avoided if possible. Unavoidable situations should be followed by a check on the health of the system and any necessary

adjustments. Some conditions may simply result in a short-term reduction in treatment efficiency, while others may require adjustments of maintenance to restore performance.

Extremely high concentrations of contaminants, even for a short period, could shock the organisms or have a toxic effect. Sudden spikes in concentration may also be inadequately treated, even if they don't stress the system. Spikes of new or rare contaminants, such as a different solvent from a periodic maintenance operation, may also not be adequately treated. The basic reason is that the biological system must maintain an adequate population of organisms to consume the specific organics in the air stream. There may not be an adequate population of the necessary organisms to handle a sudden increase in loading or new contaminants, even though those populations will adapt to the variations in the food source over time. The system design should avoid shock or uncontrolled loadings whenever possible.

Temperature extremes affect the system. A short-term cold event due to colder inlet air or a loss of supplemental heat normally results in less biological activity and a reduction in treatment efficiency. Most systems recover quickly once temperatures return to normal. An extremely hot inlet episode could stress or kill the organisms and take a longer time for recovery. Again, consider temperature concerns during the system design process.

Most biological treatment systems are not designed to handle particulate loadings. The particulate can clog or smother the biological media, or cause chemistry imbalances within the sump water. Normally, particulate should be controlled prior to the biofilter. Care should be taken during activities such as maintenance of baghouses to avoid slug loadings of particulates into the biological treatment systems.

Coordinating the operation of the treatment system with the facility operations can provide some opportunities for savings. While constant airflow is needed to maintain oxygen levels, the airflow can be adjusted according to production activities. For example, if the production operation is one shift, six days per week, the system could be adjusted so it operates at full design airflow during production, but then "idles" at a fraction of that airflow nights and weekends, saving costs on electricity and make-up air. Another example would be to adjust flows and areas to draw from according to operations – such as full flow from a paint booth during the coating operation, followed by 50% flow from the drying oven for 3 hours, followed by 15% flow from the shop area until the next painting cycle. The goal is to maximize the capture and treatment of the contaminants while minimizing the energy and operating costs for the facility.

Balance Air Movement Throughout the Collection System

The overall efficiency of a pollution control system is the product of the capture efficiency and destruction efficiency. Capture efficiency is simply what percent of the contaminants are collected for treatment; while the destruction or removal efficiency is what portion of the captured contaminants are destroyed by the treatment process. Economical operations require high capture efficiency, but without excessive dilution air that increases treatment costs and energy use.

The collection system must be carefully designed and operated to capture the contaminants with minimal dilution air or unwanted contaminants. For example, a sliding valve on a collection hose for a mixing tank could allow operators to take efficient control of the situation – have it full open during addition of solvents to capture all fumes, keep it only partially open during mixing so fumes don't escape the tank but airflows don't create excessive evaporation, and keep it fully shut during addition of powder pigments so particulates are not drawn into the system.

The airflows also need to be balanced against OSHA and worker exposure standards, such as the required face velocity for paint booth operations. Opportunities may arise to follow a priority of sources for the best results. For example, the treatment system may be required and designed for control of solvents from a certain production process. However, during the non-production hours the system may be able to treat tank vent emissions or organic odors from a different part of the operation.

6.10.5 Recommended Monitoring and Maintenance.

Routine Observations and Monitoring

Most biological treatment systems have limited operation and maintenance requirements. However, regular monitoring to insure operating parameters are within normal ranges is important to detect and correct an imbalance quickly. Biological systems by their nature have much slower response and reaction times than mechanical systems. By monitoring system parameters regularly, the health and performance of the system can be maintained. Each manufacturer has recommended monitoring and testing schedules, but they may include parameters, operating ranges, and timing such as:

- Temperature (75 to 105 F)   daily
- Airflow (within 10% of design)   daily
- Back Pressure/Vacuum (no abrupt changes)   daily/weekly
- pH (6 to 8)/Conductivity (< 2500)   weekly/bi-weekly
- Sump Nutrients – N-P-K (per manufacturer)   monthly
- Removal Efficiency   as required by permits
- BOD (sump water)   as required by permits
- Sump/Media observation (appearance/condition)   weekly

Recommended Maintenance

Maintenance for the mechanical and biological systems will include tasks such as:

- Check and replace fan belts, etc.
- Check and clean pump inlets and spray nozzles
- Check and clean sensors and controls
- Replace biological media per manufacturer's recommendations – typically each 3-5 years

6.10.6 Troubleshooting Biological Treatment Systems.

a. **Monitoring and Control System**

   Trouble: Entire system off

   Possible reason: Power Failure

                       Alarm conditions in system logic

                       Electrical circuit breaker tripped

b. **Fan or Blower System**

   Trouble: Fan motor/unit above normal operation temperature

   Possible reason: Blower operating below minimum airflow

                       Blower motor cooling fan inoperative

                       Inlet manifold plugged/obstructed

c. **Vent stack plugged/obstructed**

   Trouble: Fan Motor not operating

   Possible reason: Blower shut down due to thermal overload

                       Control system shut blower down

                       System main power off

d. **Water Recirculation Pump**

   Trouble: Pump not pumping

   Possible reasons: System turned off

                        No water in sump

                        Broken/clogged transfer line(s)

                        Inlet of the pump plugged

                        Breaker for system has tripped

e. **Pump motor damaged**

   Trouble: No water to sprayer system

   Possible reason: Water lines plugged

                       Excessive silt build up in nozzles

                       Pump motor shut down/out of service

f. **Water Makeup Valve**

   Trouble: High water level in sump

Possible reasons: System turned off

Broken/clogged transfer line(s)

Water level controls damaged/dirty

g. Biological Media Appearance

Trouble: Dry appearance on the surface of biological media

Possible reasons: No water in sump

Broken/clogged transfer line(s)

Overhead spray watering nozzle clogged

Breaker for system has tripped

Pump motor damaged

h. Biological Media Appearance

Trouble: Excessive moisture (wet) appearance on the bio-media

Possible reasons: Sump water level too high

Broken overhead spray watering nozzle

Watering cycle duration too long

High relative humidity from inlet source

6.10.7 Successfully Managing System Changes.

Changing Airflow Through the Bio-treatment System

The treatment efficiency of biological systems is typically influenced by the air velocity and residence time within the treatment units. If a system or operational change reduces the airflow (increases the residence time) a simultaneous increase in removal efficiency would be expected. Similarly, if the airflow increases, the system performance should be evaluated, as the removal efficiency is likely to decrease. Any time airflows must be changed, the balance through the collection system should be reviewed to assure effective collection. For example, if the airflow is increased throughout the collection system, rather than balanced according to specific needs, increased airflow across the top of a mixing tank could result in excessive evaporation of solvents – wasting raw materials and increasing the loading to the treatment system. Discussing the planned changes with the system manufacturer can allow them to review the design airflows against the changes, and recommend the most effective operational mode for the new conditions.

Changing Organic Loading in the Air Stream

Changes in the mass loading of organic contaminants may have a significant impact on the treatment system performance. An appreciable increase or decrease in the food source available to the microbes can affect their natural balance and ability to efficiently remove the contaminants. Most systems are sized based on both the design airflow and the organic

loading, so a discussion with the system manufacturer is strongly recommended.

Changes in the chemistry of the contaminants can also affect the system performance. For example, a shift from solvent-based coatings to water-based coatings may result in a higher proportion of water-soluble contaminants, which may be more easily treated in the bioscrubber portion of the system. Also, changes in the types of contaminants may require a time period for the biological community to adapt and increase the population of appropriate microbes before the new chemical will be effectively treated.

Be sure to review the entire organic content of the air stream. A change in contaminants may not be an air quality permit issue, but it may affect system performance. For example, consider a system designed to treat solvents, including hazardous air pollutants (HAPs) from a coating operation. If the coating formulator substitutes a large quantity of acetone, an exempt compound, for a portion of the regulated HAPs, the acetone will still be an organic load on the treatment system that could affect treatment capability. Do not assume that the reduced HAP or VOC content has reduced the organic loading that must be treated. Again, discussing the proposed changes with the manufacturer and getting their recommendations on system adjustments can avoid unexpected results.

6.11   MECHANICAL COLLECTORS

6.11.1 Introduction. Mechanical collectors utilize the laws of physics to separate dust from an air stream. The type of collector chosen is determined by the desired quality of the end product, collection efficiency, energy consumption, economics, or the life expectancy desired.

6.11.2 Cyclone Collectors. Cyclones use centrifugal force to throw particles out of an air stream. The air/dust mixture enters a cyclone in a tangential manner to induce a spin. The much heavier particles are forced to the wall and down the bottom to the discharge while the cleaner air makes it way out the top (see Figure 6-34). Pressure drops for cyclones typically range from 3 to 8 "wg. Collection of particles less than 10 microns in size is limited unless high efficiency designs are considered.

All cyclone designs will not produce the same results. Cyclones specifically designed for an application can produce very high collection efficiencies even on particles less than 10 microns in size. Generally, cyclone efficiency is related to a cyclone's inherent aspect ratio (height divided by width). Therefore, a cyclone that resembles a pencil is likely to be more efficient than the "pot belly" type cyclones often seen on paper trim systems (see Figure 6-35). The tighter spinning action, and the actual number of turns that the air makes internal to the cyclone, give the particles more time to have the centripetal force of the cyclonic action to act upon them. The more turns in a cyclone, the greater the pressure drop.

Accurate data must be obtained to ensure the cyclone design

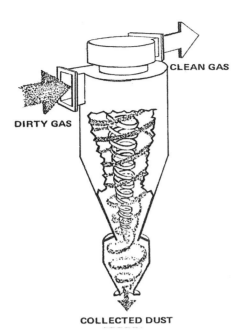

FIGURE 6-34. Cyclone collector

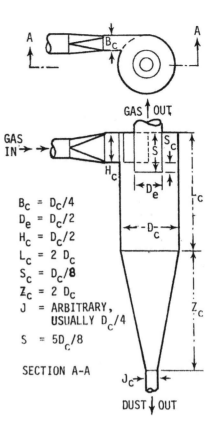

$B_c = D_c/4$
$D_e = D_c/2$
$H_c = D_c/2$
$L_c = 2\ D_c$
$S_c = D_c/8$
$Z_c = 2\ D_c$
$J = $ ARBITRARY, USUALLY $D_c/4$
$S = 5D_c/8$

SECTION A-A

FIGURE 6-35. Sample high-efficiency cyclone dimensions

is optimized. Data required include a complete description of the air that will enter the cyclone (volumetric rate, temperature, pressure, moisture content) and the particulate entrained in this air stream (rate, specific gravity, sizes). Experienced cyclone manufacturers have developed geometric relationships to maximize performance. The differences in efficiency between low and high efficiency cyclone designs can be dramatic. A cyclone that is inappropriately designed can waste money and resources when the expected efficiency is not achieved.

Advantages:

*   Instrumentation is typically not required – an occasional check of the pressure drop (differential static pressure at inlet/outlet) will confirm any operational changes,

*   Low maintenance (no moving parts),

*   Removal of large particles versus small (classification),

*   Economic considerations better than other collector types.

Disadvantages:

*   Efficiency on particulates below 10 microns may be less than with baghouse or scrubber,

*   Changes in flow will affect pressure drop, which can affect induced draft fan operation,

*   Vertical space may be a factor, especially on high efficiency types,

*   Will remove large particulate, which may aid in removal/agglomeration of very fine dusts from fabric filters.

6.11.3 Troubleshooting Cyclone Collectors. Table 6-20 displays potential problems and solutions for various situations using a Mechanical Collector.

6.11.4 Dropout Box Collectors. A dropout box relies on inertial and gravitational forces to separate particulates from an air stream (see Figure 6-36). Depending on the fineness of the particles to be separated, a dropout box may not be suitable as a high efficiency collector. If the particulate has a reasonable density and is aerodynamically stable, a dropout box can be effective. Sand and uniform manufactured powders may be suitable, while paper punchings, feathers and other particles with unpredictable aerodynamic behaviors may not.

The dust-laden airflow enters at a high velocity making direct impingement contact with a baffle plate at high velocity. The flow is directed downward where the heavy particulate falls into a hopper. The airflow seeks the outlet on the other side of the baffle and rises at a very low velocity that does not permit material to flow with it. Although this method cannot obtain as high a collection-efficiency as a cyclone, some applications support it.

Advantages:

*   Low Pressure Drop

*   Low maintenance (no moving parts)

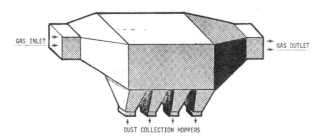

FIGURE 6-36. Simple dropout box

Disadvantages:

• Efficiency is less than that of a cyclone

• Large physical size to obtain low velocity

6.11.5 Troubleshooting Dropout Box Collectors. Table 6-21 shows typical issues and possible solutions for Dropout Box Collectors.

6.11.6 Mechanical Classifiers. Classification can be accomplished by combining gravitational, inertial, centrifugal and aerodynamic forces in a way to cut the material into fine and course fractions for sizing and de-dusting applications. Classification of materials is very common in industrial sand and aggregate mining, as well as other industries where specific size grading is needed.

Classifiers can be static or dynamic (see Figure 6-37). Static classifiers have no moving parts and rely on the aerodynamic forces outlined above, while dynamic classifier designs involve spinning wheels with blades to provide the forces required for separation. Static classifiers are able to cut finer material from a coarser fraction because the finer material will be lighter and can be carried away easier with a controlled air stream. Efficiencies can be tailored to the type of material, bulk density, the amount of loading and the air volume. Other factors affecting classification include:

• Particle behavior and flow characteristics

• Surface moisture

• Viscosity of gas stream

• Particulate hardness

• Particle shape, range and cut point

6.11.7 Troubleshooting Mechanical Collectors. Table 6-22 displays possible problems and solutions when troubleshooting Mechanical Classifier Collectors.

6.11.8 Managing Changes to Mechanical Collector Systems. In general, a cyclone's inherent resistance (pressure drop) will act as a function of the Velocity Pressure and would increase in pressure at a ratio of the square of the volume increase. The manufacturer should be contacted for actual pressure drop relation to volume changes.

Cyclone collectors are generally only able to be efficiently

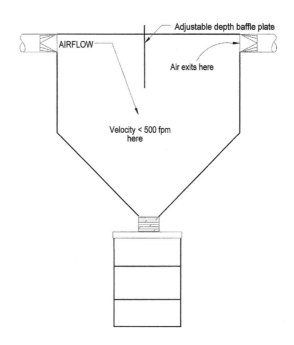

FIGURE 6-37. Simple classifier

operated at a range between 80% and 120% of the rated design volume. Lower flows can cause a short circuiting of airflow without benefit of the centrifugal action. Too high an air volume will cause rapid exit of the collector before going through centrifugal action.

TABLE 6-22. Troubleshooting Guide – Cyclone Collectors

CYCLONE COLLECTOR TROUBLESHOOTING		
Symptom	Possible Problem	Solution
1. Pressure drop is too high	Too high a gas flow rate resulting from incorrect initial design of the duct or fan	Leave alone unless it is causing process problems. If so, change fan operation or add additional flow restrictions in the system to reduce flow rate and cyclone ΔP
	Leakage into the system ahead of the cyclone	Repair duct or hood leaks
	Cyclone has an internal obstruction	Clear internal obstruction
	Incorrect cyclone design	Redesign or replace cyclone
2. Pressure drop is too low	Too low a gas flow rate resulting from incorrect initial design of the duct or fan	Change fan operation or replace with larger fan. Redesign components with high ΔP to reduce pressure drop. See Chapter 5 for possible fan problems.
	Air leakage into the cyclone assembly	Repair
	Air leakage into downstream system components	Repair
	Incorrect initial design of the cyclone	If loss in collection efficiency is not an issue, leave it alone. If collection efficiency is too low, see symptom 3 below.
3. Low collection efficiency	Incorrect initial design or incorrect inlet flow data given	If small performance improvements and/or higher ΔP are acceptable, redesign of the existing cyclone may be possible. If higher ΔP is not acceptable and/or major improvements in collection efficiency are required, cyclone replacement will be required
	Leakage into cyclone	Repair leaks and ensure air locks are working properly and are reasonable gas-tight
	Internal obstructions or plugging	Remove obstruction(s). If persistent plugging occurs, consider alternative construction and look for determining and solving root causes such as condensation and too small a discharge diameter
	Poor inlet duct design	Redesign and replace

TABLE 6-22 (Cont.). Troubleshooting Guide – Cyclone Collectors

CYCLONE COLLECTOR TROUBLESHOOTING		
Symptom	Possible Problem	Solution
4. Plugging	Cyclone discharge is too small for actual loading	Redesign cyclone with larger discharge diameter
	Material may be accumulating in dead space if cyclone has dished head	Replace dished head with flat roof, false roof, or refractory-lined flat roof
	Material may be naturally sticky or hygroscopic	Improve internal surface finishes, PTFE coating, electropolish, etc.
		Use vibrators
		Provide easy access for cleaning
	Condensation	Insulate and/or heat trace
5. Erosion	Too high an inlet velocity	Reduce flow rate
		Redesign inlet for lower velocities
	Naturally erosive particulate	Minimize inlet velocity
		Abrasion-resistant construction
		Ensure proper cyclone geometry
		Design for easy repairs and/or replacement

TABLE 6-23. Dropout Box Troubleshooting Table

DROP OUT BOX TROUBLESHOOTING		
Symptom	**Possible Problem**	**Solution**
1. Low collection efficiency	Baffle plate altered	Check interior
	Leakage	Check for leaks
2. Plugging	Discharge too small	Enlarge discharge
	Material sticking	Improve surface finish
3. Erosion	Holes in baffle	Replace with higher Brinnell material

TABLE 6-24. Troubleshooting Mechanical Classifiers

Symptom	**Possible Problem**	**Solution**
1. Wrong cutpoint	Not set up properly, too much moisture	Change air settings
2. Abrasion	Material too hard	Appropriate liners
3. Material sticking	Too much moisture	Adjust moisture content vibrators
4. Moisture	Rain, dust suppression equipment (sprays)	Find source of moisture. Drying to reduce moisture. Wait for drier conditions.

REFERENCES

6.1   Lewandowski, D.A.; Steele, G.; Donley, E.J.: Process Design Philosophy for Waste Combustion/Destruction Systems. Pollutex Asia 1988 Conference. Process Combustion Corporation, Pittsburgh, PA (July 8, 1998).

6.2   Knight, Jr., R.B.: Air Techniques, Inc., Marietta, GA.

6.3   Hesketh, H.E.: Air Pollution Control. Ann Arbor Science Publishers, Inc., Ann Arbor, MI (1979).

6.4   Air & Waste Management Association: Air Pollution Control Engineering Manual. van Nostrand Reinhold, New York, NY (1992).

6.5   Mogar, M.: Westminster, MD.

6.6   Trion Air Purification Products. Sanford, NC.

6.7   Heumann, W.: Industrial Air Pollution Control Systems (Chapter 8). Fisher-Klosterman, Inc.

6.8   Classifiers. Buell Division of Fisher-Klosterman, Inc., Lebanon, PA.

6.9   Allan, R.A.: Turbosonic Corporation, Waterloo, Ontario, Canada.

6.10   White, H.J.: Industrial Electrostatic Precipitation. Addison-Wesley Publishing Company, Inc., London (1963).

6.11   Young, C.; Drzewiecki, G.: Wet Electrostatic Precipitator Having Movable Nested Hexagonal Collector Plates and Magnetic Aligning and Rapping Means. US Patent 4441897. INCO Limited.

Chapter 7
TROUBLESHOOTING VENTILATION SYSTEMS

7.1   INTRODUCTION

Over time, ventilation system performance will degrade due to a variety of circumstances. This may stem from poor maintenance that does not systematically remove duct buildup, unauthorized or improper system design changes, hardware failures, or other causes. A routine monitoring and maintenance program is the critical step for identifying and correcting degradation before it reduces the system performance to an unacceptable level. This chapter provides techniques to diagnose the problems that may cause degraded system performance, and to determine solutions that will either restore the system to Baseline (design specifications) or to acceptable system operation when original design data are not available.

The most important measure of a ventilation system's performance is the ability of the system to continuously control worker exposure to airborne contaminants below the level that was the basis for design. Managing a system to stay within its measurable baseline limits is predictive and prevents system-related exposures before they happen. Reactive maintenance procedures (i.e., waiting until air samples are out of limits and individuals have been exposed) must be replaced with a proactive monitoring and maintenance approach.

When solving a ventilation system problem, it is important to look at the total system and understand how all of the system components fit together. The ventilation system is composed of both exhaust air and supply air systems. The exhaust air system consists of the exhaust hoods, the duct system, the fan, and the air cleaning devices. It is necessary to understand how a problem with the duct system can affect the overall system performance to properly diagnose and fix a problem. Too often, effort focuses on a major component like the air cleaning device (e.g., a fabric filter) while ignoring the rest of the system. The operator must know the connected process, how each of the parts of the dust control system operates, the typical problems and symptoms of each part, and how a problem in one part of the system can be seen as a symptom in another part of the system.

The supply air system has air filters, air tempering components, a fan, air distribution ducts, and supply air fixtures. The supply and exhaust air systems must function in harmony for the design basis to be achieved. Inadequate supply or replacement air will affect the exhaust airflows. A poor air distribution of the supply air can create turbulent airflow in the area around exhaust hoods thus affecting hood performance.

Spaces with supply or replacement air volumes that are less than the exhaust volume develop pressures that are lower than the surrounding spaces. The resulting "negative pressure" could impact the exhaust airflow and could create a situation where hood performance suffers. A check for this negative pressure can be made by observing flow through openings between spaces and noting the difficulty of opening of exterior doors. For a description of pressure readings, see Chapter 3 of this Manual.

When the system performance has deteriorated, the plant should follow a prescribed process to identify the problem, determine the cause, and fix the problem. The flow chart in Figure 7-1 shows the process for troubleshooting problems encountered in the ventilation system. The primary steps include: the Evaluation of the Problem, System Walkthrough, Measurement and Data Evaluation, System Restoration, and Validation of Results. These are described later in this chapter.

7.2   EVALUATION OF THE PROBLEM

7.2.1 Initial Steps. The first step in troubleshooting a problem is to gather information concerning the system. New problems may often be a result of changes in the configuration, use, or condition of the system. Several questions should be asked to understand if system changes have occurred. Some of these important questions are shown in Table 7-1. The answers to these questions will help direct the troubleshooting investigation.

In addition to asking these questions, additional baseline data should be gathered to determine the original design for the system and other pertinent system information as outlined in Table 7-2. The test and balance or acceptance test reports should include volumetric flow and static pressures from a variety of locations throughout the system. See Chapter 4 of this Manual on Balancing for more information. These reports can be used for comparison with the design and current configuration. An examination of maintenance records may uncover processes or hoods that have not functioned properly and may provide data on the performance of fans or air cleaning devices. Following the compilation and review of these drawings, records and reports, the operations team should be prepared to conduct the walkthrough.

TABLE 7-1. Important Questions to Ask

1. When did you notice problems starting?
2. Any recent operating problems?
3. Any work procedure changes?
4. Any ventilation system changes?
5. Any changes in process operation/ingredients or throughput?
6. Any change in material handling systems?
7. Any exhaust/supply fan maintenance/changes?
8. Any recurring maintenance problems?
9. Have worker/air monitoring samples changed? Are they out of limits? In what area of the plant?
10. Are there differences between summer and winter?
11. Any different or unusual odors or noises?

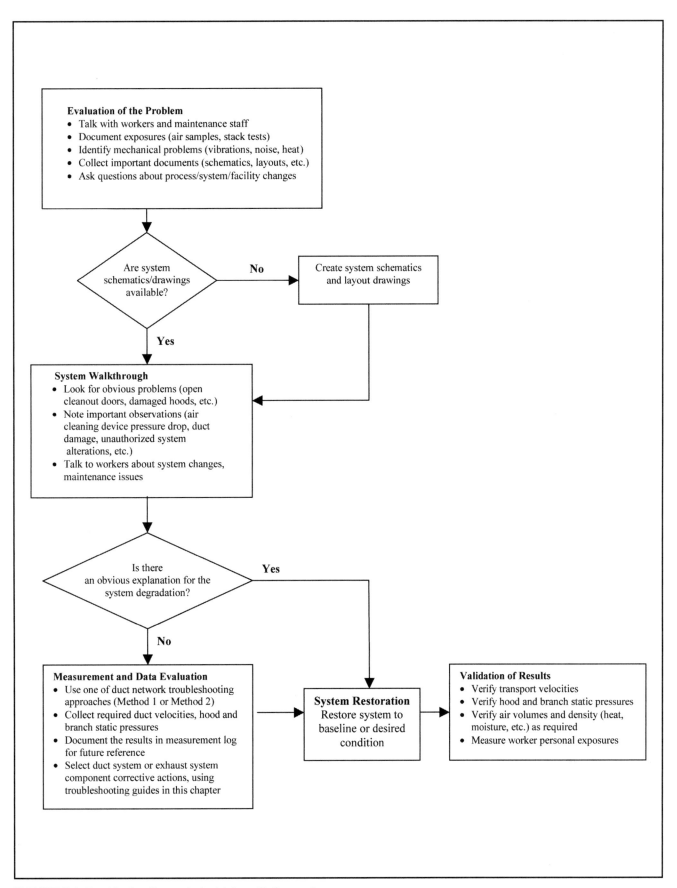

FIGURE 7-1. Troubleshooting an industrial ventilation system

TABLE 7-2. Sources of Information

1. Original design criteria

2. Facility drawings, industrial ventilation system schematics and layout.

3. If no available drawings, make a sketch of the ventilation system showing all the pickup points, blast gate locations, the duct system, the collector, the exhaust fan and the stack. Mark the drawings with anything that looks like a change.

4. Equipment vendor drawings, specifications or cut sheets.

5. If equipment information is missing or inadequate, obtain nameplate information from the equipment. Contact vendors for catalogs, fan curves, etc.

6. Design calculation sheets with static pressure and duct velocity specifications

7. Commissioning report or Acceptance test report

8. System maintenance records

9. System Test and Balance reports

10. Exposure, area, or engineering air samples

11. Environmental permit records (permit applications, installation permits, operating permits, Title V submissions, emission tests, etc.)

Where no facility schematics or drawings exist, a necessary first step in troubleshooting is to create system schematics or layout drawings. For exhaust systems, this includes documenting the process operations that have installed local exhaust hoods and making sketches (or take pictures) showing hood or enclosure design, opening sizes, estimated airflows, hood static pressures, and pertinent operational characteristics (e.g., grinding wheel size, tank dimensions for open surface tanks, etc.). The exhaust duct system should be sketched from hoods to exhaust stack and include duct diameters, lengths, numbers and angles of elbows, elbow radius, branch entry angles, other changes in duct size or direction, and test point locations. This layout drawing should also show duct elevation changes and routing throughout the plant. In a multi-floor plant, this will help ensure the right duct is traced from floor to floor. The exhaust fan inlet and outlet duct sizes and information including fan type, manufacturer, make and model, motor size, and exhaust configuration (rain stack type) should be documented.

7.2.2 Preliminary Ventilation System Data. Before conducting significant calculations, conduct a preliminary ventilation system assessment. The major components include:

1) Check System Diagram – Starting with a sketch of the ventilation system developed earlier or using any existing engineering drawings, develop a system diagram that shows the current dimensions of the system. Provide the dimensional data for all parts of the system.

   a) Flexible duct used for duct (diameters, lengths, approximate radius of turn through a duct direction change)

   b) Nominal internal duct diameters and lengths to nearest foot

   c) Number of elbows in each branch with elbow radii of curvatures (i.e., duct centerline radius of curvature is 2.0 duct diameters)

   d) Junction or "Y" fittings (branch entry angle, expansion to larger diameter angle – 15 degrees conical taper preferred, does branch enter the main directly in the tapered section or before it?)

   e) Duct expansions and contractions (provide dimensions)

   f) Exhaust fan inlet duct (diameter, lengths, straight lengths between last direction change and fan inlet)

   g) Exhaust fan stack (diameter, lengths, straight lengths between fan discharge flange and next direction change, type of stack rain preventer - no-loss, weather cap, elbow)

2) Make a table with the hood/enclosure design intent

   a) Shows every hood or enclosure on the system

   b) Describes the contaminant source being controlled by the hood

   c) Gives the dimensions of the opening

   d) Provides visual or air sample evidence of whether it is working

   e) Lists any field measurements of face velocity that might be available

   f) Collect system pressure and flow measurements – Collect the data gathered earlier in this problem solving process

3) System maintenance records – Collect any maintenance records on file for the system

4) Engineering data – Collect any system specification and design information that might be available as well as any installation drawings.

7.2.3 Supply Air Systems. For supply air systems, the fans, the heating and cooling components, air filtration devices, supply air distribution ducts, the air diffusers, estimated airflows, and the criteria for re-circulating air should be considered. Supply air inlets to workstations should be noted on sketches or system drawings. Also identify the location of local exhaust hoods and their proximity to supply air outlets.

7.3 SYSTEM WALKTHROUGH: VISUAL OBSERVATION AND ASSESSMENT

A walkthrough should be conducted to collect information on the state of the industrial ventilation system. The walkthrough relies on the team's use of their senses in identifying potential problems. The team is required to look, listen, and even smell to detect system faults and failures. This process will help identify any changes to the system that might have impacted operation including the addition of hoods to the system or open/leaking cleanout/inspection doors. The initial walkthrough may provide the information needed to resolve the problem without further investigation. At the least, it will provide important information to guide the rest of the investigation. Some important questions to consider in the initial walkthrough are shown in Table 7-3. The team should talk to the workers in each area to find out if they have noticed any changes to the industrial ventilation system or if they have made changes to the system based on problems encountered during normal operation.

A detailed review of all available system information will be needed if the initial visual inspection does not identify the problem. This information should include the design calculation sheets and commissioning report with the acceptance test results. These data can provide some insight into the as designed and installed performance of supply and exhaust air systems. Other important information includes system maintenance records and facility construction drawings. A thorough review of the maintenance and construction records will provide a history of the condition of the system when new and how it has changed over time. They should also show any changes that may have occurred to the system including fan upgrades (belt or pulley changes, motor changes) and air cleaning device service (for example, filter changes).

7.4   MEASUREMENT AND DATA EVALUATION

The approach to evaluate Industrial Ventilation System data depends on the types of data that are available. The best situation for troubleshooting occurs when data for the original duct calculations, the Baseline or previous measurements, and current measurements are available. There are approaches that can be used when one or more of the three types of data are missing as described below. Each of the methods is illustrated with ventilation system examples. Each of these methods requires measurements of static pressures and velocities within the ducts and around the air cleaning device and fan. Refer to Chapter 3 of this Manual for practical information on the instruments and methods recommended for the measurements of system parameters for monitoring system performance and troubleshooting.

Supply air system performance can be easily evaluated by noting the static pressure readings downstream from the fan or the air handling unit. If this pressure increases, it is likely that the supply airflow has decreased. The total air volume can be estimated by taking a velocity traverse across the filter bank or traversing the supply air ducts. Airflow turbulence can be determined by visual observation or measured through the use of a thermal anemometer. In all cases, they should be minimized to the level used in the initial hood design.

Local exhaust systems are more difficult to keep operating properly and have numerous components whose operation

may affect other elements in the system. Therefore, the remaining sections of this chapter will discuss methods to troubleshoot local exhaust ventilation systems.

Sometimes the preliminary measurements provide immediate indications of problems, although they may not identify the probable causes.

1) Measure the face velocities at the hoods. Most hoods are designed within the range of 75 to 150 to perhaps 200 feet per minute. Substantial velocity differences indicate either the hood opening size was modified or something changed in the connected duct network.

2) Measure duct velocities and static pressures at the main duct locations and at the collector inlet. Record the values on the system sketch. Most dust control systems are designed with conveying velocities in the range 3000 to 4500 feet per minute. Aerosol/mist or vapor collection systems might be designed for lower velocities like 2500 to 3000 feet per minute or lower since conveying velocity is not an issue. Check to see what the practice is for the industry.

3) Measure the total flow in the system. A quick comparison to the fan motor – Motor Horsepower is approximately (Total Pressure)*(Volumetric flow)/6356*(Fan Efficiency). A significant deviation may indicate major system problems.

4) Static pressure drops across a fabric filter are typically a few inches (often 2 to 4 but the range can be higher). A significantly higher pressure drop indicates problems with the air cleaning device.

7.5   INDICATIONS OF SYSTEM CHANGE

Before beginning a major investigation of a system, look for indications that the system has been changed enough that the next best step is a technical study by a trained ventilation engineer to determine what can be done to restore appropriate industrial ventilation for your process. Otherwise, there may be value in taking some further measurements to better define the problem and perhaps restore some system capability.

1) *Branch Additions* – Adding a duct without redesign does not often succeed because the exhaust fan speed should have been increased to exhaust the additional air and the fan motor may not have the capacity. This is because the increased pressure drop requirement for the higher velocity air trying to be "squeezed" through the original duct is higher. Only small additions with ducts that have cross-sectional areas 10-15% of the main duct have a chance of working without duct changes between the tap-in point and the collector.

2) *Branch Removals* – Removing a duct and blanking off the abandoned duct degrades system capacity because the duct between the blanking off point and the collector was sized for the transport velocity with that air vol-

TABLE 7-3. Walkthrough Observation Checklist

Is this condition present?	Y / N	Describe
1. *Contaminants escaping hood?* Visual emissions, accumulations around the hood, observed odors, etc.	Y / N	
2. *Adequate hood draft?* Use smoke visualization methods to demonstrate airflow into the hoods.	Y / N	
3. *Clogged hoods?* Debris or papers covering opening or slots, cleanout boxes overflowing, excessive material or equipment in hood, etc.	Y / N	
4. *Hoods modified?* Dents, access doors cut into hood, slots modified, etc.	Y / N	
5. *Hood Openings.* Measure length and width of the hood openings.		L = W =
6. *Duct Connection.* Measure diameter of duct connected to hood, in.		Dia =
7. *Difficult Exhaust?* Sources of moisture, wet or sticky material, corrosive or abrasive material, observed odors, hot sources or flame, agitation inside hood, etc.	Y / N	
8. *Dampers adjustment?* Frequently adjusted, no mark or locking device to indicate correct position.	Y / N	
9. *Branch additions:* Duct branches joining main headers and the header diameter does not get larger between the addition point and the collector.	Y / N	
10. *Branch removals:* Duct branches cut off and opening covered with blanking plates/flanges.	Y / N	
11. *Plugged ducts:* Tapping duct with broomstick shows duct sections that do not sound hollow.	Y / N	
12. *Damaged duct:* Dents, holes, rust.	Y / N	
13. *Audible leakage:* Hissing at inspection doors, cleanout doors, flanges, other fittings.	Y / N	
14. *Cleanouts?* Open cleanouts, missing access doors, leaks in access doors, etc.	Y / N	
15. *Test points:* Few or no pressure/flow measurement holes in the duct network.	Y / N	
16. *Air Cleaner?* External signs the collector is not operating correctly (see appropriate Air Cleaning Device chapter).	Y / N	
17. *Air Cleaner Information:* Obtain nameplate data, pressure drops, type of fabric, water flow, etc.	Y / N	
18. *Fan Information:* Nameplate data (fan: vendor, model number, serial number; motor: horsepower, RPM, full load amps). Obtain a copy of the fan operating curve from plant records or the equipment vendor.	Y / N	
19. *Fan Operation:* Check proper rotation, belt tension, inlet or outlet damper position, etc.	Y / N	
20. *Fan makes unusual sounds:* Squeaks/squeals on startup, new sounds, fan surging-hunting.	Y / N	
21. *Emissions?* Visible emissions at stack or deposited on roof.	Y / N	
22. *Negative Pressure?* Inadequate replacement air, high velocity airflow through windows and doors, etc.	Y / N	
23. *Air turbulence?* Cooling fans, supply air drafts, entrained air from process, etc. Smoke visualization helps to identify and qualify.	Y / N	

ume and the system balance is now changed. The correct way to make this change is to change the ducts and system balance to deal with the reduced air volume, but this can be expensive. A lower cost option is to size and install an orifice plate for the pressure drop of the removed duct branch and deliberately bleed air to maintain the downstream transport velocity and fan sizing.

3) *Data that show the system has no Baseline* – There are two simple indications that this was never done:

   a. Few or no test ports on duct network to take airflow and static pressure measurements.

   b. Blast gates have no mark or locking device. Baselining a system requires adjusting the blast gates after taking an initial set of airflow and static pressures around the system. Even if there are some test points, if there has been no effort to control the blast gate positions, they may have been adjusted away from their original settings, disrupting original airflows.

4) *Does exhaust fan capacity match hood airflow requirements?*

   a. Is the fan delivering the airflow and static pressure intended for the original condition when it was shipped by the vendor? With a serial number and the information above, a phone call to the vendor will tell you if the fan has been changed from the original order and what its ultimate capacity is with the attached electric motor.

   b. Estimate the airflow requirement. Using the area of the hood openings, make a simple table of assumed face velocities or use hood dimensions and VS prints from *Industrial Ventilation: A Manual of Recommended Practice for Design* to estimate the airflow required for each hood. This will provide a range of possible airflows that when totaled will indicate whether the fan could possibly deliver the needed airflow.

5) *Correct collector high differential pressure* – A high pressure loss at the air cleaning device will reduce airflow from the rest of the system. See the appropriate section of the Air Cleaning Device Chapter for specific collectors and how to solve high differential pressure problems.

6) *Fix any audible leaks* – Leaks allow air to bypass the hoods by going on an easier path of resistance closer to the fan.

7) *Determine if there are internal duct problems preventing flow.*

   a. If the dampers do not have marks or locks, the system may be out of balance. This may require balancing as described in Chapter 4.

   b. Repair obviously damaged ducts (i.e., dents, holes, missing duct, etc.) that can change the airflow.

   c. Check the branches, submains, and mains for blockage.

      i. Taping on the ducts may show blockage. If there is no hollow sound when tapped, the duct may be plugged.

      ii. If they do not exist, drill test point holes in proper locations on every branch and every main duct (where the branches connect to go on to the collector). Note, in many systems this will require a hot work permit.

      iii. Methods developed below will provide a method to predict potential blockages from static pressure or velocity readings.

      iv. The Duct Network Troubleshooting Table (Table 7-5), when velocities are either above or below the transport velocity range typically used for the contaminants, often indicates the locations of potential obstructions. A sudden step change in velocity values from one test point to the next (either up or down) of more than 20% probably indicates a change between those test points.

7.6 SELECTION OF TROUBLESHOOTING METHODS

The most important information needed to troubleshoot a local exhaust system is its Baseline data (or startup proof of performance values), both static pressure and airflow or duct velocity, for all parts of a system, and an acceptance range of the observed variability. The measurement data should include air temperature, moisture content, and elevation, values that affect air density and can greatly impact system performance. Without reference values, none of the troubleshooting methods in this section will work. The amount of data available will dictate how troubleshooting is done for the system.

7.6.1 Acceptance Range. The methods discussed below calculate a parameter and compare it to a Baseline or reference value. In an ideal system, with no normal variability in the ventilation system and no variability in the measurements, any deviation from the Baseline indicates a problem in the system. Since ventilation systems do have variability (dust cake buildup on a fabric filter, change in temperature at warm processes, windage from falling material in hoppers and conveyors, temporary blockage of hood or slot opening by personnel or materials, etc.) and there can be significant variability in reading the static pressures (measurement errors), the parameters (e.g., ratios of hood static pressures, ratios of hood static pressure to the branch static pressure, etc.) will have some variability when there is no true change in the system. Consequently, an acceptance range is set. When the parameter is outside the range, remedial action is indicated. The remediation may consist of cleaning the duct, patching eroded or corroded holes in the duct, repairing damaged hoods or duct, repositioning a damper, correcting malfunction in the air cleaning device or fan, or other appropriate actions.

If the acceptance range for the calculated parameter is too small, the evaluation may conclude a malfunction when the system is functioning correctly. If the range is too large, the evaluation may conclude the system is functioning correctly when it is not performing adequately. Selection of the proper acceptance range will depend on an understanding of the system and the measurement methods, as well as the consequences of making the wrong decision. Some considerations in determining the site specific acceptance range include:

- **Reflect Reality:** When an inspection determines a system is not functioning correctly, it means the volumetric flow through the hood is outside an acceptable range (too high or too low). Since the ventilation system is designed to protect the operator from overexposure (or collect contaminants at a point source for environmental reasons), the volumetric flow is a surrogate for the more critical parameter. Experience shows that a system fails either catastrophically (belt break, damper changes position, obstruction on the damper, fork truck hits the hood or duct, etc.) or gradually (accumulation of dust in the duct, erosion or corrosion of the duct, abrasion or buildup on a damper or orifice plate, etc.). For catastrophic failures, almost any trigger level is adequate. For slow changes, periodic monitoring changes can demonstrate the slow deterioration.

- **System Inherent Variability:** If volumetric flow of an exhaust system with a fabric filter varies by ± 5% because of the changing pressure drop across the filter, the acceptance range should be larger. The amount of variability in the volumetric flow caused by the change in pressure drop across the fabric will depend on the fan selection and the total system resistance.

- **Toxicity of the Contaminant:** Consider two identical material handling systems. If one contains 1% quartz and the other 10% quartz (the balance in both cases being nuisance dust), the second (more hazardous) could have a tighter range than the first (less hazardous).

- **Cost of Accepting a System With a Problem:** Here the inspection does not uncover an existing problem. At least one hood is not performing adequately. This will happen more frequently with a higher acceptance range. An inspection may miss an increased operator exposure. If the system is sufficiently robust, the increase in exposure may still be below acceptable levels. If the system is marginal, the increased exposure may not be acceptable. It is important to understand the strengths and limitations of the ventilation system when setting the acceptance ranges for a ventilation system.

- **Cost of Rejecting a System That Has No Problem:** Here the inspection shows a problem where there is no problem. This will happen more frequently with a low acceptance range. To remedy the problem, the system may be shut down and the ducts cleaned or visually inspected or some other remedial action. In addition to the cost of the remedy, there can be sufficient costs associated with the process down time. In addition, "crying wolf" frequently may cause disregard of a significant problem.

- **Experience:** The range may change with time. Starting with a tight range will cause more frequent cleanout of the duct or other remedial action. If experience shows that the ventilation system performs adequately at the extremes of the range, it may be appropriate to increase the range. Moreover, experience may show that once the buildup begins, it accelerates. Early action, at the potential cost of responding to a minor problem, may be beneficial.

- **Inspection Frequency:** If an inspection shows significant deterioration (many hoods or branches) at each inspection, the range may be adequate but the frequency of inspection inadequate. For example, if all the ducts show plugging during a yearly inspection, the frequency of the inspections should be increased (monthly or weekly) before considering lowering the acceptance range.

- **Staged Trigger:** In a process that operates nearly continuously, one range may cause cleaning of the duct system the next down day. A second (higher) range may cause the process to shut down to clean the duct system.

- **Biased Trigger:** The trigger need not be symmetric. A trigger may be set at -10% and +20% of the Baseline. This works best for the Baseline Deviation Method or in a system with variable pressure losses, like a system with a fabric filter.

- **Increase the Baseline:** If the inspections cause too much down time, increase the system volumetric flow by 5% and the acceptance range by about 8%. Consider a hood that requires 1000 acfm at 1.00 "wg with an acceptance range of 10%. A volumetric flow less than 900 acfm would result in remedial action. If the baseline flow were increased by 50 acfm (1050 acfm) the static pressure would increase to about 1.10 "wg. The same minimal airflow, 900 acfm, would be a reduction of 14% from the new baseline. Consequently, increasing the flows and the acceptance range would provide the same degree of protection but would trigger fewer remedial actions. If process down time is expensive, the cost savings may counteract the increased cost of systems operation (both the exhaust and the supply systems).

- **Cost of Cleaning:** In some cases, cleaning small amounts of fresh accumulations more frequently may be less expensive than cleaning larger amounts of old accumulations less frequently.

7.6.2 Outline of Troubleshooting Methods.
There are three methods to locate obstructions and alterations that interfere with ventilation system baseline conditions. These methods offer relative advantages of accuracy and simplicity. The practitioner can use either method based on individual system requirements.

Baseline Deviation Method – This method compares current static pressure measurement data with Baseline or previous performance data. For a specific location in the exhaust system, the current static pressure is compared to the static pressure initially measured when the system was commissioned. When deviation from Baseline for one or more system test points exceeds ± 20%, this indicates a developing problem. A troubleshooting table indicates the possible cause and the location of the system malfunction (see Section 7.7).

Branch Pressure Ratio Method – The branch pressure ratio method compares before and after values of the ratio of hood static pressure (SP_h) to static pressure at the end of the branch (SP_{end}), BrRatio = SP_h/SP_{end}. By comparing values taken at two different time periods, the method can predict probable blockage in the branch. A change of more than 10% in this ratio is significant. The method is useful in predicting where an obstruction exists in a branch (see Sections 7.8, 7.8.3).

End Pressure Ratio Method – The end pressure ratio method is intended to predict problems in a submain or main. It calculates the ratio of the Static Pressure in the upstream end of the segment to the down stream end. EndRatio = $SP_{end_{up}}/SP_{end_{dn}}$. By comparing values taken at two different time periods, the method predicts probable blockage in a submain or a main. A change of more than 10% in this ratio is significant. The method is useful in predicting where an obstruction exists in a branch (see Sections 7.8, 7.8.5).

Equivalent Resistance Method – This method determines the equivalent resistance — in simplest systems, the sum of the loss coefficients — for a segment. Comparison of the equivalent resistance at two different time periods allows a prediction of possible problems and an indication of the magnitude of the problem (see Section 7.9).

In analyzing the data, there are several possible physical causes of system alteration. The vertical duct sections are unlikely to plug unless a rag or something similar is snagged and caught by a damper, sheet metal screw, or a jagged piece of sheet metal pushed into the airflow during assembly. Plugging caused by dust accumulation is most likely to occur in horizontal sections or at elbows. Sometimes plugging builds up to a point but gets no worse. Sometimes it can build up and then break lose and be carried away. Most of the time, the plugging progressively becomes worse until it is cleaned out.

A leak is mostly likely to occur where ducts are joined together and where ducts are joined to "fittings," such as elbows and junctions (part that connects three or more ducts together). The single most likely cause of a leak is failing to properly connect a duct to its hood after disconnecting it for some reason. Changes at the Air Cleaning Device and the Fan can be seen throughout the system. Airflows will drop if the air cleaning device has a high differential pressure, if the fan's belts are slipping, or if someone left a duct or collector inspection door open, effectively bypassing the duct network.

7.7 BASELINE DEVIATION METHOD

Measurements of the static pressure throughout the duct system can provide indications of a problem. To effectively troubleshoot the system, it is important to know how the measurements have changed from when the system was performing correctly. The process of commissioning the system created such a data set and is an important factor in effective system operation. Measurements that indicate system performance need to be taken if an exhaust system is not performing up to expectations. Since the pressure inside the duct system causes airflow, static pressure readings at key locations in the duct system can provide an indication of potential problems.

7.7.1 Duct System Troubleshooting Guide.
Table 7-4 provides examples of several possible combinations of airflow/velocity and static pressure that suggest possible causes of deviations from pressure readings taken when the system was operating correctly. By comparing routine system monitoring static pressure data to their Baseline or proof of performance values, you can determine if the system is operating at other than the design condition. Table 7-4 indicates where to look for the cause of the problem. Static Pressure data are easier and quicker to gather than airflow or volumetric flow data. Airflow data are sometimes taken as a second step to confirm the problem, based on what the static pressure data indicate.

Table 7-4 provides possible explanations for significant static pressure variation, either high or low, at a specific test point. If airflow measurements are not available, make an assumption about whether the airflow is either high or low. Some of the possible causes will fit your situation better than others. The problem may be at an adjacent branch or from the collector or fan, and can have an impact on the entire system.

The Baseline Deviation Method compares the current measured static pressure with the baseline or previous measured results. If the measurement at one or more test points is 20% higher (plus) or lower (minus) than the Baseline value, there has probably been a change in the system. A 20% change in static pressure is roughly equivalent to a 10% change in airflow (the volumetric flow is proportional to the square root of the static pressures).

The next step is to use the Duct System Troubleshooting Guide (Table 7-4) to find which of the possible causes could fit the situation. If the situation is still not clear, take selected

TABLE 7-4. Duct System Troubleshooting Guide (Reprinted with permission from Procter & Gamble)

	High Static Pressure	Low Static Pressure

High Airflow or Velocity	1. Branch airflow greater than design
	  - Restrictions in an adjacent duct branch:
	    - Duct plugged?
	    - Balancing orifice too small?
	    - Blast gate closed too far?
	    - Air bleed blocked?
	2. Total system airflow greater than design:
	  - Fan inlet slide gate open too far?
	  - Fan speed too high?
	    - Belt pulley diameter correct?
	    - Fan motor speed correct?
	  - Filter differential pressure low?
	    - Pressure indicator functioning?
	    - Bag cleaning too often?
		1. Branch airflow less than design
		  - Branch resistance less than design between duct branch air inlet and test point:
		    - Duct access door open?
		    - Hole in duct?
		    - Balancing Damper open too far?
		    - Orifice missing?
		    - Orifice too large/small?
		    - Hood modified?

Low Airflow or Velocity	1. Branch airflow less than design
	  - Restrictions between duct branch air inlet and test point:
	    - Duct plugged?
	    - Poorly cut flange gasket partially blocking duct?
	    - Orifice too small?
	    - Blast gate closed too far?
	    - Air bleed blocked?
		1. Branch airflow less than design
		  - Restrictions between the test point and the system fan:
		    - Downstream duct plugged?
		    - Downstream damper too closed?
		    - Poorly cut flange gasket partially blocking duct?
		2. Openings in other parts of system allow airflow to bypass test point duct branch:
		  - Duct access door open?
		  - Filter inspection door open?
		  - Missing orifice?
		  - Blast gate open too far?
		  - Leakage around damper seals?
		3. Total system airflow less than design:
		  - Fan performance?
		    - Incorrect fan rotation?
		    - Loose or broken belts?
		    - Small drive pulley diameter?
		    - Large driven pulley diameter
		    - Wrong fan motor speed?
		    - Fan in unstable region on performance curve?
		    - Fan overload on cold start?
		  - Filter differential pressure high?
		    - Pressure indicator function ok?
		    - Incorrect bag cleaning cycle?
		    - Moisture, bags blinded?
		  - Fan damper closed too far?

airflow measurements to provide more information to make a decision of where to enter the system to correct the problem. This section gives several examples on how to use the method.

7.7.2 Key Assumptions. The key assumptions in the method are:

1) There are test point holes in straight sections of duct in each branch or main of the system. For the branches where air first enters the duct, the best location is between any installed balancing device and the duct connection to the main.

2) Baseline or previous measurements (while the system is functioning correctly) are available:

   a) Set of Baseline static pressures and airflows for the test points of the system.

   b) Sketch or isometric that shows the locations of the test points, ducts and other components of the system.

3) Routine static pressure monitoring data are taken for selected test points and recorded on a trend plot. (Chapter 3 describes the equipment and techniques of measurements and Chapter 5 describes ventilation system monitoring and maintenance.)

4) At least one of the test points is more than 20% above or below its Baseline value.

7.7.3 Steps of the Baseline Deviation Method. The steps in this methold are as follows:

1) Walk the entire system to observe that nothing obvious is out of its ordinary place (i.e., a duct cleanout door is open, the fan is turned off, broken belt, etc.). It is helpful to bring the system sketch to make sure that you have seen all parts of the system.

2) Collect a set of static pressure data for all the test points or use the recent monitoring data.

3) Set up a spread sheet with test point, the measured static pressure reading, and the baseline data (see Table 7-5 for an example).

4) Calculate the percent deviation from Baseline for all test points as a percentage (Measured – Baseline)/Baseline * 100%). Note the results as HI if the value is greater than 20% or LO if the value is less than -20%. The HI is important since a system with too much air at one hood will likely have too little air at another hood.

5) On a diagram of the system, note with arrows whether the percent change is HI (plus 20%) with an upward arrow or LO (minus 20%) with a downward arrow.

7.7.4 Example 7-1: Baseline Deviation Method. Consider the system in Figure 7-2. Measured static pressure and baseline data are shown in the second and third columns of Table 7-5. Determine if the system has a potential problem and identify the likely cause.

Solution: Complete the Percent of baseline calculation in the fourth column of Table 7-5. Evaluate which test points are HI or Lo or within the limits (YES if greater than -20% and less than +20%).

Using a sketch of the system, mark it with arrows by each of the test points to show if the data are above or below Baseline values. Use an up arrow (↑) for values above Baseline and a down arrow (↓) for values below Baseline. Use double arrows (↓↓) for larger relative deviations. Refer to Figure 7-2 below. The test points are marked with letters.

The reversal in arrow directions in Figure 7-2 shows that something has changed in the duct system between test points F and two upstream points, C and E. If there was a problem that affected the whole system caused by reduced flow through the fan or increased pressure drop at the air cleaning device, all the arrows would be pointed down. Refer to the Duct System

TABLE 7-5. Baseline Deviation Method – Example 7-1

Test Point	Measured Static Pressure	Baseline Value	Percent of Baseline = (Measured – Baseline)/Baseline * 100%	In limits? Yes/HI/LO
A	- 1.58	- 2.26	(1.58 - 2.26)/2.26 * 100% = - 30%	LO
B	- 3.27	- 4.54	(3.27 - 4.54)/4.54 * 100% = - 28%	LO
C	- 3.41	- 4.87	(3.41 - 4.87)/4.87 * 100% = - 30%	LO
D	- 7.22	- 5.64	(7.22 - 5.64)/5.64 * 100% = + 28%	HI
E	- 3.69	- 5.35	(3.69 - 5.35)/5.35 * 100% = - 31%	LO
F	- 7.21	- 5.77	(7.21 - 5.77)/5.77 * 100% = + 25%	HI
G	- 9.26	- 7.35	(9.26 - 7.35)/7.35 * 100% = + 26%	HI
H	- 9.76	- 7.81	(9.76 - 7.81)/7.81 * 100% = + 25%	HI
I	- 8.75	- 7.00	(8.75 - 7.00)/7.00 * 100% = + 25%	HI
J	- 14.32	- 11.83	(14.32 - 11.83)/11.83 * 100% = + 21%	HI

Troubleshooting Guide (Table 7-4) to determine possible causes of the reversal.

Look at Table 7-5 to focus on possible reasons for the reversal. Look down the static pressure columns for the most likely cause. Look for the most likely cause of the reversal of static pressures in the Low Static Pressure column by imagining yourself at either test point C or E and asking: "What are possible reasons that Static Pressure would drop at that location?" Do the same imagination game at test point F in the High Static Pressure column to find reasons why Static Pressure would rise.

In the example, point F gets its air supply from points C and E; points C and E are connected to the fan through point F. A plugged duct, Item 1 in both columns on the Low Airflow row, is a common reason in both highlighted items and is the most likely cause. One could take airflow readings to confirm your

initial conclusion but with experience, static pressure data will usually be enough to know where to clean out a plugged duct. Another technique is to mount permanent gauges at key measurement points, marked with action limits, so that the operator can quickly identify problems and trends.

7.7.5 Interaction of System and Fan Curves. Remember that the system fan delivers an air volume based on the duct system resistance. If the system resistance is changed (which happens when there is a blockage developing in a duct for example), the airflow changes as well. This is shown in Figure 7-3.

A similar situation occurs in each branch of the system as well as the total system. However, the results will be different in some branches because a plug in one branch (and its corresponding reduction in airflow) may be seen as an increase in airflow in an adjacent branch, as the fan tries to move enough

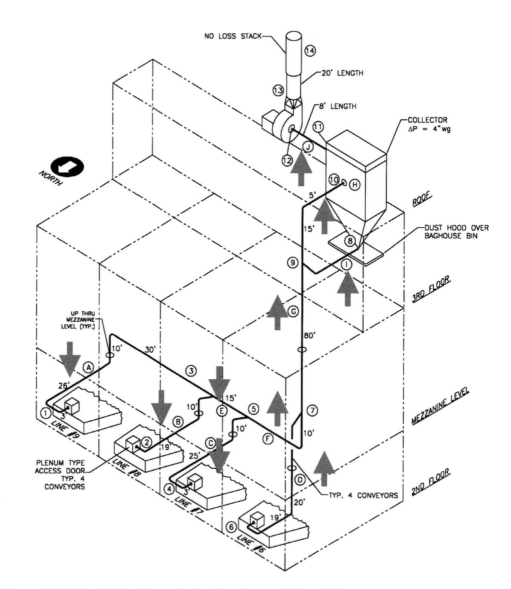

TEST PORT	BASELINE SP
A	2.20
B	4.64
C	4.87
D	5.64
E	5.35
F	6.77
G	7.35
H	7.01
I	7.00
J	11.83

FIGURE 7-2. Schematic for Example 7-1 (Reprinted with permission from Procter & Gamble)

air through an adjacent branch to match the total system resistance even though the total airflow at the fan is reduced (see Duct System Curve B in Figure 7-3). Curve C illustrates a situation where the system resistance is lower (possibly from an open duct cleanout door). More air is moved by the fan. Use the Duct System Troubleshooting Guide (Table 7-4) as a checklist of possible causes for the condition seen at each test point.

A simple memory aid that can be used to quickly evaluate Static Pressure readings when they differ from Baseline is:

- High pressure, look low in the system (towards the pickups or air inlets).

- Low pressure, look high in the system (towards the exhaust fan).

7.7.6 Example 7-2: Baseline Deviation Method. In the same system as Example 7-1, Table 7-6 shows the measured static pressure and baseline values. The percent Baseline calculations are all negative and around the same order of magnitude. The operator was concerned about the very low static pressure values and took a system airflow measurement, which was 52% of the Baseline value. Figure 7-4 shows the directional arrows all pointing down.

If all the percent of baseline calculations were low and in the same general range, it suggests the cause of the low static pressure and low airflow is system-wide. The air cleaning device, the fan or the duct downstream from the last sample

point could have that kind of impact. If the pressure drop across the air cleaning device is within the manufacturer's expected range, then a fan problem is most likely. An open cleanout door near the fan could also be causing the low static pressure readings with a large portion of the exhaust air entering the system through the open door rather than through the hoods.

In some cases, this condition could be caused by an electrical problem, either installation or maintenance. For example, reversing two of the three power leads in the three phase fan motor can cause it to rotate in reverse, delivering less than half the design airflow even though fan rotational speed (but not direction) is correct. Fans have a proper rotational direction, usually marked on the fan housing.

A common misperception about exhaust ventilation system operation is that when collector differential pressure is within the expected range, then the rest of the system is functioning correctly. This is not true. For example, a fabric filter with a cleaning cycle determined by pressure drop, will attempt to operate within the preset range of pressure drops. If the volumetric flow is low, the dust cake will be thicker resulting in the proper range of pressure drops. Also, many scrubbers will have a pressure drop determined by the depth of the scrubber liquid, not just the volumetric flow. See Chapter 6 for further details.

It is important to know how the system components per-

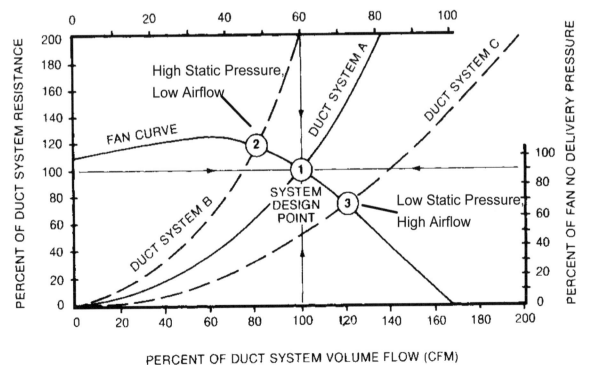

FIGURE 7-3. Interaction of system curves and fan curves

TABLE 7-6. Baseline Deviation Method – Example 7-2

Test Point	Measured Static Pressure	Baseline Value	Percent of Baseline = (Measured – Baseline)/Baseline * 100%	In limits? Yes/HI/LO
A	- 0.52	- 2.26	(0.52-2.26)/2.26 × 100 = -77%	LO
B	- 1.18	- 4.54	(1.18-4.54)/4.54 × 100 = - 74%	LO
C	- 1.41	- 4.87	(1.41-4.87)/4.87 × 100 = -71%	LO
D	- 1.47	- 5.64	(1.47-5.64)/5.64 × 100 = -74%	LO
E	- 1.28	- 5.35	(1.28-5.35)/5.35 × 100 = -76%	LO
F	- 1.27	- 5.77	(1.27-5.77)/5.77 × 100 = -78%	LO
G	- 1.84	- 7.35	(1.84-7.35)/7.35 × 100 = -75%	LO
H	- 2.11	- 7.81	(2.11-7.81)/7.81 × 100 = -73%	LO
I	- 1.68	- 7.00	(1.68-7.00)/7.00 × 100 = -76%	LO
J	- 2.96	- 11.83	(2.96-11.83)/11.83 × 100 = -75%	LO

form when working properly. For example, find and use the most recent Baseline data from when General Contractor or plant engineering turned the system over to the site. Ensure that the data are updated with any changes to reflect the "As Built" condition. Also look at the trend plots and maintenance records for the system to understand where routine cleanout and system repairs should be conducted.

Consider the future impact of the problem, its cause, and its resolution and think of ways to prevent or minimize repeat problems. For example, if a tight radius elbow in the duct network always builds up a layer of dust, would changing to a long radius curvature help reduce cleanout frequency or is the best value a well-placed cleanout door?

7.7.7 Example 7-3: Baseline Deviation Method. Table 7-7 shows the static pressure measurements and Baseline values for the system in Figure 7-5. Determine probable cause for the deviation from Baseline.

Figure 7-5 shows selected system readings. This system apparently has a problem of low airflow because nearly all the static pressures readings are HI (the Percent of Baseline values are greater then 20%). The volumetric flow through points 11 (+39%), 18 (+42%) and 23 (+22%) are high while the volumetric flow through point 26 (-5%) is about correct. Consequently, the flow though point 12 must be low. There could be a blockage or other restriction between point 12 and 15. If there is a blockage between points 12 and 15, with a design volumetric flow of 3000 acfm, the reduced flow would cause an increased flow in the other branches entering before point 26.

If only fan inlet static pressure had been taken, no problem would have been observed. Airflows in some branches were high by as much as 20 to 60% because the air inlet at point 12 was effectively blocked. Plastic bags or similar debris sucked into the inlet can cause that kind of obstruction.

7.8   PRESSURE RATIO METHODS

7.8.1 Terminology. Obstructions are most likely to appear in "branch" and "submain" ducts. A branch duct connects the hood to the rest of a duct system. It usually starts at a "takeoff" from a hood and ends in a "junction" fitting (see Figure 7-6). A submain is a duct that connects two junction fittings together. A "main" is a duct downstream of the last junction fitting. Main ducts connect the last junction to the fan or air-cleaner and the air-cleaner and fan to each other.

The static pressure method can detect and find plugging that is substantial enough to affect airflows. Large leaks are easy to detect and find if they occur well downsream of the hood static measurement location. They can be difficult to detect using these methods if they occur because a hood is left disconnected.

7.8.2 Overview of Pressure Ratio Methods. The ratio of any two pressures in one part of a ventilation system stays the same even if changes occur in a different part of the system or if the fan speed changes. They stay the same even if the filter in the dust collector is blinded, the fan belts are slipping, or the scrubber's venturi is partially blocked. In short, ratios of pressures will not change unless that section of the system has been altered or obstructed – no matter what has happened elsewhere in the system. Therefore, if the ratio has not changed in a branch, the cause is somewhere else.

On the other hand, if a ratio has changed, something has happened to that part of the system. Look in that part of the system for an obstruction, heavy dust coatings, leaks, or some other change that can impact airflows.

Although one can look at any two locations and compute the ratio for them, some locations are more useful than others. In the following sections, locations are suggested for branch ducts, submains, and main ducts.

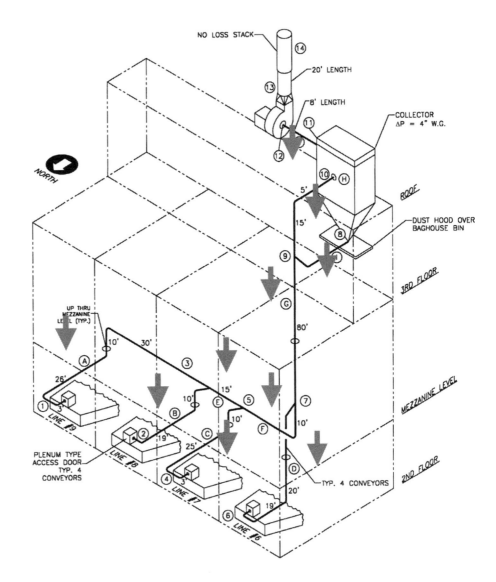

TEST PORT	BASELINE SP
A	2.20
B	4.64
C	4.87
D	5.64
E	5.35
F	6.77
G	7.35
H	7.01
I	7.00
J	11.83

FIGURE 7-4. Schematic for Example 7-2 (Reprinted with permission from Procter & Gamble)

TABLE 7-7. Baseline Deviation Method – Example 7-3

Test Point	Measured Static Pressure	Baseline Value	Percent of Baseline (Measured – Baseline)/Baseline * 100%	In limits? Yes/HI/LO
2	- 3.9	- 1.8	(3.9 - 1.8)/(1.8) × 100 = +117%	HI
4	- 3.8	- 1.7	(3.8 - 1.7)/(1.7) × 100 = +124%	HI
11	- 4.7	- 2.3	(4.7 - 2.3)/(2.3) × 100 = +104%	HI
18	- 4.1	- 2.4	(4.1 - 2.4)/(2.4) × 100 = +71%	HI
23	- 4.6	- 2.9	(4.6 - 2.9)/(2.9) × 100 = +59%	HI
26	- 4.3	- 3.0	(4.3 - 3.0)/(3.0) × 100 = +43%	HI
31	- 4.4	- 3.1	(4.4 - 3.1)/(3.1) × 100 = +42%	HI
37	- 6.4	- 6.2	(6.4 - 6.2)/(6.2) × 100 = +3%	Yes

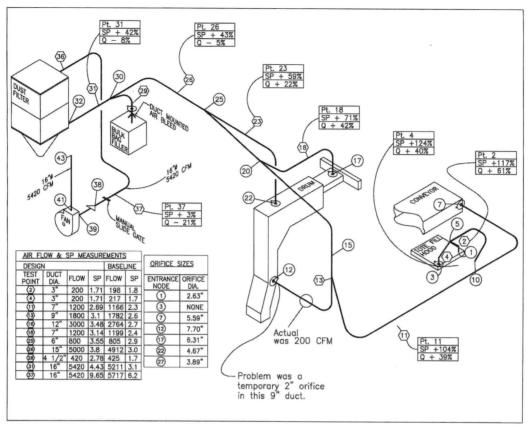

FIGURE 7-5. Schematic for Example 7-3 (Reprinted with permission from Procter & Gamble)

7.8.3 Branch Pressure Ratio Method.

The branch pressure ratio method compares before and after values of the ratio of hood static pressure (SP_h) to static pressure at the end of the branch (SP_{end}). This important Branch Ratio (BrRatio) is defined by:

$$BrRatio = \frac{SP_h}{SP_{end}}$$ [7.1]

SP_h = value measured at the hood in the branch duct

SP_{end} = value measure at end of branch duct

A change of more than 10% in BrRatio often means that something is wrong within that branch (see Table 7-8). It could be an obstruction or a leak. It could be between the hood and the end of the branch or it could be upstream of hood static pressure reading. With an obstruction between the hood and the end, the resistance in the branch would have increased and thus the Branch Ratio (SP_h/SP_{end}) would decrease (recall, SP_{end} = SP_h + losses (resistance) between the hood and the end). Likewise, if the duct leaked, more air would flow through the branch increasing the static pressure at the end, resulting in a decrease in the Branch Ratio. If Branch Ratio is zero ($SP_h = 0$), the duct is completely blocked between the hood and the end of the branch or there is a massive leak between the hood and

the end. If the duct is completely blocked upstream of the hood, the Branch Ratio would be 1 (with no flow, there would be no losses between the hood and the end so $SP_h = SP_{end}$).

7.8.4 Example 7-4: Branch Pressure Ratio Method.

Table 7-9 shows data collected on the system shown in Figure 7-6. The data were collected at two different times on the same system. Use the values of Branch Ratio to decide whether there is a problem somewhere in the system.

In fact, obstructions were actually in Branches 2-A, 4-C and in Submain C-D. The method correctly identified that there was a problem in the branches but gave no indication of the obstructed submain.

7.8.5 End Pressure Ratio Method.

The Branch Ratio Method only identifies potential problems in branches. It will not identify problems in submains. However, the End Ratio method can identify problems in submains. Hence, unless there is good reason to suspect a particular branch, it is best to employ the Branch Ratio Method and End Ratio Method at the same time. The following example problem illustrates the use of the End Ratio Method.

The End Pressure Ratio Method is intended to locate obstructions in submain ducts. To do so, we use the values of SP_{end} in two consecutive ducts to compute EndRatio:

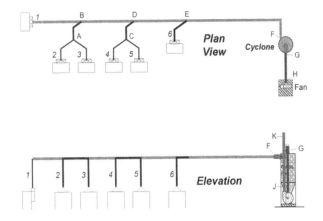

Baseline Data

ID	Type	SP_h	SP_{end0}
1-A	Brch	2.83	4.38
2-A	Brch	1.91	2.50
3-A	Brch	1.91	2.50
A-B	Subm		4.01
B-D	Subm		6.16
4-C	Brch	2.37	2.66
5-C	Brch	2.37	2.66
C-D	Subm		5.29
D-E	Brch		5.82
6-E	Brch	3.73	5.23
E-F	Main		6.24
F-G	Coll.		10.70
H-J	Fan inlet		12.20

FIGURE 7-6. Schematic for Examples 7-4, 7-5, 7-8, 7-9 and 7-10

$$BrRatio = \frac{SP_{end_{up}}}{SP_{end_{dn}}} \quad [7.2]$$

where:

$SP_{end_{up}}$ = average value of SP_{end} in the ducts immediately upstream of this duct

$SP_{end_{dn}}$ = value of SP_{end} measured in this duct

If branch ducts A and B empty into submain M, then:

$$EndRatio_M = \frac{(1/2)(SP_{end_A} + SP_{end_B})}{SP_{end_M}} \quad [7.3]$$

If there was an obstruction between the junction and the end of the segment, the static pressure at M would remain the same or increase. On the other hand, the volumetric flow through A and B would be reduced, resulting in a reduction in the end static pressures for A and B. Consequently, the ratio would decrease. Likewise, significant leakage into the duct between the junction and M would decrease the static pressure ratio. These conclusions are tabulated in Table 7-8.

A change of more than 10% in EndRatio probably means that something is wrong with the downstream duct. It could be an obstruction (reduced ratio) or a leak (increased ratio).

7.8.6 Example 7-5: End Pressure Method. Table 7-10 shows the data collected at two different times for the system shown in Figure 7-6. Use the Branch Ratio Method to determine which ducts are partially obstructed or are leaking and use End Ratio Method for submains and mains.

7.8.7 More Examples Using the Ratio Methods. In this section the pressure ratio methods are applied to a series of test cases that are intended to be realistic. The numbers for the test cases were generated using a computer program that models ventilation systems. Random measurement errors were also added.

7.8.8 Example 7-6: Pressure Ratio Methods. The data

shown in the first few columns of Table 7-11 list sets of static pressure measurements for the system in Figure 7-7. The first set of data represent Baseline and the second set of data represent tests taken sometime later.

The calculations in the table are of two types. First, the Branch Ratio is calculated for all the exhaust points. Then the End Ratios are calculated for the branches. Notice the up stream entries are the legs entering the branch entry while the first column of the table is the submain leaving the branch entry.

The Branch Ratio Method identifies potential problems in Branches 2-B and 9-F. The End Ratio Method identifies the submain, D-C. The false positive for the air-cleaner would be expected for a fabric filter since the pressure drop may not change with a change in volumetric flow when the unit pulses at a fixed static pressure.

7.8.9 Example 7-7: Pressure Ratio Methods. This example uses the same system shown in Figure 7-7. The data shown in Table 7-12 list data measured initially and at some later time. Note that at the second round of measurements about half of the ducts had a light coating inside and another branch (4-A) had been added since the original measurements were taken.

7.9   EQUIVALENT RESISTANCE METHOD

When the acceptance range is appropriately selected, the Pressure Ratio Methods should detect most obstructions large enough to shift airflow sufficiently.[7.1, 7.2, 7.3] However, changes to pressure ratios do not directly indicate the magnitude of the change in resistance due to the obstruction. With a greater investment of effort (static pressure and velocity pressure measurements throughout the system), the Equivalent Resistance Method described below provides an indication of the magnitude of the problem.

7.9.1 Equivalent Resistance. Equivalent resistance (X) is the ratio of the dissipated power (rate of energy consumed due to the internal resistance to flow of the duct) divided by the

TABLE 7-8. Action Thresholds for Pressure Ratio Methods

Method	Ratio	Measure In	Threshold	Action	If Increase	If Decrease
BrRatio	SP_h/SP_{end}	Same branch	10%	Find alteration	Obstruction upstream of hood Reduction in resistance between hood and end	Obstruction between hood and end Leak between hood and end
EndRatio	SP_{end}/SP_{end}	Different ducts	10%	Find alteration	If a significant increase, look for an obstruction in the submain in the numerator or a branch that is nearly or completely blocked. Obstructions in branches may have little effect on this ratio.	Downstream duct – obstruction If large decrease, look for an obstruction in the denominator submain. A modest change could be due to obstructions almost anywhere upstream.

TABLE 7-9. Branch Ratio Pressure Method for Example 7-4

		Measured				Branch Ratio Method			Interpretation
		Time 1		Time 2		Time 1	Time 2	Change	
ID	Points	SP_h	SP_{end}	SP_h	SP_{end}	SP_h/SP_{end}	SP_h/SP_{end}	%Change	Altered?
1-B	Branch a-h	2.83	4.38	1.87	3.02	0.65	0.62	-5%	Not Likely
2-A	Branch	1.91	2.50	1.49	1.70	0.77	0.87	13%	Likely
3-A	Branch c-j	1.91	2.50	1.28	1.72	0.77	0.75	-3%	Not Likely
4-C	Branch d-n	2.37	2.66	1.82	2.46	0.89	0.74	-17%	Likely
5-C	Branch e-o	2.37	2.66	2.12	2.44	0.89	0.87	-2%	Not Likely
6-E	Branch f-t	3.73	5.23	2.48	3.73	0.71	0.67	-6%	Not Likely

Note: Percent change calculation uses the ratio at time 1 in the denominator.

Solution: The Branch Ratio Method indicates potential problems in Branches 2-A and 4-C. Since the value of Branch Ratio for 2-A increased, it is likely that an obstruction is upstream of the hood static pressure measurement location. Since the change in Branch Ratio for 4-C is negative, it is likely that an obstruction is between measurement locations hood and end. Moreover, since all the readings were reduced, there is likely a problem after junction E.

In fact, obstructions were actually in Branches 2-A, 4-C and in Submain C-D. The method correctly identified that there was a problem in the branches but gave no indication of the obstructed submain.

TABLE 7-10. End Pressure Ratio Method – Example 7-5

ID	Type	SP$_{end}$ Time 1	SP$_{end}$ Time 2	Up IDs A	Up IDs B	Time 1: up SP$_{end}$ A	Time 1: up SP$_{end}$ B	Time 1: up SP$_{end}$ Avg	Time 2: up SP$_{end}$ A	Time 2: up SP$_{end}$ B	Time 2: up SP$_{end}$ Avg	EndRatio Time 1	EndRatio Time 2	EndRatio Change	Interpretation
1-B	Branch	4.38	3.02												
2-A	Branch	2.50	1.70												
3-A	Branch	2.50	1.72												
A-B	Submain	4.01	2.77	2	3	2.50	2.50	2.50	1.70	1.72	1.71	0.62	0.62	-1%	
4-C	Branch	2.66	2.46												
5-C	Branch	2.66	2.44												
C-D	Submain	5.29	3.78	4-C	5-C	2.66	2.66	2.66	2.46	2.44	2.45	0.50	0.65	29%	obstruction
6-E	Branch	5.23	3.73												
B-D	Submain	6.16	4.30	1-B	A-B	4.38	4.01	4.20	3.02	2.77	2.90	0.68	0.67	-1%	
D-E	Submain	5.82	4.12	B-D	C-D	6.16	5.29	5.73	4.30	3.78	4.04	0.98	0.98	0%	
E-F	Main	6.24	5.31	6-E	D-E	5.23	5.82	5.53	3.73	4.12	3.93	0.89	0.74	-17%	obstruction
F-G	Collector	10.70	11.30			6.24		6.24	5.31		5.31	0.58	0.47	-19%	change in airflow
G-H	Fan Inlet	12.20	12.30			10.70		10.70	11.30		11.30	0.88	0.92	5%	

Solution: As shown in Table 7-9, Branch Ratio changed by more than 10% for Branch 2-A (13%) and 4-C (-17%). Hence, you would expect to find an obstruction or alteration in Branch 2-A and 4-C. As shown in Table 7-10, End Ratio changed by more than 10% only for submain C-D (+29%) and main E-F (-17%). The increase in the Branch Ratio across the collector (-19%) is likely due to a change in airflow. Consequently, it is likely that there are obstructions or alterations in submain C-D and the main E-F.

kinetic energy rate.[(7.4)] The power of the airflow at any cross-section can be computed from Power = $-Q \times TP$ at that cross-section. The dissipated power due to that section is the difference between the power entering and the power exiting that section (ΔPower). The kinetic energy rate (KP) at a cross-section is computed from $KP = Q \times VP$ at that section. The equivalent resistance is $X = \Delta Power/KP$.

As with static pressure ratios, the equivalent resistance value for a given portion of a system (e.g., a branch duct) should vary little with changes to airflow. This includes changes induced by alterations to other parts of a system. Conversely, a substantial change in an X value is a strong indication that an obstruction or alteration has occurred. Those properties make observed values of X useful for troubleshooting. For a single flow in a duct, X is approximately the same as the sum of loss coefficients for the components in that section of duct. Indeed, velocity pressure coefficients can be considered as the X-values for individual components (e.g., elbows, hood entries to ducts, etc.).

Unlike the static pressure ratios described in the previous section for which different ratios are required for branches than for submains, equivalent resistances can be applied usefully to any contiguous section of ducts, including branch ducts (X_{br}), submains (X_{sub}), many air-cleaning devices ($X_{cleaner}$), the entire system of ducts upstream of the fan inlet (X_{inlet}), and the ducts connected to the exhaust side of the fan (X_{outlet}). In addition, since the parameter values are computed from a different mix of measured values, conflicts between findings with the two methods indicate measurement errors.

Since X, assuming no leaks in the system or changes in the physical state (i.e., the volumetric flow in equals the volumetric flow out), is essentially the sum of the loss coefficients in the segment under investigation, an increase in X indicates an increase in a loss coefficient or an addition of a loss coefficient. For example, damage to the duct, an obstruction, or accumulation of material in the duct would, in effect, add a loss coefficient to the system. On the other hand, if there is a leak upstream of the end of the segment, the volumetric flow changes. Q_1 (flow at beginning of segment) is greater than Q_2 (flow at end of segment). Note, this assumes a negative pressure exhaust system. Then $X = (Q_2 TP_2 - Q_1 TP_1)/Q_2 VP_2$ would decrease.

7.9.2 Basic Formulas. The values for the various parts of a system can be computed from the following relationships:[(7.1)]

Fan Inlet: $X_{inlet} = \dfrac{-(SP_{inlet} + VP_{inlet})}{VP_{inlet}}$ [7.4]

where:

SP_{inlet} = static pressure measured just upstream of the fan inlet

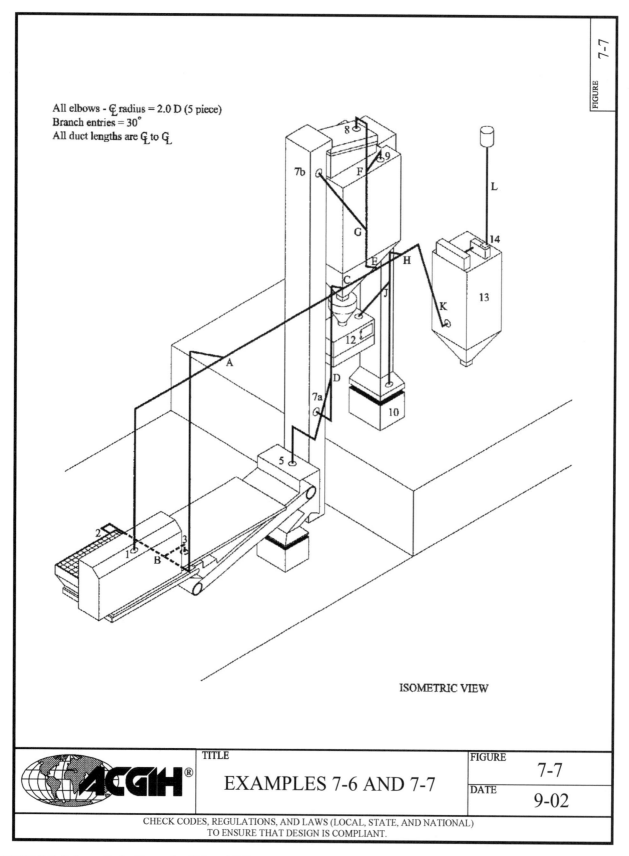

All elbows - C$_L$ radius = 2.0 D (5 piece)
Branch entries = 30°
All duct lengths are C$_L$ to C$_L$

7-7

FIGURE

ISOMETRIC VIEW

	TITLE		FIGURE	
ACGIH®	**EXAMPLES 7-6 AND 7-7**		7-7	
			DATE	
			9-02	

CHECK CODES, REGULATIONS, AND LAWS (LOCAL, STATE, AND NATIONAL)
TO ENSURE THAT DESIGN IS COMPLIANT.

FIGURE 7-7. Schematic for Examples 7-6 and 7-7

TABLE 7-11. Branch Ratio and End Ratio Methods – Example 7-6

	Original		Later		BrRatio Method			End Ratio Method								Location of Obstruction
Duct	SP_{b0}	SP_{end0}	SP_{b2}	SP_{end2}	$BrRatio_0$	$BrRatio_2$	%Change	Upstream	SP_{endA_0}	SP_{endB_0}	$Ratio_0$	SP_{endA_2}	SP_{endB_2}	$Ratio_2$	%Change	
1-A	3.52	4.51	3.83	5.17	0.78	0.74	-5%									
2-B	1.71	2.04	1.76	2.39	0.84	0.74	**-12%**									Branch
3-B	1.48	2.05	1.74	2.38	0.72	0.73	1%									
5-D	1.31	1.89	0.94	1.33	0.69	0.71	2%									
7a-D	1.64	1.93	1.16	1.43	0.85	0.81	-5%									
8-F	2.05	3.17	2.31	3.53	0.65	0.65	1%									
9-F	1.83	2.69	2.2	2.89	0.68	0.76	**12%**									Branch
10-J	2	2.61	2.33	2.87	0.77	0.81	6%									
12-J	1.59	2.18	1.67	2.47	0.73	0.68	-7%									
7b-G	1.61	2.69	1.81	2.96	0.60	0.61	2%									
B-A	3.83			4.34				2-B, 30B	2.04	2.05	0.53	2.39	2.38	0.55	3%	
C-A	4.18			4.55				1-A, B-A	4.51	3.83	1.00	5.17	4.34	1.05	5%	
D-C	3.73			4.15				5-D, 7a-D	1.89	1.93	0.51	1.33	1.43	0.33	**-35%**	Submain
C-E	3.91			4.52				A-C, D-C	4.18	3.73	1.01	4.55	4.15	0.96	-5%	
F-G	2.92			3.38				8-F, 9-F	3.17	2.69	1.00	3.53	2.89	0.95	-5%	
G-E	3.59			4.01				7b-G, F-G	2.69	2.92	0.78	2.96	3.38	0.79	1%	
J-H	3.67			3.99				10-J, 12-J	2.61	2.18	0.65	2.87	2.47	0.67	3%	
E-H	4.02			4.39				G-E, C-E	3.59	3.91	0.93	4.01	4.52	0.97	4%	
H-K	4.61			5.48				J-H, E-H	3.67	4.02	0.83	3.99	4.39	0.76	-8%	
Air-Cleaner	8.55			8.31				H-K	4.61		0.54	5.48		0.66	22%	False positive?
Fan Inlet	8.63			8.4				Air-Cleaner	8.55		0.99	8.31		0.99	0%	
Fan	8.54			8.45				Fan Inlet	8.63		1.01	8.4		0.99	-2%	
Fan Exhaust	0.44			0.55				Fan	8.63			8.4				

TABLE 7-12. Branch Ratio and End Ratio Methods - Example 7-7

Branch Ratio Method

Duct	SP_{h0}	SP_{end0}	SP_{h2}	SP_{end2}	$BrRatio_0$	$\%BrRatio_2$	%Change	Location of Obstruction
	(Original)	(Original)	(Later)	(Later)				
1-A	3.52	4.51	2.5	4.45	0.78	0.56	28%	Branch
2-B	1.71	2.04	1.65	2.11	0.84	0.78	7%	
3-B	1.48	2.05	1.44	2	0.72	0.72	0%	
4-A			2.02	4.45		0.45		
5-D	1.31	1.89	1.58	2.33	0.69	0.68	2%	
7a-D	1.64	1.93	1.59	2.38	0.85	0.67	21%	Branch
8-F	2.05	3.17	2.65	3.97	0.65	0.67	-3%	
9-F	1.83	2.69	2.34	3.33	0.68	0.70	-3%	
10-J	2	2.61	2.67	3.31	0.77	0.81	-5%	
12-J	1.59	2.18	1.97	2.7	0.73	0.73	0%	
7b-G	1.61	2.69	1.97	3.4	0.60	0.58	3%	
B-A		3.83		3.62				
A-C		4.18		5.08				
D-C		3.73		4.3				
C-E		3.91		4.82				
F-G		2.92		3.52				
G-E		3.59		4.58				
J-H		3.67		4.45				
E-H		4.02		5.09				
H-K		4.61		5.92				
Air-Cleaner		8.55		21.1				
Fan Inlet		8.63		21.84				
Fan		8.54		22.08				
FanExhaust		0.44		0.47				

End Ratio Method

Upstream	SP_{endA_0}	SP_{endB_0}	SP_{endC_0}	$Ratio_0$	SP_{endA_2}	SP_{endB_2}	SP_{endC_2}	$Ratio_2$	%Change	Location of Obstruction
2-B, 3-B	2.04	2.05		0.53	2.11	2		0.57	-6%	
1-A, B-A, 4-A	4.51	3.83		1.00	4.45	3.62	4.45	0.82	18%	Submain
5-D, 7A-D	1.93	1.93		0.52	2.38	2.38		0.55	-7%	
A-C, D-C	4.18	3.73		1.01	5.08	4.3		0.97	4%	
8-F, 9-F	3.17	2.69		1.00	3.97	3.33		1.04	-3%	
7b-G, F-G	2.69	2.92		0.78	3.4	3.52		0.76	3%	
10-J, 12-J	2.61	2.18		0.65	3.31	2.7		0.68	-3%	
C-E, G-E	3.91	3.59		0.93	4.82	4.58		0.92	1%	
E-H, J-H	4.02	3.67		0.83	5.09	4.45		0.81	3%	
H-K	4.61			0.54	5.92	4.45		0.28	48%	False Positive?
Air-Cleaner	8.55									
Fan inlet	8.63									
Fan	8.54									

Solution: Table 7-12 shows the Branch Ratio and End Ratio calculations. Since the new branch was added at the junction point A, the End Ratio for A-C averages the end static pressure for three branches (1-A, 4-A, and B-A).

The Branch Ratio method identifies potential problems in two branches (1-A and 7a-D). The End Ratio method suggests an obstruction in the submain A-C.

In the calculations, the End Ratio was occasionally greater than 1. However, the static pressure at the end of the leg should be less than the static pressure at the end of the submain, unless there is regain in the duct. Consequently, the End Ratio should be less than 1. When the End Ratio exceeds 1, the calculations indicate potential error in the measurements (as was introduced into the example).

TABLE 7-13. Action Threshold Limits for Equivalent Resistance Methods

Location	Parameter	Threshold	Action	If Increase	If Decrease
Hood	X_h	20%	Find alteration	Obstruction upstream of the hood	Leak upstream of the hood
Branch	X_{br}	20%	Find alteration	Obstruction between the hood and the end	Leak upstream of the hood or a leak between the hood and the end
Submain	X_{sub}	40%	Find alteration	Obstruction within the submain	Leak within the submain

VP_{inlet} = velocity pressure measured just upstream of the fan inlet

X_{inlet} = equivalent cumulative resistance upstream of the fan inlet

Hood: $X_h = \dfrac{-(SP_h + VP_h)}{VP_h}$ [7.5]

where: X_h = cumulative resistance upstream of the hood

Branch: $X_{br} = \dfrac{-(SP_{end} + VP_{end})}{VP_{end}}$ [7.6]

where: X_{br} = cumulative resistance of the branch upstream of "end"

Submain: X_{sub} =

$$\dfrac{Q_a(SP_a + VP_a) + Q_b(SP_b + VP_b) - Q_m(SP_m + VP_m)}{Q_m\,VP_m} \quad [7.7]$$

where:

X_{sub} = equivalent resistance of the volume bounded by cross-sections a, b, and m (see Figure 7-8)

a, b = cross-sections near the end of the upstream ducts terminating at the junction fitting

m = cross-section near the end of the Submain duct

7.9.3 Percent Change. For all of the various forms of equivalent resistance, an increase or decrease in resistance can indicate an unwelcome development. For that reason one should look at the percentage change in the parameter's values.

$$\%X = \left(\dfrac{X_2 - X_1}{X_1}\right) \times 100\% \quad [7.8]$$

where:

$\%X$ = percentage change in X for a section of a system

In evaluating changes to X values, judicious consideration can give additional information. For examples:

1) An obstruction upstream of h should increase X_h and X_{br} by about the same deviation (not percentage) since X_{br} includes the losses up to h. For example, an obstruction that increases X_h by 0.5 should also increase X_{br} by roughly 0.5. Thus, if X_h increases substantially and X_{br} does not, it is likely that SP_h was measured incorrectly or one of the X values was incorrectly calculated.

2) If X_h and X_{br} change by roughly the same percentage and the Branch Ratio (SP_h/SP_{end}) has changed little, the value of VP_h or VP_{end} is probably incorrect.

3) X_{sub} is less reliable than X_{br} because it is affected by errors or normal fluctuations in VP_a, VP_b, SP_a, SP_b, VP_m and SP_m. The uncertainty associated with a value of X_{sub} is high because it is computed using the difference between large numbers. This is especially true if X_{sub} is relatively small. To reduce false positives, it is important to consider not only the percentage change in X_{sub} but also the magnitude of the deviation. For example, if the observed value of X_{sub} increases from 0.15 to 0.30, the increase is 100%; however, the deviation is only 0.15, a small increase in observed resistance that could easily be due to measurement errors or normal system fluctuations.

4) Obstructions can be located by noting where X first increases. For example, if X_h has not changed and X_{br} has increased substantially, then the obstruction must be between h and end (assuming SP_{end} is correct).

7.9.4 Example 7-8: Equivalent Resistance Upstream of Fan, X_{inlet}. This example uses the duct layout as shown in Figure 7-6. Measurements were taken as shown in Table 7-14 which provides the observed fan inlet mean velocity pressure (VP) and SP_{end} values for times 1 and 2. By comparing the changes to X_{inlet}, it is possible to determine whether the reduction in fan airflow is due to changes in resistance in the system or to problems with the fan.

A 6% change in resistance to flow could be attributable to random measurement error or normal system fluctuations. In addition, it is unlikely that a 28% drop in VP (and thus a 15% change in fan airflow) could be produced by a 6% increase in resistance to flow. Hence, it is most likely that the problem is with the fan itself. Note, also, that lack of substantial change in X_{inlet} does not imply that nothing has changed anywhere in the duct system. For example, profound alteration to a single branch may have very small effects on X_{inlet} if there are many branches in the system. A small change in X_{inlet} does imply that any changes that did occur in the duct system upstream of the fan should have had little effect on fan output.

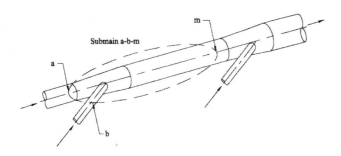

Submain a-b-m

FIGURE 7-8. Submain

7.9.5 Example 7-9: Equivalent Resistance of Branch.
Again the duct layout as shown in Figure 7-6 is used in this problem. Table 7-15 shows the measurements of the velocity pressures (VP) and SP_{end} for Times 1 and 2 in several duct branches. By comparing the changes to X_{br}, it is possible to determine which branches are most likely to have become obstructed or have been altered from Time 1 to Time 2.

The values of X_{br} changed from 5% to 43% from Time 1 to Time 2. Deviations that are above 20% are likely to correspond to significant obstructions or alterations. Branch 2-A showed a 26% drop in value, which indicates that between Times 1 and 2 a leak may have appeared, an obstruction was removed, or the duct was otherwise altered in a manner that reduced resistance to flow. The value of X_{br} for Branch 4-C increased substantially, which is consistent with an increase in resistance due to an obstruction or alteration.

7.9.6 Example 7-10: Equivalent Resistance of Submain.
The duct layout as shown in Figure 7-6 is also used in this problem. Measurements were taken as shown in Table 7-16 that provide the determination of airflows and measurement of SP_{end} in the ducts upstream of the junction fitting as well as measurement of SP_{end} in the submain. The observed velocity

pressures and SP_{end} values for the test system at Times 1 and 2 are shown in the table below. Both the magnitude and the percentage change in X_{sub} should be considered in assessing if possible blockages are present.

Example calculations:

For Submain A-B, $\Delta X_{sub} = 1.03 - 0.99 = 0.04$ %X_{sub}
$0.04/1.03*100 = 4\%$

For Submain C-D, $\Delta X_{sub} = 1.25 - 0.69 = 0.56$ %X_{sub}
$0.56/1.25*100 = 45\%$

For Submain B-D, $\Delta X_{sub} = 0.26 - 0.23 = 0.03$ %$X_{sub} = 0.03/0.23*100 = 13\%$

Note that it is convenient to list the product of Q and TP_{end} as well as Q and VP. For example, when computing the value of X_{sub} for the junction of Branches 2-A and 3-A with Submain A-B:

For Submain A-B:

$$X_{sub} = \frac{Q_{2-A}(TP_{2-A}) + Q_{3-A}(TP_{3-A}) - Q_{A-B}(TP_{A-B})}{Q_{A-B}(VP_{A-B})}$$

$$X_{sub_1} = \frac{-726 - 726 - (-3304)}{1805} = 1.03$$

$$X_{sub_2} = \frac{-362 - 422 - (-1891)}{1115} = 0.99$$

For Submain C-D:

$$X_{sub} = \frac{Q_{4-C}(TP_{4-C}) + Q_{5-C}(TP_{5-C}) - Q_{C-D}(TP_{C-D})}{Q_{C-D}(VP_{C-D})}$$

TABLE 7-14. Equivalent Resistance Method – Example 7-8

	Time 1			Time 2			Change	
ID Points	VP	SP_{end}	X_{inlet}	VP	SP_{end}	X_{inlet}	%X_{inlet}	Check fan or ducts?
H Fan inlet	0.95	- 8.01	7.43	0.68	- 6.02	7.85	6 %	fan

TABLE 7-15. Equivalent Resistance Method – Branch, Example 7-9

		Time 1			Time 2			Change	
ID	Type	VP	SP_{end}	X_{br}	VP	SP_{end}	X_{br}	%X_{br}	Check
1-B	Branch	1.95	- 4.38	1.25	1.28	- 3.02	1.36	9%	no
2-A	Branch	1.32	- 2.50	0.89	1.03	- 1.70	0.65	-26%	yes
3-A	Branch	1.32	- 2.50	0.89	0.89	- 1.72	0.93	6%	no
4-C	Branch	1.36	- 2.66	0.96	1.05	- 2.46	1.34	43%	yes
5-C	Branch	1.36	- 2.66	0.96	1.22	- 2.44	1.00	5%	no
6-E	Branch	1.78	- 5.23	1.94	1.19	- 3.73	2.13	11%	no

TABLE 7-16. Equivalent Resistance Method – Submain, Example 7-10

			Measured or given data					Calculated data, density factor = 1				
Time	ID	Type	Dia	Q	SP_{end}	V	VP	SP_{end}	$Q*TP_{end}$	$Q*VP$	Down to	X_{sub}
			inch	scfm	"wg	fpm	"wg	"wg				
1	1-B	Branch	9	2510	-4.38	5,681	2.01	-4.38	-5,943	5,051	Sub B-D	
2	1-B	Branch	9	2036	-3.02	4,609	1.32	-3.02	-3,453	2,696	Sub B-D	
1	2-A	Branch	5	637	-2.5	4,672	1.36	-2.5	-726	867	Sub A-B	
2	2-A	Branch	5	561	-1.7	4,114	1.06	-1.7	-362	592	Sub A-B	
1	3-A	Branch	5	637	-2.5	4,672	1.36	-2.5	-726	867	Sub A-B	
2	3-A	Branch	5	521	-1.72	3,821	0.91	-1.72	-422	474	Sub A-B	
1	A-B	Submain	7	1274	-4.01	4,767	1.42	-4.01	-3,304	1,805	Sub B-D	1.03
2	A-B	Submain	7	1085	-2.77	4,060	1.03	-2.77	-1,891	1,115	Sub B-D	0.99
1	4-C	Branch	6	933	-2.66	4,752	1.41	-2.66	-1,168	1313	Sub C-D	
2	4-C	Branch	6	817	-2.46	4,161	1.08	-2.46	-1,128	882	Sub C-D	
1	5-C	Branch	6	933	-2.66	4,752	1.41	-2.66	-1,168	1313	Sub C-D	
2	5-C	Branch	6	882	-2.44	4,492	1.26	-2.44	-1,043	1110	Sub C-D	
1	C-D	Submain	8	1874	-5.29	5,369	1.8	-5.29	-6,546	3367	Sub D-E	1.25
2	C-D	Submain	8	1703	-3.78	4,879	1.48	-3.78	-3,910	2527	Sub D-E	0.69
1	B-D	Submain	10	3803	-6.16	6,973	3.03	-6.16	-11,899	11527	Sub D-E	0.23
2	B-D	Submain	10	3129	-4.3	5,737	2.05	-4.3	-7,034	6420	Sub D-E	0.26

$$X_{sub_1} = \frac{-1168 - 1168 - (-6546)}{3367} = 1.25$$

$$X_{sub_2} = \frac{-1128 - 1043 - (-3910)}{2527} = 0.69$$

For Submain B-D:

$$X_{sub} = \frac{Q_{1-B}(TP_{1-B}) + Q_{A-B}(TP_{A-B}) - Q_{B-D}(TP_{B-D})}{Q_{B-D}(VP_{B-D})}$$

$$X_{sub_1} = \frac{-5943 - 3304 - (-11899)}{11527} = 0.23$$

$$X_{sub_2} = \frac{-3453 - 1891 - (-7034)}{6420} = 0.26$$

The results of computations shown on Table 7-16 indicate that Submain C-D (percentage change 45%) probably accrued an obstruction between Times 1 and 2. The conditions for other submains were probably unchanged (percentage change 4% and 13%, respectively).

7.9.7 Parameter Response to Alterations and Measurement Errors. In using the Pressure Ratio Methods and the Equivalent Resistance Method, one must be aware of the possibility of substantial measurement errors and fluctuations in the ventilations systems. Although it may be possible to measure static pressures and velocity pressures with less than 5% error under ideal conditions, in many real world situations the static pressure varies by a larger value. In addition, large errors may appear due to transcription mistakes, partial plugging of Pitot tubes, facing the Pitot tube in the wrong direction, instability in airflow, etc. For that reason, it is prudent to compare new parameter values to previous ones while taking the measurements. If the Branch Ratio, End Ratio, or X-value appears to vary outside the acceptance range, repeat the measurement. If a second set of measurements produces the same indication of substantial change, then there has probably been a change in resistance in the system due to a leak or obstruction.

Table 7-17 shows the response of different parameters to alterations and measurement errors.

7.10 TROUBLESHOOTING WHEN NO BASELINE EXISTS

Many ventilation systems are installed without adequate commissioning or even preliminary measurement of the installed systems. In spite of the important effect they will have on employee health and the high cost of installing and operating the systems, many companies turn them on and forget them. After time, a concern may develop and the systems require inspection and evaluation. The concern may develop because of the same reasons the system was first installed – operator complaints, elevated airborne exposures, OSHA citations, increased worker compensation claims, or corporate concern.

7.10.1 Initial Comparison. Since there is no baseline, there is no basis of comparison. Several approaches can be used to develop a Baseline for comparison.

1) Compare the system to existing drawings.

2) Compare the system to existing design calculations.

3) Compare the system to recommended approaches such as in *Industrial Ventilation: A Manual of Recommended Practice for Design.*

4) Compare the system to Permit Applications or Title V submissions.

5) Walk through the system and determine the required ventilation at each potential exposure point and estimate the needs of the system.

Once a basis of comparison is determined, the evaluation would consist of measuring the ventilation system to compare it to the existing system. The Baseline and the required measurements will depend on the available information and the amount of work required in obtaining the Baseline.

7.10.2 Compare the System to Existing Drawings. When drawings of the ventilation system are available, the first step is to see if the system was installed as designed. Reproduce the drawings and walk the system. Mark the drawings with changes and observations. Note apparent changes in the process and any additional potential sources. With significant emphasis on production rates, many plants have increased the contaminant generation rate without increasing the ventilation rates. Often line speeds change the required capture velocity, reducing the effectiveness of the exhaust ventilation. In addition, significant changes in the drawings indicate a change in the process or an installation modification by the contractor.

If the walkthrough shows major problems (disconnected duct, holes in the duct, major operator modifications to the hoods, etc.), fix the problems before conducting major measurements.

Once the drawings have been adequately marked (often called red lined), determine the appropriate airflow. Many drawings will indicate the volumetric flow at the hoods. In other situations an approximation can be made from the size of the connecting duct. In dust conveying systems, it is usual that the duct velocities are about 4000 fpm to prevent deposition of dust in the duct. Use the continuity equation ($Q = VA$) to estimate the volumetric flow at the hoods. For solvent systems, it is difficult to estimate the duct velocity. However, the duct velocity is often similar in all branches.

From the drawings and field observations determine the fan capacity. Most drawings will call out the make and model of the fan and the operating point (volumetric flow, fan static pressure, speed of rotation, and motor horsepower). Contact the fan manufacturer to obtain a fan curve for the operating conditions.

With the fan volumetric flow, compare the flow to the sum of the calculated volumetric flows at the hoods. If the values are close, the assumption on duct velocities is reasonable. If not, reconsider the duct velocity and recalculate the volumetric flow at the hood.

Measure the corresponding values in the system. Specifically, determine the volumetric flow at the hoods, the total flow through the system, the operating parameters of the fan (inlet and outlet static pressures, fan speed (rpm), motor amperage) and the volumetric flow and pressure drop at the air cleaning device. Often it is not much work, and can be very useful, to determine the static pressure at all the measuring points. Chapter 3 discusses method and instrumentation for ventilation measurements.

Compare the measured results to the calculated results. Since neither the ventilation measurements nor the rough calculations are exact, some disagreement is expected between the measurements and the calculated values. The critical observations and conclusion will depend on the system. However, some possibilities are:

1) If the fan is not performing on the fan curve:

   a. Check rotation of the fan (should have been done during the field inspection or measurements),

   b. Look for a system effect on the fan (see the chapter on Fans in *Industrial Ventilation: A Manual of Recommended Practice for Design*),

   c. The fan impeller may be eroded, corroded or have significant accumulations. In some fans, the position of the impeller relative to the inlet bell or housing of the fan can be critical to performance.

2) If the fan is performing on the fan curve but the volumetric flow is incorrect:

   a. An excessive fan inlet or outlet static pressure indicates an obstruction in the duct, poor adjustment of the dampers, duct diameters too small (resulting in high velocity pressures), or problems with the air cleaning device.

   b. An excessive volumetric flow indicates a hole in the duct, lower duct velocities than expected or incorrect operation of the air cleaning device.

3) If the sum of the parts does not approximate the total flow:

   a. Less total flow than the sum indicates measurement errors.

   b. More total flow than the sum indicates leakage in the system. Check for holes in the duct.

4) If the system has multiple dampers, the damper settings may be incorrect. Use the calculated volumetric flow and follow one of the procedures for damper adjustment described in Chapter 4.

5) If a branch flow is much different from the estimate:

   a. If one branch is higher, look for leakage in the branch.

   b. If one branch is lower, look of obstruction or damage to the duct, unusually high velocity in the

TABLE 7-17. Parameter Response to Alterations and Measurement Errors

Alteration	BranchRatio	EndRatio	X_h	X_{br}	X_{sub}	X_{inlet}
Branch ducts(h at hood, end at branch junction with submain)						
Obstruction upstream of h	+	0	+	+	0	Vs+
Obstruction between h & end	-	0	0	+	0	Vs+
Leak upstream of h	Vs+	0	-	-	0	Vs-
Leak between h & end	-	0	0	-	0	Vs-
Positive error in SP$_h$ meas	+	0	+	0	0	0
Negative error in SP$_h$ meas	-	0	0	0	0	0
Positive error in SP$_{end}$ meas	-	+ or -	0	+	-	0
Neg. error in SP$_{end}$ meas	+	+ or -	0	-	+	0
Positive error in VP	0	0	-	-	+	Vs-
Negative error in VP	0	0	+	+	-	Vs+
Submain ducts						
Obstruction upstream of end	0	+ or -	0	0	+	Vs+
Leak upstream of end	0	+ or -	0	0	-	Vs-

+ = Positive change
– = Negative change
Vs = Very small change, except possibly in very small systems
0 = No change

branch, or an additional branch added to the system.

7.10.3 Compare the System to Existing Design Calculations. If the design calculations are available, they could be used as an approximation to the Baseline. Care should be used while evaluating the calculations. If the system design balanced the system by increasing the volumetric flow in a branch, the calculation sheet may not have included the impact on the hood by adjusting the volumetric flow or hood static pressure. These changes may be assumed in the subsequent calculations without changing the values in the calculation sheet. For example, following the calculation sheet in *Industrial Ventilation: A Manual of Recommended Practice for Design*, the flows and static pressures are adjusted at the junction but not necessarily carried back to the values shown at the hoods. In such a case, the adjustments made at the branch need to be carried back to the hoods. This could be a series of calculations.

A second problem is the assumption that the calculation sheet matches the installed system. In the design process, revisions in the drawings frequently occur. The calculation sheets need to match the current revision. In the installation process, some changes could be made that are not reflected in the calculation sheets. Finally, the calculation sheets may be in error.

Use the predicted values from the calculation sheet to make a Baseline. Then continue as in Section 7.10.2.

7.10.4 Compare the System to Recommended Approaches Found in Industrial Ventilation: A Manual of Recommended Practice for Design. If there are no available drawings or calculations, the investigator should set a reference. The Ventilation Sketches (VS Prints) in *Industrial Ventilation: A Manual of Recommended Practice for Design* give a recommendation for hood volumetric flow and a formula for hood static pressure. Unfortunately, most operations do not have a corresponding VS Print. In some cases, similar operations provide a suggestion for the hood. In other cases, the investigator can apply an appropriate capture velocity to the hood to determine the flow. *Industrial Ventilation: A Manual of Recommended Practice for Design* discusses capture velocities and provides some information on converting a capture velocity to volumetric flow.

Once a Baseline is determined, and a sketch of the system developed, the system can be evaluated as described above.

7.10.5 Compare the System to Permit Applications or Title V Submissions. Often environmental regulations require installation and operating permits or reporting of the potential emission points. Such sources provide a gross description of the ventilation systems. Further analysis would require an approach as described above.

7.10.6 Determine the Required Ventilation at Each Potential Exposure Point. When all else fails, begin at the beginning. This approach essentially provides a concept design of the ventilation system. Sources such as *Industrial Ventilation: A Manual of Recommended Practice for Design* become essential in the process. The resulting Baseline may be very different from the original design. Comparison of the existing system to the concept design shows where significant differences exist and may allow focus on the highest priorities.

7.11   AIR HANDLING UNIT TROUBLESHOOTING

The supply system is critical to the performance of the exhaust systems. Trouble shooting the system is similar to an exhaust system. The most significant difference is that a supply system is positive pressure while the exhaust system should be negative pressure.

Table 7-18 shows some air handling unit problems and possible causes.

7.12   VALIDATION OF RESULTS

Following the completion of any corrective actions, the system performance will need to be validated. This step should include the measurement of volumetric flows and static pressures at the hoods, fan and selected branches; air temperature, air moisture, and barometric pressure; volumetric flow, inlet and out fan static pressure, fan speed, and motor amperage; and pressure drop across the air cleaning device after system adjustment and balancing. These readings will give the facility engineer/ventilation system designer confidence that the system has been properly restored to the desired conditions.

These measurements will also provide the baseline for future troubleshooting efforts. Therefore, it is critical to thoroughly document the system parameters at all important points throughout the system. It is also important to verify that the ventilation systems meet process needs.

The most critical validation procedure is the measurement of worker exposure. The local exhaust ventilation system exists to provide a healthy working environment for the employee. Worker exposure should be evaluated by a qualified industrial hygienist to verify that the measured concentration meets all applicable occupational exposure limits. Personal exposures should be collected in accordance with the methods documented by NIOSH/OSHA.

REFERENCES

7.1   Guffey, S.E; Booth, D.W.: An Evaluation of Industrial Ventilation Troubleshooting Methods in Experimental Systems. Am. Ind. Hyg. Assoc. J., Vol. 62, No. 6, pp. 671-679 (2001).

7.2   Booth, D.W; Guffey, S.E.: An Evaluation of Industrial Ventilation Branch Screening Methods for Obstructions in Working Exhaust Systems. Am. Ind. Hyg. Assoc. J., Vol. 62, No. 4, pp. 401-410 (2001).

7.3   Booth, D.W.; Guffey, S.E.: Field Evaluation of Methods for Determining the Obstructed Section of Branches of Industrial Ventilation Systems. Journal of Occupational and Environmental Hygiene, Vol. 1, No. 4 (April 2004).

7.4   Guffey, S.E.: Quantitative Troubleshooting of Industrial Exhaust Ventilation Systems. Appl. Occup. Env. Hyg., 9(4): 267-280 (1994).

TABLE 7-18. Air Handling Unit Troubleshooting

PROBLEM	CAUSE
Facility (room) static pressure very positive	Too much replacement air (relative to exhaust air). Replacement air fan greater than needed or fan rotating too fast. Rip or tear (blow by) in filter section (low differential pressure drop across filters) or air bypass through heating, cooling, or humidification section.
Facility (room) static pressure very negative	Too little replacement air (relative to exhaust air). Replacement air fan less than needed or fan rotating too slow. Clog in filters (high differential pressure drop across filters), clog in heating or cooling coils, or clog in humidification section.
Dirty replacement air	Dirty filters. Air bypassing filter section (rip or tears in filter). Dirty air handling cabinet housing.
Facility (room) temperature too high or low	Improper heating or cooling unit operation. Replacement fan not operating properly. Thermostat or controls?
Facility (room) humidity too high or low	Improper humidification equipment operation. Replacement fan not operating properly.
Visible mold or slime	Drain pans not operating properly or drain pans overflowing.

Chapter 8
MODIFYING INDUSTRIAL VENTILATION SYSTEMS

8.1   INTRODUCTION

Over the life of a typical industrial ventilation system, many changes can be made. New equipment arrives, obsolete equipment is removed, line speed increases, raw material or products are changed, changes in OSHA or environmental regulations occur, or the plant is reorganized for more efficient operation. Each time a change is made, new demands are placed on the industrial ventilation system. This chapter addresses guidelines for making changes to industrial ventilation systems without impairing or defeating the operation of the system.

8.1.1 Change Management. Just as changes in the process are not made without evaluating the consequences, it is necessary to ensure that changes made to the system or the manufacturing processes do not inadvertently compromise the ventilation systems. Things that can impact industrial ventilation system performance include changes in raw materials, formulations and operating conditions, as well as process equipment changes and exhaust ventilation system changes.

A good Change Management Program is one in which the Change Reviewer is seen as a resource and not as the enforcer of a set of rules. However, the most important objective at all times must be to ensure safe operations. For that reason, changes in the ventilation system should be reviewed and approved before they are implemented.

The industrial ventilation system Change Reviewer is the key to managing ventilation system modifications. This person must be knowledgeable in both the processes that are controlled and the systems and equipment designed to capture and control the contaminants. The ventilation system Change Reviewer must be able to recognize when changes can adversely impact the performance of a system and know when changes are needed and how to implement them to maintain the proper system performance.

The velocity pressure calculation sheets and the start up balance reports are the central documents of exhaust ventilation system change management. They provide design and actual values of system airflows and static pressures. They also provide details on fan operating parameters and balancing required to achieve the design values. These documents must be kept up to date and used to control changes to the industrial ventilation system.

8.1.2 The Characteristics of a Good Management System. The general characteristics of a Change Management System should include:

1. Workforce knowledge of Change Management System and commitment to use it
   - Importance to plant health and safety
   - How the Change Management System works
   - Technical resources available
   - Individual responsibilities
   - Periodic retraining

   - New hire training
2. Procedure for change management
   - All change proposals reviewed by the ventilation system Change Reviewer:
   - Reformulations
   - Minor equipment modifications
   - Simple and easy to use
   - Minimum request review and approval time
   - Backup when primary ventilation system Change Reviewer not available
3. Knowledgeable technical resources available
   - Plant process systems
   - Plant exhaust ventilation systems
   - Control technology
4. Verification and documentation of changes
   - Follow up on change requests
   - System design calculation, balance reports and other design information updated after changes
5. Auditing Change Management System performance
   - Annually by plant audit team
   - Audit results checked by Change Reviewer

8.2   MANAGING INDUSTRIAL VENTILATION CHANGES

Major project work is the easiest to control. The industrial ventilation system Change Reviewer should be a part of the approval process for the project. The final ventilation system construction authorization should not be given until the request has been reviewed and approved by the ventilation system Change Reviewer.

Minor modifications and maintenance changes are much more difficult to monitor and control because these do not have to be approved as projects do. When a project is completed under a maintenance budget or attached to a small equipment change, the change ventilation review process is often overlooked. These modifications can still cause problems.

All process changes should be reviewed by the ventilation system Change Reviewer. It is much better to take the time to review the numerous changes that may not increase the risk in a process rather than to have an apparently "minor" change slip through and cause an incident.

8.2.1 Activities That Challenge the Operation of a Change Management System. Certain activities often increase the level of risk of poor performance by the industrial ventilation system unless carefully controlled. These activities are discussed below.

Plant startup activities are times of rapid process and equipment change, often under extreme time pressures. Process changes often are made on an expedited basis and exhaust ventilation system change management might be compromised.

Formulation changes should be investigated for possible control implications. The most effective time to make input to formulation changes is before people are committed to making the change. Changes in raw materials, even "identical" raw materials from two different suppliers, may lead to different results.

Production rates can have a significant impact on contaminant generation or the effectiveness of the ventilation system. For example, increasing the line speed on a coating or impregnating process from 400 fpm to 500 fpm increases the application of coating (paint, resin, solvent, etc.) by 25%. If the same percent of contaminant escapes from the web, the potential release could increase by 25%. In addition, the windage at the hoods is increased with line speed, resulting in a reduction in the capture efficiency of the hood. The two factors can combine to increase operator exposures. In many cases, modifications to the ventilation system may be indicated. If the ventilation changes are considered during the process modification, they can be included in the capital authorization request. It is always easier to obtain funds when there is a corresponding increase in revenue. In addition, the entire cost of the project, including the ventilation changes, should be available to management when decisions are made.

8.3   VENTILATION CHANGE REVIEW

The industrial ventilation system Change Reviewer acts as a gatekeeper to evaluate whether or not the change request has the potential for ventilation system impact. When there is potential for an adverse impact, changes in the ventilation system must be made to maintain the proper system operation. When not sure of potential impact, involve an exhaust ventilation engineering resource for design expertise.

8.3.1 Information Gathering. To assess if potential changes will affect the ventilation system performance, the following information is needed:

- Description of the existing manufacturing process

- Description of existing ventilation systems, both supply and exhaust, with current static pressures, airflows, fan speed and fan amps, duct layout drawings, and details of the air cleaning devices

- Description of the proposed changes, including any new ingredient data, sketch of equipment changed and required opening sizes, sketch of hood/enclosure affected, Plant and Equipment Flowsheet, etc.

- Other pertinent information, such as studies or reports on similar production processes, ventilation system control equipment information, etc.

- Room Air Balance Diagrams for the areas with the exhaust ventilation system in question

8.3.2 Changes to the Manufacturing Process. Process/product modifications can affect the contaminant characteristics. Table 8-1 shows some considerations. If the process change significantly affects the characteristic of the contaminant, the ventilation system may require modification.

In addition, some process considerations exacerbate contamination generation.

1. Equipment motion can create air currents that in turn generate airborne dust.

2. Equipment motion, vehicular traffic and supply air can cause air currents that interfere with the collection efficiency of the exhaust hoods. Increasing production can often result in increasing room air currents.

3. Vehicular traffic can re-entrain spilled or deposited dust.

8.3.3 Changes to Local Exhaust Ventilation Systems. Examples of changes affecting hood and enclosure performance:

1. Modifying access doors or openings on an enclosure

2. Changing hood location relative to the contaminant source

3. Changing static pressure available to draw air into hood

Table 8-1. Changes to Process That Affect Contaminant Generation Rates

Dust:	*Liquids/mists:*	*Vapors:*
1. Product mass or volume flow increase	1. Volume throughout increases	1. Volume throughout increases
2. Particle size reduction	2. Greater system pressure	2. Higher temperature, closer to boiling point
3. Product becomes more fragile	3. Greater spills of liquid outside equipment	3. Greater volatility (i.e., higher Vapor Pressure)
4. Changes in moisture content	4. Lower liquid viscosity	4. Greater agitation or other mechanical work added
5. Product becomes stickier or moisture introduced	5. Greater liquid surface tension	

4. Increase in exhausted air without increase in makeup air to room

Examples of changes affecting duct system performance:

1. Inadequate ventilation system maintenance

2. Adding a duct branch to the system

3. Removing a duct branch from the system

4. Modifying a duct system

5. Throttling flow of a fan inlet

6. Sealing air bleed openings

7. Altering or removing flow control dampers

Examples of changes made that affect fan performance:

1. Duct system flow resistance difference

2. Fan speed

3. Air density

4. Fan throttling damper adjustment

Examples of changes in Indicators, Controls, and Interlocks that affect ventilation system performance:

1. Startup/shutdown sequence

2. Dust plugging of sensors used

3. Different logic for automatic and manual start/stop modes

8.4 INCREASING OR DECREASING THE SYSTEM AIRFLOW

Modifying the system airflow rate is perhaps the simplest change that can be made to a system. However, planning and analysis must be made to ensure that there will be no damage to the system components caused by the change.

Speeding up the fan and the corresponding airflow will increase the static pressure in the ducts. At higher speeds, the forces on the fan and bearings increase. At some point the higher speed can adversely affect the structural stability of the fan and bearings. The designer must check to see if the increased static pressure is within the design tolerance of the duct. The increased flow can overtax the fan motor, the electrical supply equipment, and/or the emission control equipment.

Slowing down the fan may reduce the hood volumes below the point where adequate capture can be maintained. Reduced duct velocity can allow particulate to accumulate and plug the branches.

8.4.1 Dampers. Increasing or decreasing the system volumetric flow may sometimes be accomplished by using dampers installed in the system. Many systems have an inlet or outlet damper installed on the fan. Adjustments to these dampers will affect the total system volume. Changing damper positions is generally a quick and easy way to change the volumetric flow over a limited flow range. The amount of flow

increase is determined by the starting and ending damper position. Because the dampers increase the resistance to the system, modifying the dampers may significantly increase the energy use for the system. Often, changing the fan speed by changing the sheaves and belts or using a variable frequency drive can reduce the operating costs with a short payback for the modifications.

Other systems may also have balancing dampers installed at each branch. These dampers may be effective at reducing the system volumetric flow somewhat, but will require a full system rebalance at the reduced volume. As described in Chapter 4, the insertion losses for a damper are not linear so increasing the insertion depth an equal amount in each damper is unlikely to produce the desired results.

8.4.2 Variable Frequency Drives and Belt Drive Changes. The best method for large changes in the total system volume is by changing the speed of the fan. This results in the most efficient use of energy for operating the fan. This change can be accomplished either by a change in the motor speed or by a change in the sheave diameters.

Over the past several years, technology improvements have made variable frequency drive units more affordable and appropriate for use on industrial ventilation systems. The variable frequency drive (VFD) unit allows the user to select the proper speed for operation of the exhaust system based on the conditions found during operation. This method is best suited for systems where the operating conditions change on a regular basis and constant control of the exhaust volume is required. Examples of this condition are a push-pull system where the amount of exhaust cannot drop below a certain value or there is a loss of capture, or a carbon bed filtration system where the final differential pressure on the filter media is several times the initial pressure.

In most cases, the fan speed is determined by the ratio of sheave sizes on a belt drive system. Changing the speed of the fan can only be accomplished by changing the sheaves and belts. At a one to one ratio, the fan impeller rotates at the same speed as the fan motor. If the fan sheave is larger than the motor sheave, the fan will run slower than the motor and conversely. Sizing fan sheaves and belts is a specialized task requiring some skill and experience. This work is generally done by a representative of the drive manufacturer. However, the ventilation engineer must be able to determine the speed ratio and determine the amount of power to be applied to the fan.

8.4.3 Determining the Revised Fan Speed. The revised fan speed is determined by using the fan laws. In an isothermal system, the change in fan speed is directly proportional to the change in volume. Therefore, a 5% increase in fan speed will result in a 5% increase in volumetric flow. On the other hand, the static pressure increases by the square and the system horsepower increases by the cube. The same 5% increase in fan speed will result in an increase in static pressure of 10%

and the power requirement (the brake horsepower) will increase by 16%.

The fan laws are presented here in a slightly different format than in Chapter 7 of *Industrial Ventilation: A Manual of Recommended Practice for Design.* In that chapter, the fan laws were used to show the difference in the fan curve and fan properties when the fan operating conditions change. In this chapter we are concerned with the effect that the fan changes will have on the system.

The change in system volume is proportional to the fan speed ratio.

$$\frac{Q_1}{Q_2} = \frac{RPM_1}{RPM_2} \qquad [8.1]$$

The system static pressure ratio is proportional to the square of the fan speed ratio.

$$\left(\frac{RPM_1}{RPM_2}\right)^2 = \frac{SP_1}{SP_2} \qquad [8.2]$$

The system power ratio is equal to the cube of the fan speed ratio.

$$\left(\frac{RPM_1}{RPM_2}\right)^3 = \frac{HP_1}{HP_2} \qquad [8.3]$$

For changes in density, the flows are not changed. However, both the static pressure and the power requirements change by the ratio of the densities.

In most cases, a change in the speed of the fan will act proportionally over the entire system as long as no resistances are changed in any of the branches. If the system volume is increased by 10%, then each individual branch volume will be increased by 10%. This does not occur in all cases. If the temperature of the various branches is changed by the changes in volume, the proportional amount of air from the branch will change as well. Consider a system that has one branch located at a hot source. As the exhaust volume increases, the air temperature from this hot source decreases (the heat loss is about the same but the mass of the airflow increases). The temperature change affects the density of the air and consequently the resistance to flow through the section and the mass flow rate of the air. The other hoods on the system are at ambient temperature. In this case, the volume from the hot source will not change proportionally to the other hoods. The hot branch will increase proportionately less than the other sources. This effect may be significant on systems with many sources operating at different volumes and temperatures. In that case, a full velocity pressure calculation should be used to determine the revised mix temperatures, operating static pressures and air densities.

Another time the flow change will not be proportional is when there is a source of significant non-turbulent resistance in the branch. An example of this effect can be found on sys-

tems where some of the hoods have pre-filters installed. The resistance on most kinds of filters increases in direct proportion to the increase in the flow rate (for example a 10% flow increase = 10% static pressure increase). The turbulent flows in these ducts increase resistance as the square to the change in volume (for example a 10% flow increase results in a 21% increase in static pressure). If the fan speed is increased on a system with filters on only some of the hoods, then the hoods with filters will receive a greater proportional increase in flow than the unfiltered hoods.

Another consideration is the air cleaning device. The pressure drop across the fabric filter is affected by the flow, but also by the dust cake. The frequency and duration of the cleaning cycle can maintain a preset pressure drop independent (within limits) of the volumetric flow through the system. The pressure drop across some scrubbers depends on the water level in the scrubber, not the volumetric flow.

The first task is to determine if the equipment is adequately sized to handle the additional load. Fans, dust collectors and other control devices will usually operate over a range of airflows and contaminant loadings. The additional load must be compared to the manufacturer's recommended operating capacity. The amount of air is the obvious factor, but changes in the level of contamination in the collected air and changes in the static pressure requirements are other factors that must be reviewed.

The fan must operate in the proper speed range as specified by the manufacturer. Excessive fan speed can lead to reduced bearing life, wheel imbalance and excessive vibration. In extreme cases, catastrophic failure can occur. The motor must be sized to handle the increased load.

An increase in fan speed, with no other changes to the system, will increase the static pressure in the ducts. The duct construction should be reviewed to ensure that the metal gauges and stiffeners are adequate for the increased pressure.

8.4.4 Example 8-1. At the commissioning of a new industrial ventilation system, it was found that field revisions to the duct reduced the system volume below the specification. The system was designed to operate at 20,000 acfm at 10 "wg static pressure. The measured operating volume was 18,000 acfm at 12 "wg. The operating power was measured at 22 hp.

1. What changes to the fan are needed if the fan is currently operating at 1460 rpm?

2. If the maximum safe speed of the fan is 1800 rpm, will the fan require replacement?

3. The motor is 30 hp. Will the motor require replacement?

Assume the system will follow the fan laws.

Solution

If the initial volume is 18,000 acfm at 1460 rpm, the revised fan speed will be 1460 rpm * (20,000 acfm/18,000 acfm) =

1622 rpm. The static pressure will be 12 "wg * (20,000 acfm/18,000 acfm)^2 = 14.81 "wg. The revised fan speed is lower than the maximum safe speed. The power requirement will increase equal to 22 hp * (20,000 acfm/18,000 acfm)^3 = 30.18 hp.

The power requirements are right at the listed power for the motor. The fan laws show the power required at the fan (brake horsepower). They do not show the required motor horsepower. If the fan is belt driven, there will be additional drive losses. As described in Chapter 6 of the 25th Edition of the Industrial Ventilation Manual, the losses for a 30 horsepower motor are between 3% and 7%. Consequently, the motor needs to operate between 31 and 32 horsepower. If the motor has a motor safety factor greater than 1.0, it should be able to operate at the small amount of overage calculated. The operating power should be measured after the change to ensure that the motor is not operated over the listed capacity (including the safety factor). If the motor must be replaced, the starters, disconnects, wiring and other electrical components must be reviewed to see if they meet the new power requirements.

Note: The duct construction should be reviewed to ensure that it is adequate for the increased static pressure. Details of duct construction are shown in several SMACNA publications (Sheet Metal and Air Conditioning Contractors Association.)[8.1, 8.2]

8.5   ADDING A DUCT BRANCH

One of the most common requests of the ventilation engineer is to add a new exhaust point (hood) to an existing industrial ventilation system. The task of the engineer is to determine if the requirements for the new exhaust point can be met by the current system.

8.5.1 Considerations. There are several important considerations when determining if an additional branch can be added to a system.

1. Can the conveying velocity be maintained in all branches of the system?

2. Will the velocity be excessive on all or part of the system?

3. What other hoods will be affected by the change to the system?

4. Is the air cleaning equipment sized to handle the additional airflow and contaminant load?

5. Does the fan speed need to be revised?

6. Are the fan, motor and electrical connections adequate for the changes?

All local exhaust hoods have a volumetric flow requirement and many exhaust systems have a minimum. In most cases, neither of these numbers is fixed, but includes a range of values. A revision to a ventilation system must maintain both the minimum transport velocities and the hood volumes for con-

tinued proper operation.

8.5.2 Procedure. The steps to add a hood to a system are:

1. Know the existing system. Determine the required volumes for each hood on the system. Determine the minimum conveying velocity. Determine the current volumetric flow and static pressure requirements for the system fan. Determine the operating range for the control equipment.

2. Review the abrasive qualities of the conveyed material to see if the revised velocity is too high.

3. Determine the airflow and static pressure requirements for the new hood.

4. Determine the optimum location for adding the branch.

5. Determine what changes to the branches or submains are needed to maintain proper velocity.

6. Determine if changes are needed for the fan and/or the control equipment.

8.5.3 Example 8-2. In Chapter 5 of the 25th Edition of the Industrial Ventilation Manual, the first example problem shows a dust collection system consisting of a single grinder hood. Figure 8-1 shows the system. This example examines what will happen if a second identical hood is added to the system. The modified system is also shown in Figure 8-2. The velocity pressure calculation sheet is modified to show the hood and duct as a second branch on the system.

Figure 8-2 is a calculation sheet for the original problem and the modified problem (Figure 8-1). Using the ventilation sketches in the Industrial Ventilation Manual, both Hood A and Hood A1 will require a nominal 390 acfm. If no other changes are made to the system, other than adding the branch shown in Figure 8-1, the velocity in the main branch (B1 to B) after the junction increases to 9610 fpm. The velocity pressure, assuming a density factor of 1, increases from 1.25 "wg to 5.76 "wg. The fan inlet static pressure changes from -6.19 "wg. to -15.71 "wg. The air to cloth ratio for the dust collector will double. The fan and collector will probably need to be changed, the duct velocity is excessive for grinding dust and the duct will need to be reinforced or replaced sooner. Simply adding another grinder severely compromises the existing system.

A second option for revising the system is to make changes to the duct so that a uniform velocity is maintained in the system. This arrangement is shown in Figure 8-3.

The revised velocity pressure calculation sheet is shown in Figure 8-4. In this case, the fan inlet system static pressure has been changed from -15.71 "wg to -7.04 "wg. However, the fabric filter and possibly the fan will still be undersized. This shows that even though the duct design is proper for the change, there are several other items that will require serious attention when changes are proposed.

8.5.4 Example 8-3. A new dust hood is required to control a bin. The airflow required is 450 acfm. The fabric filter dust

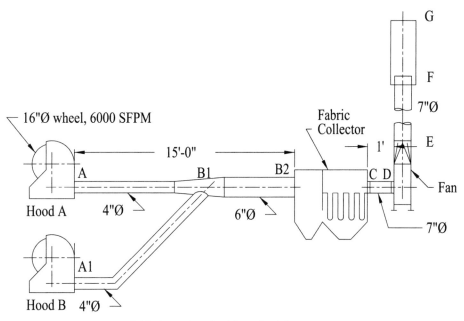

Added new hood with resized duct

FIGURE 8-1. Example 8-2 – Hood addition

collector has 160 bags, each bag has a 6" diameter and is 10 feet in length. The rectangular section of the collector is 10'-6" x 6'-0". The collector is shown in Figure 8-5. The material to be filtered doesn't change. The current airflow is 10,500 acfm with a fan static pressure of 9.2 "wg. The ductwork is redesigned so that the new operating parameters are 10,950 acfm with 10.6 "wg fan static pressure. The design limits for this dust in the collector are a 4.5:1 air to cloth ratio and a can velocity of 300 fpm. The fan has a maximum safe speed of 3350 rpm and a 25 hp motor. Is the collection equipment adequate for this application?

Solution

First, the changes to the fan must be determined. Since the revisions to the system change both the system and the fan operating parameters, the fan manufacturer must be contacted to determine if and how to change the fan to meet the new operating requirements. THE FAN LAWS CANNOT BE USED TO PREDICT THIS TYPE OF CHANGE. The fan manufacturer has determined that the new operating conditions will be a fan speed of 3024 rpm and 25.0 brake horsepower. Since the operating brake horsepower does not include drive losses, the actual power requirement will be 3% to 5% higher than the 25 horsepower needed for the fan. The motor is found to have a 1.1 service factor. This means that the motor is designed to provide up to 10% more power than the rated horsepower on a continuous basis. The motor is adequate and need not be changed.

The dust collector evaluation begins with determining the available filter area. The surface area (minus the bag ends) is calculated as the surface of a cylinder times the number of bags. Each bag has πDL square feet of media. This is computed as $\pi * 0.5$ ft $* 10$ ft $= 15.7$ ft^2 per bag. The total area is 15.7 ft^2 * 160 bags = 2512 ft^2. The air-to-cloth ratio is equal to the total system airflow divided by the filtration area. This is the new flow of 10,950 acfm by the filter area of 2512 ft^2. This equals 4.36:1. The air-to-cloth ratio is within the guidelines.

The can velocity is the updraft velocity at the base of the bags. *Note: Not all fabric filter collectors have updraft airflow to the filter media. Some collectors use an inlet on the side of the bag section and some use a downdraft flow. These collectors require an alternate internal flow analysis. Contact the manufacturer of these types of filter collectors for more information on recommended airflows.* To determine the can velocity, first the flow area must be determined. This is equal to the area of the cross–sectional area of the collector minus the cross sectional area of the bags. The collector has an area of 10.5 ft by 6 ft. The area is 63 ft^2. Each bag has an area of πr^2 or 0.1963 ft^2. For 160 bags the total bag area is 31.4 ft^2. The net area for airflow is 63 ft^2 minus 31.4 ft^2, or 31.6 ft^2. Since V = Q/A, the can velocity is 10,950/31.6 or 347 fpm. This is in excess of the maximum can velocity for this application. When the can velocity is exceeded, the collected dust is unable to fall to the collection hopper due to the high updraft velocity. If the collector is used as it is currently configured, the dust layer on the bags can thicken, increasing the filter resistance, this increases the system static pressure and reduces the airflow below design. In the worst case, the fabric filter can become plugged with dust and the airflow will drop to a frac-

ACGIH® Velocity Pressure Method Calculation Sheet Elevation (z) 0 ft   Date _____

Project Example 8-2 (Figures 8-1 and 8-2)   Designer _____

* Input Data
** Shaded lines 5, 6, 7, 8 & 14 are used for non-standard calculations
std is for standard calculations and nstd is for non-standard calculations
*** std is for standard calculations

Equations column:

1. $\omega = \#H_2O / \#Dry\ Air$
2. $df = df_e \cdot df_p \cdot df_t \cdot df_m$
   $df_e = [1 - (6.73 \times 10^{-6})(z)]^{5.258}$
   $df_p = (407 + SP)/(407)$
   $df_T = (530)/(T + 460)$
   $df_m = (1+\omega)/(1 + 1.607\omega)$
3. $Q_{duct} = Q[(1+\omega)/df]$
4. $V = 4005\sqrt{VP/df}$
5. $VP = df(V/4005)^2$
6. 90 Deg Elbow Loss Coefficients (5 Piece)

R/D	Fel
1.5	0.24
2.0	0.19
2.5	0.17

7. Branch Entry Loss Coefficients

Angle	Fen
15°	0.09
30°	0.18
45°	0.28

8. $F_d\left(\frac{metal}{plastic}\right) = 0.0307(V^{0.533}/Q^{0.612})$
   $F_d(flexible) = 0.0311(V^{0.604}/Q^{0.639})$
9. $VP_r = (Q_1/Q_3)(VP_1) + (Q_2/Q_3)(VP_2)$
10. $Q_{corr} = Q_{design}\sqrt{SP_{gov}/SP_{duct}}$
11. SYSTEM SP = $SP_{out} - SP_{in} - VP_{in}$
    SYSTEM SP provides the FAN SP for fan selection (see 5.8.4)

1-A (2) Row 31: See Appendix A.5.1

Col				Original System				Added Branch					
				A-B	B-C	C-D	E-F	A-B1	A1-B1	B1-B	B-C	C-D	E-F
1*	Duct Segment Identification												
2*	Dry-Bulb Temperature	T	F	70	70	70	70	70	70	70	70	70	70
3*	Flow Rate (Dry Air)	Q	scfm	390	390	390	390	390	390	836	836	836	836
4*	Minimum Transport Velocity	V_t	fpm	4000	4000	3000	3000	4000	4000	4000	3000	3000	3000
5*	Lbs Water per minute	$\dot{m}_{H_2O}$	#H₂O/min										
6*	Lbs Dry Air per Minute	$\dot{m}_{da}$	#da/min										
7	Density Factor	df	Eqn 2	1	1	1	1	1	1	1	1	1	1
8	Duct Flow Rate	Q_{duct}	acfm	390	390	390	390	390	390	836	836	836	836
9	Target Duct Area	A_t	(3/4std)(8/4nstd)	ft²	0.098	0.098	0.130	0.130	0.098	0.098	0.209	0.279	0.279	0.279
10	Selected Diameter	d	inches	4		5	5	4	4	4	5	5	5
11	Selected Duct Area	A	ft²	0.087		0.136	0.136	0.087	0.087	0.087	0.136	0.136	0.136
12	Duct Velocity	V_d	(3/11std)(8/11nstd) fpm	4483		2868	2868	4483	4483	9613	6149	6149	6149
13	Duct Velocity Pressure	VP_d	Eqn 5	"wg	1.25		0.51	0.51	1.25	1.25	5.76	2.36	2.36	2.36
14*	Total Heat	h	branch balance	btu/#da ft³									
15*	Slot Area	A_s	ft²										
16*	Slot Loss Coefficient	F_s	VP/slot										
17*	Acceleration Factor		0 or 1										
18	Slot Velocity	V_s	(3/15std)(8/15nstd) fpm										
19	Slot Velocity Pressure	VP_s	Eqn 5	"wg									
20	Slot Loss in VP		16+17	VPtotal									
21	Slot Static Pressure	SP_s	20x19	"wg									
22*	Hood Entry Coefficient	F_h	VP/hood			0.5		0.65	0.65			0.5	0.5
23*	Acceleration Factor		1 or 0			1		1	1			1	1
24	Hood Entry Loss in VP		22+23	VPtotal			1.5		1.65	1.65			1.5	1.5
25	Hood Entry Loss		24x13	"wg			0.77		2.06	2.06			3.54	3.54
26	Other Losses			"wg										
27	Hood Static Pressure	SP_h	21+25+26	"wg			0.77		2.06	2.06			3.54	3.54
28*	Straight Duct Length	L	ft	15		1	10	10	15	5		1	10
29*	Duct Friction Factor	F_d	Eqn 8	VP/ft	0.0704		0.0555	0.0555	0.0704	0.0704	0.0663		0.0523	0.0523
30*	No. of 90 Degree Elbows									0.5				
31*	Elbow Loss Coefficient	F_{el}	Table 6	VP/90°el					0.19					
32*	Branch Entry Coefficient	F_{en}	Table 7	VP/en					0.28					
33*	Special Fitting Coefficient			VP										
34	Duct Friction Loss in VP		28x29	VP	1.06		0.06	0.56	0.70	1.06	0.33		0.05	0.52
35	Elbow Loss in VP		30x31	VP	0				0	0.10				
36	Duct Loss in VP		32+33+34+35	VP total	1.06		0.06	0.56	0.70	1.44	0.33		0.05	0.52
37	Duct Loss		36x13	"wg	1.33		0.03	0.29	0.88	1.79	1.9		0.12	1.23
38	Other Losses			"wg		2					2			
39	Weighted Average VP	VP_r	Eqn 9	"wg						1.46				
40	Loss From Velocity Increase		13-39(if>0)	"wg						4.30				
41	Segment Pressure Loss		27+37+38+40	"wg	-3.39		-0.80	0.29	-2.94	-3.85	-6.20		-3.66	1.23
42	Governing Static Pressure	SP_{gov}		"wg	-3.39	-5.39	-6.19	0.29	-3.85	-3.85	-10.06	-12.05	-15.71	1.23
43	Cumulative Static Pressure	SP_{cum}		"wg	-3.39	-5.39	-6.19	0.29	-2.94	-3.85	-10.05	-12.05	-15.71	1.23
44	Corrected Volumetric Flow	Q_{corr}	Eqn 10	acfm					446	390	836	836	836	836
45	Corrected Velocity	V_{corr}	44/11	fpm					5130	4483	9613		5130	6149
46	Corrected Velocity Pressure	VP_{corr}	Eqn 5	"wg					1.64	1.25	5.76			2.36
			Column Number	A-B	B-C	C-D	E-F	A-B1	A1-B1	B1-B	B-C	C-D	E-F

FIGURE 8-2. Calculation Sheet for revised system for Example 8-2

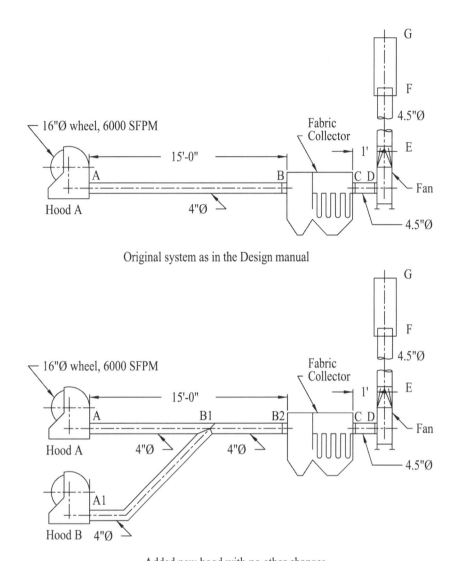

Original system as in the Design manual

Added new hood with no other changes

FIGURE 8-3. Example 8-2 – Duct revision for uniform transport velocity

tion of the intended flow rate.

Even though the air to cloth ratio is within the system design limits, the high can velocity will require changes to the collector in order for the system to continue to operate properly.

8.6   REMOVING A DUCT BRANCH

The changes to remove a hood are much simpler.

8.6.1 Air Bleed In. The simplest way to remove a hood is to disconnect the branch and install an air bleed to take the place of the hood. The air bleed has a damper or orifice plate to simulate the resistance of the removed branch. Thus the airflow through the system remains the same after the hood is no longer used. Leaving an open duct with no added resistance will draw in too much air and disrupt the operation of the other hoods on the system.

8.6.2 Capped Hood. The hood may be capped to reduce energy usage or to improve the operation of the control equipment as long as duct transport velocity is not compromised. This may require re-sizing the duct main, replacing the sheaves and belts on the fan, and may possibly require changes to the control equipment.

8.6.3 Example 8-4. A table saw is removed from a dust collection system in a woodshop. The saw currently exhausts 550 acfm. The system's total volume before the change was 17,650 acfm. The fan operates at a static pressure of 12 "wg. The table saw branch is not the governing leg and the static pressure for the governing leg will not change significantly if the volume is reduced. The table saw is the last branch before the collector and the main is 28" in diameter. The conveying velocity is 4000 fpm. Will any changes be required if this branch is capped?

ACGIH® Velocity Pressure Method Calculation Sheet   Elevation (z) 0 ft   Date _____

Project Example 8-2 (Figures 8-1 and 8-2)   Designer

* Input Data
** Shaded lines 5, 6, 7, 8 & 14 are used for non-standard calculations
*** std is for standard calculations and nstd is for non-standard calculations

See Figure 8-1

Line	Symbol	Description	Basis / Eqn	Units	A-B1	A1-B1	B1-B	B-C	C-D	E-F
1*		Duct Segment Identification								
2*	T	Dry-Bulb Temperature		F	70	70	70	70	70	70
3*	Q	Flow Rate (Dry Air)		scfm	390	390	836	836	836	836
4*	V_t	Minimum Transport Velocity		fpm	4000	4000	4000	4000	3000	3000
5*	$\dot{m}_{H_2O}$	Lbs Water per minute		#H2O/min						
6*		Lbs Dry Air per Minute		#da/min						
7	df	Density Factor	Eqn 2		1	1	1	1	1	1
8	Q_{duct}	Duct Flow Rate	Eqn 3	acfm	390	390	836	836	836	836
9	A_t	Target Duct Area	(3/4std)(8/4nstd)	ft2	0.098	0.098	0.209	0.209	0.279	0.279
10	d	Selected Diameter		inches	4	4	6	7	7	7
11	A	Selected Duct Area		ft2	0.087	0.087	0.196	0.267	0.267	0.267
12	V_d	Duct Velocity	(3/11std)(8/11nstd)	fpm	4483	4483	4267	3132	3132	3132
13	VP_d	Duct Velocity Pressure	Eqn 5	"wg	1.25	1.25	1.14	0.61	0.61	0.61
14*	h	Total Heat	branch balance	btu/#da						
15*	A_s	Slot Area		ft2						
16*	F_s	Slot Loss Coefficient		VP/slot						
17*		Acceleration Factor		0 or 1						
18	V_s	Slot Velocity		fpm						
19	VP_s	Slot Velocity Pressure	(3/15std)(8/15nstd)	fpm						
20		Slot Loss in VP	16+17	VPtotal						
21	SP_s	Slot Static Pressure	20x19	"wg						
22*	F_h	Hood Entry Coefficient		VP/hood	0.65	0.65			0.5	
23*		Acceleration Factor		1 or 0	1	1			1	
24		Hood Entry Loss in VP	22+23	VPtotal	1.65	1.65			1.5	
25		Hood Entry Loss	24x13	"wg	2.06	2.06			0.92	
26		Other Losses		"wg						
27	SP_h	Hood Static Pressure	21+25+26	"wg	2.06	2.06			0.92	
28*	L	Straight Duct Length		ft	10	15	5		1	10
29*	F_d	Duct Friction Factor	Eqn 8	VP/ft	0.0704	0.0704	0.043		0.0365	0.0365
30*		No. of 90 Degree Elbows				0.5				
31*	F_{el}	Elbow Loss Coefficient	Table 6	VP/90° el		0.19				
32*	F_{en}	Branch Entry Coefficient	Table 7	VP/en		0.28				
33*		Special Fitting Coefficient		VP						
34		Duct Friction Loss in VP	28x29	VP	0.7	1.06	0.22		0.04	0.37
35		Elbow Loss in VP	30x31	VP	0	0.10				
36		Duct Loss in VP	32+33+34+35	VP total	0.7	1.44	0.22		0.04	0.37
37		Duct Loss	36x13	"wg	0.88	1.79	0.25		0.02	0.23
38		Other Losses		"wg				-2		
39	VP_r	Weighted Average VP	Eqn 9	"wg						
40		Loss From Velocity Increase	13-39(if>0)	"wg						
41		Segment Pressure Loss	27+37+38+40	"wg	-2.94	-3.85	-0.25	-2	-0.94	0.23
42	SP_{gov}	Governing Static Pressure		"wg	-3.85	-3.85	-4.10	-6.10	-7.04	0.23
43	SP_{cum}	Cumulative Static Pressure		"wg	-3.85	-3.85	-4.10	-6.10	-7.04	0.23
44	Q_{corr}	Corrected Volumetric Flow	Eqn 10	acfm	446	390	836	836	836	836
45	V_{corr}	Corrected Velocity	44/11	fpm	5130	4483	4267	3132	3132	3132
46	VP_{corr}	Corrected Velocity Pressure	Eqn 5	"wg	1.64	1.25	1.14	0.61	0.61	0.61
		Column Number			A-B1	A1-B1	B1-B	B-C	C-D	E-F

Formula reference column:

1* — $\omega = \#H_2O / \#\text{Dry Air}$

2* — $df = df_e \cdot df_p \cdot df_T \cdot df_m$
$df_e = [1-(6.73\times10^{-6})(z)]^{5.258}$
$df_p = (407 + SP)/(407)$
$df_T = (530)/(T+460)$
$df_m = (1+\omega)/(1+1.607\omega)$

3* — $Q_{duct} = Q\left((1+\omega)/df\right)$

4* — $V = 4005\sqrt{VP/df}$

5* — $VP = df(V/4005)^2$

6* — 90 Deg Elbow Loss Coefficients (5 Piece)

R/D	Fel
1.5	0.24
2.0	0.19
2.5	0.17

7 — Branch Entry Loss Coefficients

Angle	Fen
15°	0.09
30°	0.18
45°	0.28

8 — $F_{d\,(metal)} = 0.0307(V^{0.533}/Q^{0.612})$
$F_{d\,(plastic/flexible)} = 0.0311(V^{0.604}/Q^{0.639})$

9 — $VP_r = (Q_1/Q_3)(VP_1) + (Q_2/Q_3)(VP_2)$

10 — $Q_{corr} = Q_{design}\sqrt{SP_{gov}/SP_{duct}}$

11 — SYSTEM SP = $SP_{out} - SP_{in} - VP_{in}$
SYSTEM SP provides the FAN SP for fan selection (see 5.8.4)

1-A (2) Row 31: See Appendix A.5.1

FIGURE 8-4. Calculation Sheet for revised system for Example 8-2

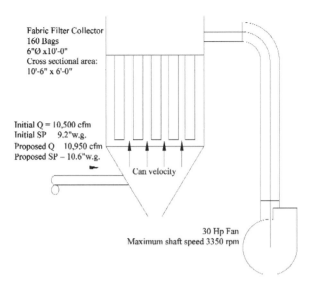

FIGURE 8-5. Fabric filter for Example 8-3

Solution

If the branch is capped, the volume in the main will be 17,650 acfm - 550 acfm = 17,100 acfm. The 28" main has an area of 4.276 ft². Using the formula V = Q/A the revised duct velocity will be 3999 fpm. Since this is only 1 fpm less than the minimum conveying velocity, the velocity should be adequate. The fan will now operate at 17,100 acfm at 12 "wg. Since this change does not follow the fan laws, the fan manufacturer should be contacted for a revised fan speed. If a fan inlet damper is installed, the damper can be used to reduce the flow rate with only a small penalty in operating power.

8.6.4   Example 8-5. A machine hood operating at 1250 acfm is located at the end of a branch with four other hoods. This branch is not the governing leg. If the machine is removed and the inlet is capped, the rest of the branch will operate below the minimum conveying velocity. A contractor has estimated that the replacement duct will cost $22,000 to fabricate and install. The fan power requirement will drop from 32 bhp to 29 bhp. The system operates 2000 hours per year. The cost of electricity is 7.5 cents per kilowatt hour. If the company standard payback period is one year, should the branch be changed, or should air be bled into the system where the hood was installed?

Solution

The energy savings is 3 hp or 2238 watts. Over a one year period the energy cost is [2238 Watts * 2000 hours/1000 W/kW]*0.075 cents / kWh = $335. The cost of the duct revision would have a 66 year payback. The duct change should not be made and air should be bled into the duct where the hood was installed previously.

An option would be to use the additional air to increase the hood volumes at the other hoods on the branch. Since this is not the governing leg, some or all of the removed volume may

be used at the other hoods on the branch without affecting system performance. Note: A change of this type will have an effect on the conveying velocity in portions of the branch. Review the air distribution to ensure that no section conveying particulate falls below the minimum conveying velocity established for the conveyed dust.

8.7   INCREASE OPENING ON ENCLOSING HOOD

8.7.1   Procedure. If the opening to an enclosing hood is enlarged, the amount of air exhausted from the hood should be increased to maintain the same capture velocity. The opening may be changed for better access to the equipment in the enclosure, to provide better exhaust of the process, or to allow larger items to enter and exit the enclosure. The relationship between the opening size and airflow is proportional to the size of the opening. The formula is as follows:

$$Q_2 = Q_1 * (A_2/A_1) \hspace{2cm} [8.4]$$

where:

> Q_1 is the original volume
> Q_2 is the revised volume
> A_1 is the original area
> A_2 is the revised area

Once the revised volume is calculated, the steps outlined in the previous sections should be followed to correct the system volume.

8.7.2   Example 8-7. A new part is to be painted in an automated paint booth. The part is larger than the old part and the entrance and exit to the booth must be increased in size from 12" x 12" to 12" x 24". The booth has a regulatory requirement that the in draft velocity will be 200 fpm. There are other openings into the booth totaling 2.5 ft².

The original volume is equal to 200 fpm times the open area. The inlet and outlet were 1 ft² each so the total open area was 4.5 ft². This area equates to an exhaust volume requirement of 900 acfm. The new openings add two additional square feet to the current openings. This increases the area to 6.5 ft². The revised volume is 1300 acfm.

The volumetric flow increase will be about 45%. If there are no changes in the duct, the resistance in the duct will more than double. The required fan horsepower (from HP = TP*Q/η*6345, η is the fan efficiency and TP is the total pressure for the system) will increase by a factor of three. Unless the fan and motor were significantly oversized, they will likely require replacement.

8.7.3   Non-enclosing Hoods. The procedure for a non-enclosing hood is similar. However, the capture velocity is not a face velocity as it is in an enclosing hood. In a capture hood, the contaminants are generated outside the hood. For several types of hoods, the Industrial Ventilation Manual provides formulas relating the capture velocity with the volumetric flow required to achieve the capture velocity.

8.8   MOVING A HOOD IN RELATION TO THE DUST SOURCE

Moving a hood in relationship to the dust source will affect the volume of air required to properly exhaust the source. The revised hood volume can be calculated using the concepts in Chapter 3 of the 25th Edition of the Industrial Ventilation Manual. Figures 3-8 to 3-11 in that Manual show the relationship between hood volume and capture velocity. As the distance from the hood increases, the volume increases by various amounts depending on the hood type. In most cases, this is considerably more than a proportional amount. If the hood is moved closer to the source, significantly less air may be required. Even less air will be required if the open hood is changed to an open faced enclosure that surrounds the contaminant source.

The steps to determine the revised volume to maintain the current level of capture velocity are:

1. Measure the hood airflow, or determine the airflow from records of system performance.

2. Measure the distance from the source to the hood.

3. Calculate the current capture velocity.

4. Pick the new hood location.

5. Using the calculated capture velocity, recalculate the hood volume using the revised distance in the formula.

8.8.1 *Example 8-8.* A change to a piece of equipment has required that a plain end hood has to be moved from 16" to 24" from a source. The hood inlet is 6" in diameter and has a current exhaust volume of 785 acfm.

To determine the new volume, first determine the current capture velocity. The formula for a plain end hood is $Q = V(10X^2 + A)$. Rearranging the formula to calculate the formula gives $V = Q/(10X^2 + A)$. So the result is $V = 785$ acfm/$(10*(16"/12")^2 + (0.1963\ ft^2)) = 44$ fpm. Plugging this result and the new distance into the original formula results in a new hood volume of $Q = 44fpm\ (10*2^2 + .1963) = 1768$ acfm. This is an increase of 2.25 times the original volume.

If the conveying velocity in the duct was 4000 fpm, the new duct size will be 9" diameter. If possible, the hood should be increased in size to match the duct. This will have a small effect on the revised volume. Using the new hood size (9" diameter) in the formula, the hood volume is 1779 acfm.

REFERENCES

8.1   Sheet Metal and Air Conditioning Contractors' National Association, Inc.: Round Industrial Duct Construction Standards, Second Edition, Chantilly, Virginia, 1999.

8.2   Sheet Metal and Air Conditioning Contractors' National Association, Inc.: Rectangular Industrial Duct Construction Standards, Second Edition, Chantilly, Virginia, 2004.

Chapter 9
OPERATOR SKILLS AND TRAINING

9.1   INTRODUCTION

Industrial Ventilation System performance can drop to unacceptable levels due to special causes, i.e., the system ingests a plastic bag, or due to gradual degradation such as duct plugging. In either case, trained operators are needed to maintain the systems and correct developing problems. This chapter describes several of the functional roles that should be available at a plant with industrial ventilation systems.

Individuals in these roles work in the site's operations or maintenance departments and function at five levels of increasing skill. Each level builds on the one before it and has a minimum skill sets list. Some plants may choose to employ one individual with all five levels of skill. Other sites may choose to employ different individuals or teams of individuals with different combinations of skill levels. This is based on system management strategies.

Support roles and how they interface with system operators are also listed. In this section, the term "operators" refers to

- Individuals working around equipment served by an industrial ventilation system.

- Individuals working on a manufacturing process or in a shop facility that is served by the system but does not directly operate it.

- Individuals that have daily operating (and possibly some maintenance) responsibility for one or more industrial ventilation systems.

- Individuals that have operating, monitoring, and possibly maintenance responsibility for one or more industrial ventilation system(s).

- Individuals who are responsible for ensuring successful alterations to industrial ventilation systems.

Their suggested skill levels are referenced as well. There is also some guidance to training coordinators.

This section only addresses the ventilation training aspects for each skill level. It is expected that the Company will need to develop other training modules to address other potential hazards that arise during the testing and repair of ventilation systems in their own plant.

9.2   FUNCTIONAL ROLES

9.2.1 Operators Require Basic Skill Sets. Successful long-term operation of Industrial Ventilation Systems within the original design parameters requires trained and skilled system operators. These personnel should have clear responsibilities for operation and maintenance, appropriate skill training and sufficient time to do the work. Site management should support the operators, who frequently are serving in an auxiliary role operating a utility system rather than their main job function.

Industrial ventilation system performance begins to degrade as soon as contaminants such as dusts, mists, or vapors are pulled through them. System operators or technicians should understand how the industrial ventilation systems interact with the process, how they function, how to perform routine system monitoring and maintenance and how to correctly make changes to the systems.

Without proper training, it may not be obvious what is important to the successful operation of an industrial ventilation system. Studies show that untrained operators frequently assume that the contaminant-collecting device is the cause of all the problems. Experience shows that most problems begin with the duct network. This Manual provides training on how to use system measurements during operation (rather than direct duct inspection during shutdowns) to determine where to intervene in the system while the problem is still a small one.

Five functional roles of increasing responsibility describe how individuals interact with industrial ventilation systems in their workplace. These are not hard and fast role descriptions into which people must be placed. Depending on the size and complexity of the system, individuals might have more than one of these roles or there may be several individuals with the same skill level.

The skills and associated training materials for each of the role descriptions below are described in the Training Guides included in this section. Training Guides fit into two categories:

1) Local Exhaust Ventilation Operators, Levels 1 through 5 (Tables 9-1 through 9-5), and

2) Air Cleaning Device information for System Operators, Levels 1 through 5 (Table 9-6).

The two categories allow for flexibility to focus the training on total system operation or specifically on the Air Cleaning Devices that are in place at the site.

The skill requirements are shown in the following table as well as the sources for other training information. The tables were prepared based on the assumption that system operators have access to vendor's drawings, specifications, and training and operations manuals.

System operators who discover unacceptable emissions situations (i.e., dust leaks from baghouses, ducts) should report them to management or as directed by management as soon as the problem is discovered so appropriate action can be taken.

9.3   SKILL LEVEL 1: GENERAL AWARENESS

Plant Managers, Production Managers, maintenance personnel, cleanup personnel and other individuals who work around equipment served by an industrial ventilation system must be aware of how the system functions.

A basic knowledge of terminology, how systems operate and general airflow principles are included (see Table 9-1).

9.4   SKILL LEVEL 2: SYSTEM USER

A system user works on a manufacturing process or in a shop facility that is served by the system but does not directly operate it. The individual should be aware of how Industrial Ventilation Systems provide protection at the workstations in the area and should be aware who to communicate operational problems to (this would include process or machine operators and maintenance shop personnel). Table 9-2 assumes completion of Skill Level 1.

9.5   SKILL LEVEL 3: INDUSTRIAL VENTILATION SYSTEM OPERATORS

An industrial ventilation system operator has daily operating, and possibly some maintenance responsibility for one or more industrial ventilation systems. This includes recording routine monitoring data, performing scheduled and unsched-

uled maintenance, and communicating the need for corrective action to the system Troubleshooter when the action limits on the log sheet are exceeded. This assumes completion of Skill Level 1 and 2 (see Table 9-3).

9.6   SKILL LEVEL 4: INDUSTRIAL VENTILATION SYSTEM TROUBLESHOOTER

The Industrial Ventilation System Troubleshooter may have operating, monitoring, and possibly maintenance responsibility for one or more industrial ventilation systems. This individual troubleshoots and corrects system problems and the role can include industrial ventilation system operators and Plant Engineering or Maintenance management responsible for local exhaust ventilation operation. This assumes completion of Skill Levels 1, 2 and 3 (see Table 9-4).

TABLE 9-1. Skill Level 1: General Awareness

An Operator Should Be Able To:	Sources of Training Information
Exhibit safe behavior around Industrial Ventilation Systems.	• Purpose of local exhaust system – Read "Introduction to Local Exhaust Ventilation Systems," Section A9.1 of the Training Appendix to Chapter 9. • Use general site training to describe the Air Cleaning Devices used at the site. • Plant describes its chemical/contaminant specific work practices for equipment operation and cleanup procedures. • Plant explains its change control system and procedure so that Industrial Ventilation Systems are changed correctly.

TABLE 9-2. Skill Level 2: System User

An Operator Should Be Able To:	Sources of Training Information (Assumes completion of Skill Level 1)
1. Describe the sources of contaminant exposure in the process operator's area of responsibility.	• Plant summarizes health risks and limits, exposure sources, potential exposure routes, and routine exposure monitoring conducted at site.

2. Explain how an Industrial Ventilation System provides protection at hood or enclosures at individual workstations and how it operates as a system.	• "Fundamental Capture and Contain" in Section A9.3 of the Training Appendix to Chapter 9.
	• Plant develops operation specific training for all the hoods and enclosures in an operating area that:
	  • Shows how the hoods/enclosures capture/contain the contaminants in the operating area.
	  • Describes what to check for proper operation (i.e., visible dusting, Magnehelic gauge, face velocity, hood static pressure, etc.).

3. List safe behavior around Industrial Ventilation Systems serving the workstation.	"Recognizing Safety Hazards Around Industrial Ventilation Systems" in Section A9.2 of the Training Appendix to Chapter 9.
4. Describe basic operation of Air Cleaning Devices serving the system in your work area.	See Air Cleaning Devices Training Guides, Skill Level 2.

TABLE 9-3. Skill Level 3: Industrial Ventilation System Operators

An Operator Should Be Able To:	Sources of Training Information (Assumes completion of Skill Levels 1 and 2)
1. Explain how the local exhaust systems in area of responsibility function as both a collection of specific components and as an integrated system.	• "Advanced Capture and Contain Principles" in Section A9.4 of the Training Appendix – Chapter 9. • "Providing Exhaust Airflow to Hoods and Enclosures" in Section A9.5 and "The Fourth C: Collect" in Section A9.6 of the Training Appendix – Chapter 9. • "Local Exhaust Ventilation (LEV) System Balancing" in Section A9.9 of the Training Appendix – Chapter 9. • "Basic Local Exhaust Ventilation (LEV) System Troubleshooting" in Section A9.10 of the Training Appendix – Chapter 9. • "Impact of Improper Local Exhaust Ventilation (LEV) System Changes" in Section A9.11 of the Training Appendix – Chapter 9. • Study "How It Works" and "Operating Tips" sections of appropriate Air Cleaning Device section of Chapter 6.
2. Describe Baseline and other local exhaust ventilation technical documentation.	• "Technical Documentation" section of Chapter 5 "Monitoring & Maintenance." • Appendix 1-C "Construction Drawings" in Chapter 1, "Construction and Project Management Phase." • Review specific Industrial Ventilation System schematic diagrams and Baseline data with trainer.
3. Explain what to look for on data rounds, list the data to be recorded, and describe both the action limits suggesting corrective action and how to get troubleshooting completed.	• "Monitoring & Maintenance of Ventilation Systems," Chapter 5. • "Monitoring & Maintenance" section of appropriate Air Cleaning Device chapters. • Site's monitoring and maintenance plan and review the log sheets for daily and weekly rounds.

4. Demonstrate ability to take system measurements as required for the job:
• Static pressure
• Duct velocity/airflow
• Face velocity
• Shaft rotational speed
• Motor current
	• "Testing and Measurement of Ventilation Systems," Chapter 3.
	• Demonstrate skills to trainer during field measurements, including:
	  • How to take the measurements
	  • How to record the data
	  • How to calculate the end result
	  • How to download the data from electronic instruments (as appropriate)

5. Demonstrate ability to perform the following system maintenance tasks: • Hood/enclosure disassembly and cleaning • Duct network disassembly and cleaning • Exhaust fan lubrication and drive repairs • Air Cleaning Device routine maintenance	• Component "Monitoring & Maintenance" sections of appropriate Air Cleaning Device sections of Chapter 6 and complete other training items in the Air Cleaning Device Training Guide for Skill Level 3.
6. Describe Supply Air Systems in area and how they impact the performance of local exhaust ventilation systems.	• "Supply Air Systems;" Chapter 10 of *Industrial Ventilation: A Manual of Recommended Practice for Design.*

TABLE 9-4. Skill Level 4: Industrial Ventilation System Troubleshooter

An Operator Should Be Able To:	Sources of Training Information (Assumes completion of Skill Levels 1, 2, and 3)
1. List the references for Baseline conditions for all Industrial Ventilation Systems.	Collect copies and review all Industrial Ventilation Schematic diagrams and Baseline data.
2. Describe system Troubleshooting procedures used to restore local exhaust system to Baseline operation.	• "Introduction," "Baseline Deviation Method," and "Pressure Ratio Method" sections of "Troubleshooting Ventilation Systems," Chapter 7. • Review system component troubleshooting tables in Chapter 7.
3. Explain Troubleshooting procedures for Air Cleaning Devices used at plant and list the effects of process or ambient conditions change (i.e., temperature, humidity) on the operation of the Air Cleaning Devices.	• "Troubleshooting" section of appropriate Air Cleaning Device section of Chapter 6. • Air Cleaning Device equipment vendor Installation, Operation, and Maintenance Manual and complete the other training items in the Air Cleaning Device Training Guide, Skill Level 4.
4. Describe the Industrial Ventilation System impact of poor Supply Air operation.	Appendix
5. List environmental permit requirements, that require routine data gathering for all Air Cleaning Devices in area of responsibility.	Review all environmental permit requirements with your company's site environmental contact and check to see that system data gathering is up to date for current permit requirements.

9.7   SKILL LEVEL 5: INDUSTRIAL VENTILATION SYSTEM CHANGE MANAGEMENT

Industrial Ventilation System Change Management is responsible for ensuring successful alterations to Industrial Ventilation Systems when required to meet worker safety, production or shop facility requirements. This role includes Plant Engineering or manager/technician owner accountable to management for system performance. This assumes completion of Skill Levels 1, 2, 3, and 4 (see Table 9-5).

9.8   SYSTEM OPERATORS INTERFACE WITH OTHER PLANT PERSONNEL

In the normal course of operation, there will be times where individuals with the roles described below need to work with one or more individuals at the Operator levels. These brief paragraphs describe the capabilities desired in the role and ways people in the role interface with system operators.

Industrial Ventilation Engineer: The engineer should understand the process being controlled and the process operation in order to successfully apply industrial ventilation equipment to control exposures. They also should be familiar with Industrial Ventilation System design and connected process issues that can interfere with the system. The engineer might be involved in high level troubleshooting or in setting the design basis for a new or modified system or in proving the Baseline performance of a system. The Level 5 operator is the most likely functional role to interface with the Industrial Ventilation Engineer in discussions of system changes.

Testing and Balancing (TAB) Contractor: These specialist contractors are brought into a site to establish an initial system balance after new construction or to restore an old system to a desired Baseline. The Contractor might be certified by either the National Environmental Balancing Bureau (NEBB) or the Associated Air Balance Council (AABC). Typically, the Level 5 local exhaust ventilation operator might interface with the TAB Contractor.

Industrial Hygienist (IH): The Industrial Hygienist is responsible for the recognition, evaluation and control of health hazards. This is accomplished by observing work conditions, observing employee work habits, performing exposure assessments, and by evaluating implemented controls. After performing these tasks, the Industrial Hygienist will, as necessary, develop a hazard control strategy that will minimize risks through utilization of new or existing engineering and administrative controls, product substitution where possible, and personal protective equipment as necessary. Level 4 or Level 5 Operators are the most likely functional roles to work with the IH on troubleshooting exposure assessment and employee health protection issues. It is recommended that Industrial Hygienists performing troubleshooting where local exhaust ventilation problems are suspected either be familiar with industrial ventilation design and testing or study the training materials for Operators, Levels 1 through Level 5, and the appropriate Air Cleaning Devices.

Personnel Safety Contact: The Personnel Safety Contact has the technical skills to ensure that all safety issues are addressed prior to all operational and maintenance activities.

TABLE 9-5. Skill Level 5: Industrial Ventilation System Change Management

An Operator Should Be Able To:	Sources of Training Information (Assumes completion of Skill Levels 1, 2, 3, and 4)
1. List the common change ideas for Industrial Ventilation Systems and how they impact performance.	• "Modifying Industrial Ventilation Systems," Chapter 8. • "Managing Changes" section of appropriate Air Cleaning Device sections of Chapter 6. • Review environmental permit requirements with company site environmental contact and list change ideas that would require permit revision with regulatory authorities.
2. Collect the specification and commissioning data for all fabric filters on site.	• "Commissioning and Proof of Performance" Chapter 2 of *Industrial Ventilation: A Manual of Recommended Practice for Operation and Maintenance.* • "Balancing Duct Systems with Dampers" Chapter 4 of *Industrial Ventilation: A Manual of Recommended Practice for Operation and Maintenance.* • Search plant maintenance and engineering files and make copies of pertinent data for system data files.
3. Describe the air balance between Supply Air and Local exhaust systems in all operating areas with Local exhaust systems.	• Review plant HVAC technical documentation. • Prepare simple Air Balance diagrams if information is available.
4. Explain the site's change management procedure and your role as a member of the team.	Review plant change procedure and discuss with plant engineer.
5. Participate in equipment acceptance testing.	List the acceptance criteria to be evaluated.

Such issues may include (but not be limited to):

- Lock Out/Tag Out Programs
- Machine Guards
- Confined Space Entry procedures
- Fall Prevention and Protection equipment and procedures
- Ergonomic issues

Such issues arise around industrial ventilation systems so the Safety Contact may need to interface with Level 4 or Level 5 local exhaust ventilation operators.

Process Safety Contact: The Process Safety Contact has the technical skills to ensure that equipment is not exposed to over-pressure or under-pressure that can damage it. If explosive dusts or vapors are present, this individual insures that the equipment is adequately protected to prevent damage from these hazards as well. This individual might interface with Level 3 or Level 4 local exhaust ventilation Operators to ensure routine process safety equipment checks are completed or with Level 4 or Level 5 local exhaust ventilation Operators to follow up in problem solving efforts.

Environmental Contact: The Environmental Contact has the technical skills to ensure that environmental laws and regulations pertaining to the site are met. This person would have information on the specific operating permit requirements for each of the Air Cleaning Devices at the site. Level 3 or Level 4 local exhaust ventilation operators would need to know the operating data (i.e., baghouse or scrubber differential pressure) that must be routinely recorded during data rounds as well as maintenance documentation to meet those permit requirements.

9.9   DEVELOPING SITE-SPECIFIC TRAINING PROGRAMS

The best training program is one tailored for the site's specific needs. Key points about expectations and training include:

- Study the Training Guides and associated training materials to understand the required skills for system operation and the information available for use at the site.
- Develop written roles, skills, and training descriptions that fit your site.
- Clear designated roles, expectations, and delegated authority help guide personnel to the work needed to keep the industrial ventilation systems running correctly.
- Depending on how operating and maintenance skills are divided at the site, skills and training requirements can be clearly connected to the job descriptions.

- Use the information in this Manual as core training materials, supplemented by site-specific information from vendors and other sources. Tailor it to fit audience's needs.

- Training records and examinations help determine where additional training is needed to build skills.

- One annual re-training technique is to use the problems experienced from the previous year as the basis for refresher training for the next year.

APPENDIX A9   INTRODUCTION TO LOCAL EXHAUST VENTILATION

A9.1 INTRODUCTION TO INDUSTRIAL VENTILATION SYSTEMS

To begin a training program for system users and operators, there must be a thorough understanding of the principles of system operation and how the system is affected by changes and alterations. *Industrial Ventilation: A Manual of Recommended Practice for Design* is a good reference for the sources of this information and contains many drawings, figures and tables to illustrate system operation. These should be used in addition to some of the figures in this Appendix.

In this chapter and throughout both Industrial Ventilation Manuals certain acronyms are repeated as they define different systems and terms. An Industrial Ventilation System (IVS) includes a family of different types of systems that include:

1) Local Exhaust Ventilation (LEV) Systems – the suction system with hoods located near the pollutant source and a duct system conveying the air and particulate to a collection device,

2) Dilution Ventilation Systems (DVS) where large quantities of air are used to mix with contaminants and carry them normally through roof and wall exhaust fans,

3) Supply Air Systems that can sometimes be listed as Make-up Air (MUA) Systems or Replacement Air Systems (RAS).

A local exhaust ventilation system is designed to control and capture emissions from industrial processes. The purpose of the system is to capture the contaminant at its source before it can escape into the work environment. There are several types of contaminants that are controlled by Industrial Ventilation Systems:

- Dusts or aerosols – small solid particles from manufacturing processes or machining operations,

- Mists – very small, semi-liquid particles from different processes,

- Fumes – very small particles from hot operations such as combustion or welding,

- Vapors/odors – produced from evaporation of volatile components of liquids such as solvents or perfumes.

The system is engineered to contain and capture contaminants at their sources in the process and to bring that contaminated air to a central point for collection. It can then be recycled back into the process or sent for disposal. The basic functions of contaminant control systems (or the four Cs) are:

- Capture

- Contain

- Convey

- Collect

Figure A9-1 shows dust control of a filling machine for powdered products and illustrates the four Cs.

A9.2 RECOGNIZING SAFETY ISSUES AROUND INDUSTRIAL VENTILATION SYSTEMS

The purpose of the Industrial Ventilation System (IVS) is to protect employees from airborne health hazards, explosions, or fires. There are many safety hazards personnel may encounter when performing maintenance functions on industrial ventilation systems. It is important to remember that while performing some maintenance functions, the system will probably need to be turned off. Turning the industrial ventilation system off may expose operational employees to airborne hazards, and they should be notified of the system shutdown so appropriate precautions can be taken. Many maintenance functions are often performed on off shifts or during planned down times.

Plant safety standards and staff resources are the primary sources of safety information. Consult an Occupational Safety and Health specialist whenever a question arises regarding health and safety procedures required during maintenance functions.

This section is designed to assist trainers in the ventilation training aspects of each skill level. It is expected that the company will need to develop other training modules to address other potential hazards that arise during the testing and repair of ventilation systems. These additional modules may include but not be limited to training on the following issues:

- Control of Hazardous Energy (Lock Out/Tag Out)

- Confined Space Entry

- Fall Prevention and Protection

- Pinch Points and Other Machinery Hazards

- Respiratory Protection

- Hearing Conservation

- Other Personal Protective Equipment
  - Head Protection
  - Eye and Face Protection

TABLE 9-6. Air Cleaning Device (ACD) Training Guides

	Sources of Training Information				
	6.2 Fabric Filter	**6.3 Particulate Scrubber**	**6.4 Thermal & Catalytic Oxidizers**	**6.5. Absorber Scrubber**	**6.6 Vapor Absorption**
Level 1: General Awareness:					
Describe the ACD's used at the site	General site training information and vendor information and Appendix A9	General site training information and vendor information and Appendix A9	General site training information and vendor information and Appendix A9	General site training information and vendor information and Appendix A9	General site training information and vendor information and Appendix A9
Level 2: LEV User:					
1) Describe the basic operation of ACDs connected to the LEVs in the Operator's area of responsibility.	Read and Comprehend Fabric Filter Sections 6.2.1 through 6.2.11	Read and Comprehend Scrubber Sections 6.3.1 through 6.3.6	Read and Comprehend Oxidizer Sections 6.4.1 through 6.4.10	Read and Comprehend Absorber Sections 6.5.1 through 6.5.6	Read and Comprehend Vapor Adsorption section 6.6.2 and then the Sections that apply at your site (Rotor Concentrator Sections 6.6.3 thru 6.6.6 or Fixed Bed Vapor Adsorption Sections 6.6.7 thru 6.6.10.)
2) Explain how an individual in the work area can affect ACD operation.	Discuss with LEV System Operator	Discuss with LEV System Operator	Discuss with LEV System Operator	Discuss with LEV System Operator	Discuss with LEV System Operator
Level 3: LEV System Operators:					
1) For the ACDs in your area, list the common indicators, controls, and interlocks, describe how they work, and when the readings indicate a reduction in airflow through the ACD.	Read and Comprehend Fabric Filter Sections 6.2.12 through 6.2.18	Read and Comprehend Scrubber Section 6.3.7	Read vendor manual and describe devices used for oxidizer airflow, temperature, fuel burners,	Read vendor manual and describe devices used for scrubber liquid flow, pH control, scrubber differential pressure, etc.	Read vendor manual and describe devices used for vapor adsorption, vapor desorption, and final vapor concentrate treatment, etc.
2) Explain what to look for on data rounds, list the data to be recorded, and describe both the action limits suggesting corrective action and how to get the troubleshooting completed.	Review the data logsheet, read Vendor Manual, and discuss with LEV System Troubleshooter	Review the data logsheet, read Vendor Manual, and discuss with LEV System Troubleshooter	Review the data logsheet, read Vendor Manual, and discuss with LEV System Troubleshooter	Review the data logsheet, read Vendor Manual, and discuss with LEV System Troubleshooter	Review the data logsheet, read Vendor Manual, and discuss with LEV System Troubleshooter
3) Describe the power sources and emergency shutdowns for the ACD's electrical systems.	After a walkthrough, make a diagram of all the electrical distribution components between the filter and the Motor Control Center	After a walkthrough, make a diagram of all the electrical distribution components between the scrubber and the Motor Control Center	After a walkthrough, make a diagram of all the electrical distribution components between the oxidizer and the Motor Control Center	After a walkthrough, make a diagram of all the electrical distribution components between the Absorber and the Motor Control Center	After a walkthrough, make a diagram of all the electrical distribution components between the Vapor Adsorption system and the Motor Control Center
4) Summarize the operating tips for your ACD	Read and Comprehend Fabric Filter Sections 6.2.20 through 6.2.23.	Read Scrubber Section 6.3.7	Read and comprehend Oxidizer Sections 6.4.11 through 6.4.14	Read and comprehend Absorber Section 6.5.7	Read Vapor Adsorption Section 6.6.8
5) Explain the routine monitoring & maintenance requirements for your ACD	Read and comprehend Fabric Filter Section 6.2.24 to 6.2.30	Read and Comprehend Scrubber Section 6.3.8	Read Oxidizer Sections 6.4.15 through 6.4.16	Read and comprehend Absorber Section 6.5.8	Read and Comprehend Vapor Adsorption Section 6.6.4-5 or Fixed Bed Sections 6.6.9-10
6) Other considerations			Read Oxidizer Section 6.4.17 (Heat Exchanger Cleaning)		
Level 4: LEV System Troubleshooter:					
1) Demonstrate how to take airflow, temperature (wet and dry bulb), face velocity, static pressure, shaft RPM, motor current/voltage measurements.	Read "System Measurements" chapter and demonstrate measurement skills in the field.	Read "System Measurements" chapter and Demonstrate measurement skills in the field.	Read "System Measurements" chapter and demonstrate measurement skills in the field.	Read "System Measurements" chapter and Demonstrate measurement skills in the field.	Read "System Measurements" chapter and Demonstrate measurement skills in the field.
2) Explain the impact of environmental and process changes of temperature, humidity, etc., on ACD operation how to troubleshoot the problems when action limits are exceeded.	Read Fabric Filter Section 6.2.24 and discuss with LEV Change Manager	Read Scrubber Section 6.3.9 and discuss with LEV Change Manager	Read Oxidizer Section 6.18. and discuss with LEV Change Manager	Read Absorber Section 6.5.9 and discuss with LEV Change Manager	Read these sections and discuss with LEV Change Manager: Vapor Adsorption 6.6.6 Fixed Bed Adsorption 6.6.10
3) List environmental permit requirements, which require routine data gathering for all fabric filters in area of responsibility.	Review all environmental permit requirements with your company's site environmental contact.	Review all environmental permit requirements with your company's site environmental contact.	Review all environmental permit requirements with your company's site environmental contact.	Review all environmental permit requirements with your company's site environmental contact.	Review all environmental permit requirements with your company's site environmental contact.
4) Special considerations	Read specific vendor literature for on-site filters and Demonstrate how to adjust bag-cleaning system "On time" and "Off time" (Duration and Interval) and how to rebuild or replace defective solenoid and diaphragm valves	Read specific vendor literature for on site scrubbers and demonstrate how to adjust scrubber water flow and scrubber differential pressure	Read specific vendor literature for on site oxidizers and demonstrate how to set unit temperature and residence time.	Read specific vendor literature for on site oxidizers and demonstrate how to set unit temperature and residence time.	Read specific vendor literature for on site vapor adsorption systems and demonstrate how to set unit temperature and residence time.
Level 5: LEV Change Management:					
1) List the common change ideas for your ACD and how they impact system performance.	Read "Managing Changes" section of Fabric Filter chapter (6.2.28 through 6.2.30)	Read and Comprehend "Managing Changes" section of Particulate Scrubbers (6.3.10)	Read "Managing Changes" section of Oxidizers (6.4.19)	Read Absorber Section 6.5.10 and discuss with LEV Change Manager	Read Vapor Adsorption Section 6.6.11 and discuss with LEV Change Manager
2) Collect the specification and commissioning data for all fabric filters on site.	Read "Commissioning" chapter. Search plant maintenance and engineering files and make copies of pertinent data.	Read "Commissioning" chapter. Search plant maintenance and engineering files and make copies of pertinent data.	Read "Commissioning" chapter. Search plant maintenance and engineering files and make copies of pertinent data.	Read "Commissioning" chapter. Search plant maintenance and engineering files and make copies of pertinent data.	Read "Commissioning" chapter. Search plant maintenance and engineering files and make copies of pertinent data.
3) Explain the site's change management procedure and your role as a member of the team.	Review plant change procedure and discuss with Plant Engineer	Review plant change procedure and discuss with plant engineer	Review plant change procedure and discuss with plant engineer	Review plant change procedure and discuss with plant engineer	Review plant change procedure and discuss with plant engineer

TABLE 9-6 (Cont.). Air Cleaning Device (ACD) Training Guides

| | Sources of Training Information | | | | |
	6.7 Fiber Bed Filtration	6.8 Electrostatic Precipitators (ESP)	6.9 Wetted Electrostatic Precipitators (Wet ESP)	6.10 Bioscrubbers and Biofilters	6.11 Mechanical Collectors
Level 1: General Awareness:					
Describe the ACDs used at the site	General site training information and vendor information and Appendix A9	General site training information and vendor information and Appendix A9	General site training information and vendor information and Appendix A9	General site training information and vendor information and Appendix A9	General site training information and vendor information and Appendix A9
Level 2: LEV User:					
1) Describe the basic operation of ACDs connected to the LEVs in the Operator's area of responsibility.	Read Fiber Bed Filtration Sections 6.7.1 thru 6.7.4	Read ESP Sections 6.8.1 thru 6.8.4	Read Wet ESP Sections 6.9.1 & 6.9.2	Read Bioscrubber Sections 6.10.1 thru 6.10.3	Read Mechanical Collector sections below that apply to equipment at your site: 6.11.2 Cyclones 6.11.4 Dropout Box Collectors 6.11.6 Mechanical Classifiers
2) Explain how an individual in the work area can affect ACD operation.	Discuss with LEV System Operator	Discuss with LEV System Operator	Discuss with LEV System Operator	Discuss with LEV System Operator	Discuss with LEV System Operator
Level 3: LEV System Operators:					
1) For the ACDs in your area, list the common indicators, controls, and interlocks, describe how they work, and when the readings indicate a reduction in airflow through the ACD.	Read vendor manual and describe the Fiber Bed Filtration equipment installed at your site	Read vendor manual and describe the ESP equipment installed at your site.	Read vendor manual and describe the Wet ESP equipment installed at your site.	Read vendor manual and describe the Bioscrubber or Biofilter equipment installed at your site.	Read vendor manual and describe the Mechanical Collector equipment installed at your site.
2) Explain what to look for on data rounds, list the data to be recorded, and describe both the action limits suggesting corrective action and how to get the troubleshooting completed.	Review the data logsheet, read Vendor Manual, and discuss with LEV System Troubleshooter	Review the data logsheet, read Vendor Manual, and discuss with LEV System Troubleshooter	Review the data logsheet, read Vendor Manual, and discuss with LEV System Troubleshooter	Review the data logsheet, read Vendor Manual, and discuss with LEV System Troubleshooter	Review the data logsheet, read Vendor Manual, and discuss with LEV System Troubleshooter
3) Describe the power sources and emergency shutdowns for the ACD's electrical systems.	After a walkthrough, make a diagram of all the electrical distribution components between the Fiber Bed Filtration system and the Motor Control Center	After a walkthrough, make a diagram of all the electrical distribution components between the ESP system and the Motor Control Center	After a walkthrough, make a diagram of all the electrical distribution components between the Wet ESP system and the Motor Control Center	After a walkthrough, make a diagram of all the electrical distribution components between the Bioscrubber/Biofilter system and the Motor Control Center	After a walkthrough, make a diagram of all the electrical distribution components between the Mechanical Collector system and the Motor Control Center
4) Summarize the operating tips for your ACD	Read Fiber Bed Filtration Section 6.7.11	Read ESP Sections 6.8.5-6	Read Wet ESP Sections 6.9.3 through 6.9.6	Read Bioscrubber/Biofilter Section 6.10.4	Read Mechanical Collector sections 6.11.3 - Cyclones 6.11.5 - Dropout Boxes 6.11.7 - Mechanical Classifiers
5) Explain the routine monitoring & maintenance requirements for your ACD	Read Fiber Bed Filtration Sections 6.7.5 & 6 and Sections 6.7.8 & 9	Read ESP Section 6.8.5	Read Wet ESP Section 6.9.7 (10 in writeup)	Read Bioscrubber/Biofilter Section 6.10.5	Read Mechanical Collector sections 6.11.3 - Cyclones 6.11.5 - Dropout Boxes 6.11.7 - Mechanical Classifiers
6) Other considerations					
Level 4: LEV System Troubleshooter:					
1) Demonstrate how to take airflow, temperature (wet and dry bulb), face velocity, static pressure, shaft RPM, motor current/voltage measurements.	Read "System Measurements" chapter and Demonstrate measurement skills in the field.	Read "System Measurements" chapter and Demonstrate measurement skills in the field.	Read "System Measurements" chapter and Demonstrate measurement skills in the field.	Read "System Measurements" chapter and Demonstrate measurement skills in the field.	Read "System Measurements" chapter and Demonstrate measurement skills in the field.
2) Explain the impact of environmental and process changes of temperature, humidity, etc., on ACD operation how to troubleshoot the problems when action limits are exceeded.	Read Fiber Bed Filtration Sections 6.7.7 and 6.7.10 and discuss with LEV Change Manager	Read ESP Section 6.8.6 and discuss with LEV Change Manager	Read Wet ESP Sections 6.9.8 & 9 (listed as 11 & 12 in writeup) and discuss with LEV Change Manager	Read Bioscrubber/Biofilter Section 6.10.7 and discuss with LEV Change Manager	Read Mechanical Collector sections 6.11.3 - Cyclones 6.11.5 - Dropout Boxes 6.11.7 - Mechanical Classifiers
3) List environmental permit requirements, which require routine data gathering for all fabric filters in area of responsibility.	Review all environmental permit requirements with your company's site environmental contact.	Review all environmental permit requirements with your company's site environmental contact.	Review all environmental permit requirements with your company's site environmental contact.	Review all environmental permit requirements with your company's site environmental contact.	Review all environmental permit requirements with your company's site environmental contact.
4) Special considerations	Read specific vendor literature for on site fiber bed filtration systems and demonstrate how to use fiber bed differential pressure to section action limits and to monitor collected liquid flow for proper drain operation.	Read specific vendor literature for on site ESP systems and demonstrate how to analyze for the causes of sparking	Read specific vendor literature for on site Wet ESP systems and demonstrate how to analyze for the causes of sparking	Read specific vendor literature for on site Bioscrubber/Biofilter systems and list the extra steps to be taken for proper care and feeding of a biological system	Read specific vendor literature for on site Bioscrubber/Biofilter systems and list the extra steps to be taken for proper care and feeding of a biological system
Level 5: LEV Change Management:					
1) List the common change ideas for your ACD and how they impact system performance.	NO CHANGE MANAGEMENT SECTION	Read ESP Section 6.8.7 and discuss with LEV Change Manager	Read Wet ESP Section 6.8.10 (listed as 13 in writeup) and discuss with LEV Change Manager	Read Bioscrubber/Biofilter Section 6.10.7 and discuss with LEV Change Manager	Read Mechanical Collector Section 6.11.8 and discuss with LEV Change Manager
2) Collect the specification and commissioning data for all fabric filters on site.	Read "Commissioning" chapter. Search plant maintenance and engineering files and make copies of pertinent data.	Read "Commissioning" chapter. Search plant maintenance and engineering files and make copies of pertinent data.	Read "Commissioning" chapter. Search plant maintenance and engineering files and make copies of pertinent data.	Read "Commissioning" chapter. Search plant maintenance and engineering files and make copies of pertinent data.	Read "Commissioning" chapter. Search plant maintenance and engineering files and make copies of pertinent data.
3) Explain the site's change management procedure and your role as a member of the team.	Review plant change procedure and discuss with plant engineer	Review plant change procedure and discuss with plant engineer	Review plant change procedure and discuss with plant engineer	Review plant change procedure and discuss with plant engineer	Review plant change procedure and discuss with plant engineer

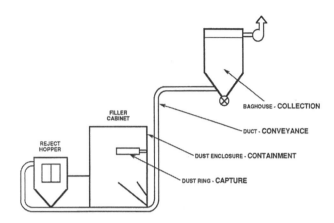

FIGURE A9-1. Carton filling dust control system illustrating the 4 Cs (Reprinted with permission from Procter & Gamble)

- Hand and Body Splash Protection
- Foot Protection
- General Hazards
  - Slips, Trips, and Falls
  - Loose clothing
  - Jewelry
  - Lighting
- Toxic materials through any route of exposure

A9.2.1 Hazardous Operations. There must be equipment or procedures (or both) in place to prevent personal injury and equipment damage due to dust or vapor deflagration. This also includes over-pressure or under-pressure conditions in the process. There must be fire protection equipment installed on the process as well. Be familiar with the site's safe operating practices around Hazardous Operations, as well as NFPA and other standards and regulations in effect.

A9.3 FUNDAMENTAL "CAPTURE AND CONTAIN" METHODS (THE 4 Cs)

The fundamental concepts of how hoods and enclosures provide protection are explained in the following sections. The "Cs" refer to Figure A9-1.

A9.3.1 The First "C": Capture (Hoods). A capture point or 'hood' is an area in which air and dust are being drawn into the duct network. Hoods may be found inside containment areas, such as the dust ring in the filling machine (see Figure A9-1).

Ideally, dust or other contaminant generation can be eliminated through the use of less hazardous materials, product redesign, or process equipment selection. Hoods or enclosures are required when changes to the process or product to eliminate dust/aerosol sources are not technically feasible. In these cases, hoods and enclosures are used to capture and contain contaminants at the point of generation. Capture and contain-

ment at the point of generation prevent the contaminant from migrating and being spread throughout the facility as well as meeting occupational health exposure limits.

The local exhaust hood is the point of entry of the airborne contaminant into the exhaust system. The primary function of the hood is to capture contaminants, before they reach the worker's breathing zone. ***If the hood fails to capture the contaminant, it does not matter how well the rest of the industrial ventilation system performs.***

Exhaust hoods, by definition, include all suction openings regardless of their configuration. Exhaust hoods can be grouped into two general categories: enclosing and exterior.

- Enclosing hoods completely or partially enclose the process or contaminant generation point. A laboratory glove box is an example of a complete enclosure. A paint booth is an example of a partial enclosure. Enclosures are always the best design to capture the contaminant.

- Exterior hoods are located adjacent to an emission source without enclosing it. Examples of exterior hoods include slots along the edge of a tank, or a flanged cone used to capture welding fumes.

Many hoods have "slotted" openings into the duct. They are carefully designed components of the ventilation system. A slotted hood distributes or balances an otherwise uneven flow of air into the hood. As with any other part of the system, the slots should remain unaltered and kept clean and clear of obstructions.

The physical characteristics of the process equipment, the contaminant, the generation mechanism, and the operator/equipment interface determine the type of exhaust hood used.

- Exterior hoods provide capture of contaminant sources at the point of generation. A hood must create an airflow pattern and capture velocity significant enough to control the motion of the contaminant laden air, plus extraneous air currents caused by room cross-drafts, vehicular traffic, or other air disturbing events. Other sources of external air motion include thermal currents from hot equipment or process, motion from machinery or material, air currents from free standing fans, open windows and doors, replacement air systems, and the motion of the operator (people walking by). That is why exterior hoods are a last resort after enclosure cannot be accomplished.

- Enclosures provide containment of contaminant sources. An enclosure must provide an adequate velocity through access openings to prevent dust migration outside of the enclosure and toward the worker. While enclosures are designed to contain dust at the access openings, they are not necessarily designed to capture or convey the contaminant within the enclosure.

A9.3.2 Limitations of Hoods. The distance over which an exhaust hood can influence air to move is small compared to the distance a stream of blown air can cause air movement. Air discharged from an opening keeps its directional effect for a considerable distance beyond the opening because of the momentum of the column of air. However, if the flow of air through the same opening were reversed so that it operated as an intake, the same volume of air becomes almost non-directional and has a reduced range of influence.

This concept is illustrated in Figure A9-2. Air discharged from the opening will have 10% of the duct velocity at 40 duct diameters from the opening. The same amount of air drawn into the opening will drop below 10% of the duct velocity at roughly one duct diameter. Hoods do not have a very long effective reach distance to capture contaminants, which is another reason to enclose the problem if possible.

Enclosures build walls around the source of contaminants. The walls function like a duct to keep the contaminants inside the equipment where an airflow pattern has already been established. The walls of the enclosure also act as barriers to prevent outside influences (such as air currents) from causing the contaminants to move outside of the containment. If care is taken to address operability issues, an enclosure will use considerably less exhaust air than an external hood.

A9.3.3 The Second "C": Contain. In Figure A9-1, containment is provided by the enclosed design and negative pressure (inward airflow) of the filler cabinet (where individual cartons are filled with powder) and the reject hopper (for dumping off-weight cartons) and other devices that restrict the dust's ability to drift out into the operator's work area. The incoming airflow at the openings pushes the dust back into the cabinet.

A containment area is an enclosure that intentionally confines dust and/or spillage for more effective capture in the ventilation system and/or clean up. It can be as small as a packing machine cabinet or as large as a process storage bin. Air is drawn into the enclosure by the dust control system either continuously through designed openings or intermittently when

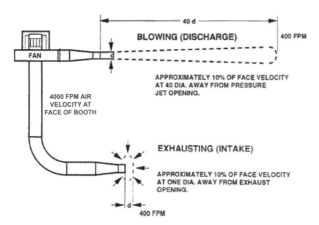

FIGURE A9-2. Blowing versus exhausting – effective reach

access doors are opened. Doors or hatches on enclosures must normally be closed to keep dust from escaping.

It is important to be especially careful to maintain gaskets, such as those on conveyors or baghouse doors. Report any leaks found to the person responsible for system maintenance. If a door will not seal as it was designed, it cannot stop dust or spilled product from escaping and contaminating a work area.

Any material spilled outside of containments can become airborne dust. There are two ways this can happen:

1) Air currents from ventilation or equipment mechanical action can make particles airborne,

2) Passers-by or forklift traffic step on and crush the material into small particles and track the material around the operating area causing the dust to be entrained in room air currents. (Smaller particles are lighter and are more easily entrained in air currents.)

Airborne contaminants created from spilled material can be responsible for a significant part of exposure. It is important to keep the material inside the equipment through good operating and maintenance procedures. Ventilation systems are designed to confine contaminants and collect them at the source, *not to correct process material handling flaws or to overcome the need for good housekeeping and maintenance.*

Dust and spillage inside a containment area (for example, filling machines and belt conveyors) are inevitable. Containment areas exist to confine dust in a small zone where it can be more easily cleaned up or captured by the dust control system. An effective dust control system will keep dust within a containment area, but the system is *not designed to eliminate all dust and spillage* from the area. Enclosures will ALWAYS require routine cleanout.

A key method for containing contaminants is to ensure that air flows smoothly and uniformly into the plane of the openings in the enclosure. This is known as the "face velocity" of the opening. Face velocity is based on a knowledge of the contaminant sources and air velocities required to keep the contaminants inside the enclosure.

When cleaning a containment area (filling machine, belt conveyor housing, etc.), personal protective equipment (PPE) should be used as appropriate or required by company safety policy.

A9.4 ADVANCED CAPTURE AND CONTAIN PRINCIPLES

The art of capturing and containing the pollutant before it gets to the operator or out into the plant involves many design considerations. If the original design is altered in the plant (putting cardboard over hood openings or changing blast gate settings, etc.), the system will not operate as designed. This section reviews basic concepts required for good design and operation.

A9.4.1 Hood Definitions (Refer to Chapter 6, Figure 6-1 in Industrial Ventilation: A Manual of Recommended Practice for Design).

Capture	Air velocity at any point in front of the hood or at the hood opening necessary to overcome opposing air currents and to capture the contaminated air at that point by causing it to flow into the hood.
Face	Air velocity at the plane of the hood opening or enclosure access opening.
Slot	Air velocity through the opening in a slot type hood. It is used primarily as a means of obtaining uniform air distribution across the face of the hood.
Plenum	Air velocity in a hood plenum or through the cross-sectional area of an enclosure.
Duct	Air velocity through the duct cross section. When solid material is present in the air stream, the duct velocity must be equal to or greater than the minimum air velocity required to move the particles in the air stream.
Conveying	The minimum duct velocity required to keep the collected particles suspended in the air stream.

A9.4.2 Hood Components.
The shape of the hood, its size, location, and volumetric airflow rate are important hood characteristics. Machinery operation and contaminant generation vary; consequently, there are many different hood designs. Besides the hood body or casing itself, common hood components include slots, plenums, baffles, flanges, and take-offs.

Slots

The function of slots on a hood is solely to provide uniform air distribution across the hood face. (Slot velocity does not contribute toward capture velocity.) Slots are defined as having a width to length ratio (W/L) of 0.2 or less. In some cases, the slot may be covered with a wire mesh or a perforated plate to prevent items (i.e., paper or rags) from being intentionally or inadvertently drawn or deposited into the exhaust hood.

Paint booths with a perforated plate may periodically need to be stripped of paint to keep the slots open. Oily, sticky or dusty operations must be cleaned frequently. A typical design slot velocity is 2,000 fpm.

Obstructions that block the slots will seriously degrade hood performance and should be removed when they are found. Even a layer of dust on a protective screen becomes extra resistance that greatly reduces airflow through the hood.

Plenums

A plenum is an enclosed space where the pressure is lower than the outside atmosphere. The purpose of a plenum is to distribute the air drawn into the slot uniformly across the length of the slot. In most cases, this is accomplished by designing the plenum air velocity to be half of the slot velocity. Because the plenum velocity is lower than the slot velocity, some material (contaminant) may settle out inside the plenum. Keep the plenum clean and free of obstructions or clogging. Inspect the plenum for physical damage.

Some exhaust hoods or plenums are installed with cleanout doors. These doors allow access into the hood or plenum. Ensure the doors are closed while the local exhaust system is operating. Inspect the doors to ensure proper sealing and that there is no physical damage.

Baffles or Flanges

A baffle is a surface that provides a barrier to unwanted airflow from the front or sides of the hood. A flange is a surface at and parallel to the hood face that provides a barrier to unwanted airflow from behind the hood. Baffles and flanges are used to direct the hood capture where it is most effective at capturing contaminants. Baffles and flanges are fixed or hinged to the hood. Ensure the baffles and flanges are clean, undamaged, operating properly, and do not obstruct airflow into the hood.

Duct connections positioned too close to enclosure access openings will result in non-uniform velocity across the opening, leaving zones of the opening with insufficient containment velocity. A baffle may be required to achieve uniform face velocity as shown in Figure A9-3.

Take-Offs

The hood take-off connects the hood, slot, or plenum to the exhaust system duct. If a large hood, slot, or plenum is used, multiple take-offs or tapered inlets are installed to ensure even airflow distribution at the hood opening. Inspect the take-off and duct network for physical damage or clogs.

Other Hood Components

Some exhaust hoods will contain all of the previously mentioned components, and they can be easily recognized. However, on others, the components may not be easily identifiable. Because hood construction varies as much as industrial operations and processes do, hood components may not look typical, but the function they serve will fall into one of the above categories. For example, in large paint booths the floor grille acts as slots and the basement as the plenum. Some machines, especially in the woodworking field, have the exhaust hood built into the machine itself. Other hoods such as paint booths may have filters built into the hood body or at the take-off. Ensure all hood designs are free of obstructions, physical damage, plugs or clogs.

Portable Exhaust Hoods

Portable exhaust hood units incorporate a local exhaust hood, some duct, an air pollution filter, and an exhaust fan into a single unit. It is important to remember that portable collectors re-circulate the air back into the workspace. Only use portable collectors when the contaminant is not toxic. Spark arrestors are sometimes installed in hoods that could release very hot particles into the duct and collector. They are commonly found on welding hoods. Refer to the manufacturer's specifications for operating and maintenance guidance for

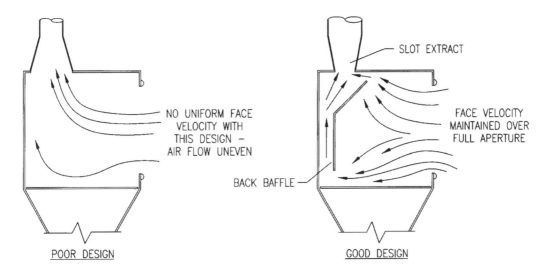

FIGURE A9-3. Impact of baffle on hood face velocity profile (Reprinted with permission from Procter & Gamble)

portable exhaust hoods.

A9.4.3 Hood Containment and Access Doors. Special consideration must be given to enclosures through which airflow is not constant. Enclosures with access doors, for example, generally have restricted airflow when access doors are closed, but have very free airflow when a door opens. The system must be able to keep contaminants from escaping through an open access door and yet stay in balance when that door is shut, restricting airflow through the enclosure again.

When the enclosure is a sealed device such as a belt conveyor or a surge bin, the sealed device may be connected to the system to keep it under negative pressure and prevent contaminant escape when access doors are opened. Most of the time, there is not a path for air to enter the system through the equipment. In those cases, an air bleed is provided to allow a path for air to enter the duct takeoff whenever the access doors are shut.

Leaving an access door open might seem a simple solution. However, doing so would defeat the containment purpose of the enclosure, and in the case of multiple doors, reduce the face velocity (the speed of air through an opening) below what is needed for effective control in the enclosure.

An air bleed is designed to protect balance among all of the branch ducts. All enclosed containment housings with access doors (such as conveyor housings, storage or use bins, mix drums, etc.) must have air bleeds. Duct mounted air bleeds are used when dust controlled equipment is site cleared and the air used by that equipment is still needed for local exhaust ventilation balance.

A9.5 PROVIDING EXHAUST AIRFLOW TO HOODS AND ENCLOSURES

This section describes how the duct, collector, and fan provide the correct exhaust airflow to each hood or enclosure.

A9.5.1 The Third "C" – Convey (The Duct Network). Duct networks have the task of carrying air and entrained contaminants from the hood, through the system, through an air-cleaning device (ACD), into the exhaust fan, and out the exhaust stack into the atmosphere. Once the captured contaminant has entered the duct network, the key maintenance focus is to keep the contaminated air moving within its required transport or conveying velocity range. System monitoring and maintenance is focused on knowing the few spots in the duct network where plugging begins. Keep those spots clean with scheduled maintenance, and the system will deliver design transport velocities for years.

The size or cross-sectional dimension of the duct depends on the required transport velocity needed to prevent the contaminants from settling out of the air stream. This velocity, referred to as conveying velocity or minimum transport velocity (MTV), depends on the nature of the contaminant in the industrial ventilation system. Gases and fumes have lower MTVs (2000-3000 fpm or lower) than heavy dusts or sticky materials (3000-5000 fpm). Changing the duct size or the airflow through any duct changes the conveying velocity and airflow throughout the entire system. If one part of the system is impaired, the effectiveness of the whole system is diminished.

As the air and dust flows along surfaces inside a duct, some dust may stick to the duct walls. When this occurs, the previously smooth surfaces of the duct walls are rougher. As the walls become rougher, friction increases and additional deposits of dust adhere to the old makeup until the duct becomes plugged. Duct cleaning is then required to keep the Local Exhaust Ventilation (LEV) system within the designed range of conveying velocities.

Problems with dust deposits are more frequent where airflow changes direction such as in elbows and branch or Y connections. Figure A9-4 shows one common example of direction change – elbows.

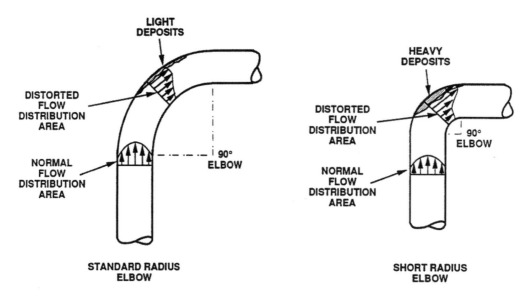

FIGURE A9-4. Duct elbows (Reprinted with permission from Procter & Gamble)

To ensure that conveying velocity specifications are met, the Industrial Ventilation System (IVS) operator must routinely measure air velocity and static pressure. These techniques are described in Chapter 3, "Testing and Measurement of Ventilation Systems."

Sharp turns create plugging in a duct for two reasons. First, moving air and dust naturally resist any change of direction. Notice that the airflow, indicated by the arrows in Figure A9-4 of the short radius elbow, actually compresses more against the outer surface of the elbow and speeds up. Likewise, dust that has more weight than air turns less easily than the air and impacts the duct wall. If it is sticky, the dust forms on the duct wall, forming a rough spot that accelerates the plugging of the duct.

A9.5.2 Elbows and Branch Fittings. Figure A9-5 shows a 90-degree elbow with 2 ½ duct diameter turn radius. Note how the 2 ½ duct diameter is measured. The 2 ½ duct diameter (or larger) turn radius is preferred, regardless of the degree of turn; it minimizes dust buildup (also called makeup) and resistance to flow (pressure drop). More information on elbows is available in Chapter 5 of *Industrial Ventilation: A Manual of Recommended Practice for Design.*

Connections at duct branches are designed to allow as smooth a merging of airflows as possible through the transition from two ducts to one duct. Gradual merging of air streams reduces dust impact buildup on the duct wall at the merging or "Y" connection. Figure A9-6 is an example of a "Y" connection, also known as a branch entry or fitting.

Figure A9-6 also shows a larger duct diameter (12 inches) beyond the merge point. Combined air from the 6-inch and 10-inch branches needs a larger diameter duct to keep the air moving within design conveying velocity. Higher velocities create more friction, deposits, and cleanup requirements.

Air streams carrying dust need to merge gradually, maintaining conveying velocity through the merge zone. The 15 degree taper cone in these fittings provides the best available conveying velocity. The angle of entry depends on the characteristics of the contaminants. Very sticky dusts should enter at a shallow angle like 15 degrees (12 degrees is shown in Figure A9-6). Thirty degrees and even 45 degrees are commonly used for most contaminants.

Ninety degree entries are NOT RECOMMENDED because of the air turbulence, fitting wear and high loss of energy as the air travels through the fitting.

Routine cleaning is an essential part of keeping the duct network operating within the design velocity range. The local exhaust ventilation operator will periodically coordinate cleaning so that makeup of dust deposits will never become a serious problem.

By monitoring the most common trouble spots, users and operators can minimize the effort needed to maintain the ducts. Frequent cleaning of points in the duct network that plug first can reduce the need for major network cleanouts. At duct locations of rapid or frequent makeup, cleanout doors or access doors make cleaning much easier. A cleanout door, however, can create an irregular, rough surface at the very spot where a problem already exists; therefore, cleanout doors and other accesses must be carefully designed. Figure A9-7 shows a common design known as a "flat back elbow." This is used for high wear points in the system and can be fitted with a hinged access door or bolted replacement sections.

A9.5.3 Duct System Standards for Installation.

- Use smooth wall duct (welded seams or drawn tubing) – no spiral wound duct for local exhaust ventilation, as joints and other rough surfaces more easily catch contaminants and hamper cleaning interior surfaces.

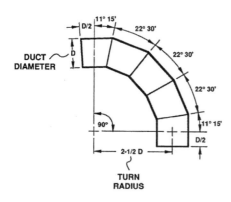

FIGURE A9-5. Standard elbow (90°) (Reprinted with permission from Procter & Gamble)

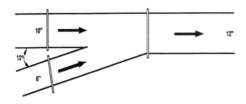

FIGURE A9-6. "Y" connection or branch entry (Reprinted with permission from Procter & Gamble)

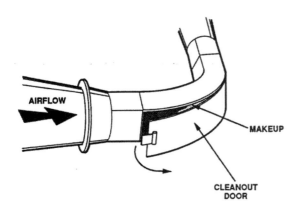

FIGURE A9-7. Flatback elbow (with optional cleanout door) (Reprinted with permission from Procter & Gamble)

- Minimize use of flexible hose. The resistance to flow is twice that of metal duct and the relatively rough inner surface will more rapidly build up with contaminants. Maintain 24" long sections or less.

- Minimize use of elbows to reduce system pressure requirements; maximize straight runs of duct.

- Avoid back-to-back elbows; target at least 5 to 7 diameters of straight duct between elbows so conveyed contaminants can get back up to speed before the next turn.

- Branch entries to main duct from side or top, not from bottom. Otherwise contaminants rolling along the bottom of the duct will fall into the low point provided by the branch entry and will block the entry branch.

- Provide 5 diameters of straight duct at hoods and equipment connections prior to an elbow; avoid elbows directly at hoods or equipment connections if possible.

- To minimize air leakage, install gaskets at each flanged connection.

- Ensure that gaskets do not protrude into duct. They can become a hidden orifice.

- Install duct supports that prevent duct shifting (in vertical or horizontal plane) when components are removed for inspection and clean-out. Put supports on the straight ducts on both sides of elbows that are removed for cleaning. Without them, the ducts will spring out of position and be very difficult to get back into place during reassembly.

- Match mark adjoining duct sections to aid in correct and efficient re-assembly.

Inspect all duct components regularly for physical damage (rips, tears, or dents), corrosion and abrasion, and plugging or clogging (low MTV).

A9.6 THE FOURTH "C": COLLECT

The collector is the device that protects the environment from excessive amounts of contaminants. The federal, state and/or local government, through an environmental permit system, regulates most collectors – also called Air Control Devices (ACD). This permit describes the special operating conditions necessary for compliance and maximum emissions. Particulate collectors can be dry filter type (baghouse), wet collectors (scrubbers), electrostatic (ESPs) or combinations (wet ESPs). They can also be specially designed for removal of vapors such as oxidizers and there are many types of these designs. Chapter 6 of this Manual describes the operation and key design features of these types of units and the local exhaust ventilation operator may also have responsibilities for their operation.

A9.7 EXHAUST FANS

Fans, sometimes referred to as blowers, are the primary air moving devices used in industrial applications. Fans can be divided into three basic groups: Axial, Centrifugal, and Special types. The focus of this section is directed towards axial and centrifugal fans. Chapter 7 in *Industrial Ventilation: A Manual of Recommended Practice for Design* discusses fans in detail for training purposes.

Axial fans have propeller type rotors. The airflow is straight through the rotors. A box fan in a window is an example of an axial fan. The axial fan category is determined by its casing style. They are not often used in local exhaust ventilation systems because they are low static pressure fans.

Centrifugal fans have an airflow that enters the fan rotor and is turned 90° in all directions (see Figure A9-8). The air is then captured in a scroll shaped casing housing and pushed through the fan outlet. Fan rotation gives the incoming air kinetic energy that is converted into static pressure by the shape of the casing or housing. The fan shaft on most fans is supported from two bearings on one side of the impeller, a cantilever design.

The amount of air a fan can move depends on the resistance to airflow (called static pressure) of the connected system. This is represented by a fan performance curve as can be seen in Chapter 7 of *Industrial Ventilation: A Manual of Recommended Practice for Design*. With minimal resistance, the fan is in a "free air" mode and can move its maximum amount of air where the curve crosses the horizontal axis of the graph. With increased resistance, represented by the curve drawn between the horizontal and vertical axes, the amount of airflow decreases. The resistance or pressure drop through the local exhaust ventilation system is represented by curve B. More pressure drop is required to pull a greater amount of airflow past the resistance of the hoods, duct, collector, etc. The fan requirements are represented by the intersection of the two curves, also known as the design operating point.

The fan vendor helps with the selection of a fan to deliver your ventilation systems' requirements and will provide the Fan Operating Curve when the fan is specified. The volume of air the fan delivers changes as the fan speed changes. Typical fans rotate at speeds ranging from 900 to 3600 revolutions per minute (rpm), depending on the IVS requirements.

Belt drives are used frequently with local exhaust ventilation fans to allow small fan speed changes. Belts and sheaves are available in many combinations providing a quick and easy way to change fan speed and its capacity to match up with a change in system requirements. Belt guards fully enclose the rapidly moving pulley belts to prevent pinch point injury. The motor, the pulley belts, and the fan shaft must be carefully aligned to prevent damaging vibration that will cause fan failure.

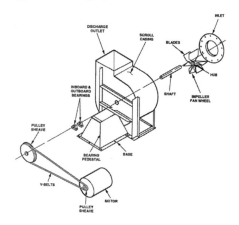

FIGURE A9-8. Centrifugal fan housing and drive (belt guard not shown) (Reprinted with permission from Procter & Gamble)

The maintenance frequency required for a fan is influenced by its operating condition. Fans operating under dusty or corrosive conditions require more frequent attention than those handling clean air. There are manuals provided by the vendor with required maintenance and operating instructions.

A9.7.1 Fan Safety. Allow only trained operating or maintenance personnel to work on fans. Fans have rotating parts that must be isolated from sources of energy to protect the maintenance worker. The fan motor or other driver must be locked out. Industrial environments generally are designed under a slight negative or positive pressure relative to the atmosphere. This slight pressure difference can cause fan blades to rotate due to back flow into the building even when the fan is shut off. This hazard requires blocking the fan impeller to prevent rotation when the fan is turned off and being maintained or cleaned.

A.9.7.2 Fan Components. Common components of axial and centrifugal fans are: bearings, shafts, belt sheaves, belts (V-belts), blades, body or housing, connectors (flexible), isolation foundations or platforms, louvers or dampers (inlet and outlet), motors, and pressure gauges.

Blades and Body (Housing)

Anything that changes the shape of the airflow within the fan housing will hurt fan performance. A buildup of foreign material on the fan blades causes imbalance, vibration, and loss of capacity (reduced airflow). Collection of foreign material in the fan housing reduces fan capacity.

Incorrect fan impeller rotation also significantly reduces fan capacity. The proper direction of fan wheel rotation is with the wheel perimeter rotating toward the fan discharge outlet. The blade direction is not the important factor.

NOTE: A centrifugal fan that is rotating backwards will deliver about 50% of the required airflow. Don't always believe the manufacturer's fan rotation arrows if the fan is not performing to specification and you have tried everything else.

Check for vibrations generated by the fan blade or shaft. Uneven material loading on the blades can cause vibration and imbalance. An unbalanced fan can cause the blades to sheer off and separate from the hub. If this condition is expected, use extreme caution when approaching the moving fan.

Inspect the fan body for physical damage, rust, and corrosion. Repair and paint the fan body if necessary. **Make sure not to paint over the fan manufacturer's nameplate.**

Bearings

Fan shaft bearings have a reputation as being the single greatest source of trouble for fans. Actually, bearings are very reliable. With proper maintenance and troubleshooting, a long bearing life can be achieved. The number of bearing types and fan applications are unlimited. Bearing life is reduced by overly tightened or excessively loose fan belts, fan vibration, uneven loading on the fan blades, high ambient operating temperatures, misalignment between the fan and motor shafts, and improper (over or under) lubrication.

Since every fan application is different, an exact lubrication schedule can only be determined by experience and manufacturer's guidance. REMEMBER, *MORE IS NOT BETTER IN FAN LUBRICATION*. EXCESSIVE LUBRICATION HAS BEEN THE CAUSE OF MANY FAN FAILURES.

Shafts

While inspecting bearings, you should also inspect the fan shaft. It must be strong and robust so it can carry the inertia of the rapidly spinning fan impeller. Shaft failure can lead to catastrophic damage and possibly injury. Inspect the shaft alignment and make sure the shaft is not bent. Ensure the shaft guard is clean, properly aligned, and secure.

Inlet and Outlet Dampers

Some fans have inlet or outlet dampers to adjust airflow or pressure (see Figure A9-9). They may be manually, pneumatically, or electronically controlled.

Belts

Maintenance increases the life and improves the overall performance of V-belts. With regular maintenance, V-belts should last for several years. Maintaining correct belt tension provides 50% to 100% longer belt life. Audible belt squealing during startup indicates insufficient belt tension. Make sure the belt guard is clean, properly aligned, and secured.

Motors

Before performing any work on the motor, ensure all power sources and switches are locked out. Motor maintenance is generally limited to cleaning and lubrication. Make sure the motor nameplate can be read. Many motors are permanently lubricated for life and require no further lubrication. Lubricate the motor only if fittings are provided and according to manufacturer's recommendations. Ensure the motor operating voltage is within ±10% of the nameplate voltage. Ensure the motor base is secure and all shims and belts are properly aligned.

Flexible Duct Connectors

Flexible connectors are used to isolate fan vibrations from the building and the remainder of the industrial ventilation system. Flexible connectors attach the ventilation system duct to the fan while eliminating fan vibration that may travel through the ventilation system duct.

Isolation Foundations

Isolation foundations eliminate fan vibrations that may travel through to the building or neighboring equipment. Ensure isolation foundations are level and all bolts are secure. Ensure that the springs were released after the unit was transported to the final location. Manufacturers frequently bind the springs for stability during shipping.

A9.8 EXHAUST STACKS AND FLOW OVER BUILDINGS

The exhaust stack is an extension of the duct, located after the fan, dispersing contaminants into the atmosphere. The exhaust stack should extend high enough to escape wind patterns around the building envelope. Otherwise, these wind patterns will draw the exhaust down to ground level because of the slight vacuum created in the wake of a building; this is known as building downwash. Note that the air is sufficiently clean to meet all regulations but may be a nuisance if it contains heat, moisture or slight odors.

Additionally, the air exit velocity and location of the exhaust stack is important. A good air exit velocity (3000 fpm) will disperse the exhaust in the atmosphere and prevent re-entry

Opposed Blade Dampers – Located in Fan Discharge

Variable Inlet Vane Dampers – Located in Fan Inlet to Pre-swirl the Entering Air

FIGURE A9-9. Fan volume adjusting dampers

into return air systems. Also, ensure exhaust stacks are not upstream of fresh air intakes on the roof or on the sides of higher parts of the building.

Weather Caps (Not Recommended)

A component found on many exhaust stacks is the weather cap or rain cap. *Do not use these weather caps!* They direct the air downwards, towards the roof, increasing the possibility for re-entry of the exhaust into return air systems. Additionally, maintenance personnel are exposed to contaminants when on the roof. They also require more fan energy to overcome the added system resistance that air experiences as it passes around the parts of the cap. Instead of a weather cap, use an "offset" exhaust stack or "no-loss" exhaust stack.

Gravity Shutoff Dampers

While not recommended, some facilities use gravity back draft dampers or similar devices to keep rainwater out of the stack when the system is not operating. Snow load can impede the damper from opening. In the past, bushings failed and the damper components rusted in place. Modern construction materials avert bushing failure and annual inspections should be done. Since climbing to the top of the stack is difficult, this inspection tends not to be performed. Therefore, these dampers are not recommended for local exhaust ventilation systems.

Inspect all exhaust stack components, as well as the ones included in the duct network section, regularly for physical damage (rips, tears, or dents), corrosion and abrasion, and plugging or clogging (low duct velocity). Inspect the flashing around the stack head opening in the roof to ensure that there is no rainwater leakage into the building.

A9.9 LOCAL EXHAUST VENTILATION (LEV) SYSTEM BALANCING

Duct network design uses varying sizes of duct to maintain the needed airflow at each hood and a minimum transport velocity (MTV) throughout the system. The more air needed, the greater the duct diameter required to maintain the velocity above the MTV. Note that the methods to design and manage a local exhaust ventilation (suction) system are different from the methods required for design of an HVAC (positive pressure) system.

"System balance" refers to achieving the intended airflow design in every branch of the system. If this balance is not maintained, the local exhaust ventilation system cannot function properly. The number of capture points and the volume of air drawn at each capture point determine the design and balance of the duct network. A change in the number or size of hoods can destroy the balance of the whole system.

In a multi-branch duct network, each branch has its own resistance (static pressure). The low resistance branches need additional resistance to be balanced to match the high resistance ones or else they will get all of the flow. Installing blast

gates to increase resistance does this. In some cases, orifice plates may be used also. This is shown in Figure A9-10. The circled numbers are called nodes and show where two branches come together.

The air path through nodes 1, 3, 5, 6, and 7 has the highest resistance. It is the "governing leg" for the system and sets the fan static pressure requirement. The two other air paths (nodes 2 to 3 and nodes 4 to 5) have a lower resistance to airflow than the available static pressure at the connection points on the governing leg.

A calculated amount of resistance needs to be added in these short sections so that airflow through these hoods will not bypass the hood at node 1. The SP at node 3 (3 "wg) is greater than the resistance of the branch between nodes 2 and 3 (2 "wg); an orifice or blast gate on that branch is needed to add 1 "wg of resistance (2 "wg + 1 "wg = 3 "wg). Similarly, the branch between nodes 4 and 5 requires an orifice or blast gate that adds 2 "wg of resistance.

Blast Gates and Cut-Offs

Blast gates (see Figure A9-11) are adjustable devices, used to add artificial static pressure as described above. They are also sometimes called "cut-offs." Once set, only the system designer should change the gate position or the entire local exhaust ventilation system will become unbalanced. It is recommended that the blast gate be padlocked in position.

Orifice Plates

Orifices are sometimes installed at the end of a duct branch, between the duct flanges connected to the hood or some branch in the system. This is shown in the examples of Figure A9-12. Orifices must always be in place when used to balance the system. If removed for cleaning, they must be replaced when the duct is reassembled.

A9.10 BASIC LOCAL EXHAUST VENTILATION (LEV) SYSTEM TROUBLESHOOTING

If you are able to actually see visible dust from equipment connected to the Local Exhaust Ventilation (LEV) System at your station, you may have a duct plugged with material or some other system trouble. Below are some reasons why ducts

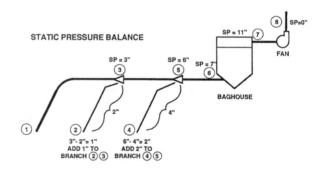

FIGURE A9-10. Balancing all the branches in a duct system (Reprinted with permission from Procter & Gamble)

FIGURE A9-11. Fabricated blast gate

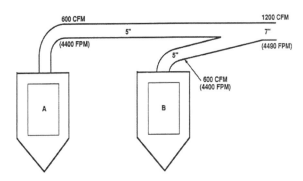

FIGURE A9-13. System balancing example (Reprinted with permission from Procter & Gamble)

may not be providing enough airflow that can be easily avoided. Refer to Chapter 7 for more detailed Troubleshooting information.

- Duct access doors are open.

- Gaskets are damaged or missing.

- Water is in the duct. Even a slight bit of moisture will cause dust to adhere to the duct wall. For this reason, introducing water into the ducts from cleaning procedures or leaks at gaskets should always be avoided. If water is used for cleaning ducts, the duct network must be thoroughly dried before being returned service. Rainwater will be pulled into outdoor ducts at leaky gaskets due to the negative pressure or vacuum inside the duct.

- Duct surfaces are dented or otherwise damaged. These irregularities in the duct cause makeup. Repair the damaged segment and have the system checked.

- Air bleeds are blocked. Blocked air bleeds actually reduce airflow in ducts downstream, leading to product/dust drop out. Air bleeds must be kept unobstructed, clean, and in good repair. If problems exist at any point in the local exhaust ventilation system, the appro-

priate person should troubleshoot the network. Any changes to the local exhaust ventilation system must be approved.

- Improper changes were made to the system, without ensuring the system was balanced after the change. See Section A9.11 for some examples of how improper changes affect system operation.

A9.11 IMPACT OF IMPROPER LOCAL EXHAUST VENTILATION (LEV) SYSTEM CHANGES

Two dust hoods, each requiring 600 cfm of air, are designed with 5-inch diameter ducts (see Figure A9-13). The 5-inch diameter is selected to maintain a conveying velocity between 3500 and 4500 fpm for 600 cfm. The combined airflow of hoods A and B (1200 cfm) requires a 7-inch duct for a conveying velocity of 4490 feet per minute. A duct diameter either larger or smaller than seven inches would cause velocities greater or less than conveying requirements and either cause the dropping out of dust or cause plugs or abrasion in the duct system.

Changing duct sizes is not the only action that destroys the balance of the local exhaust ventilation system. The most common damage to system balance occurs because hoods have been tampered with. If, for example, a new hood were added to the duct, it would change the balance of the system. Figure A9-14 shows how such a modification would affect the system.

- The new capture point C "steals" airflow designed for hood A.

- The duct between A and C drops below conveying velocity. Dust settles out. The line plugs.

- Velocity in the 5-inch duct between C and B increases beyond recommended maximum conveying velocity.

- Velocity in the 7-inch duct increases because the other connections are plugged. A sticky dust would plug the line. A coarse dust could wear the duct out near seams and elbows.

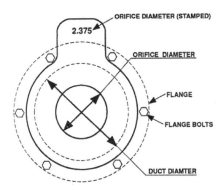

FIGURE A9-12. Plate orifice (Reprinted with permission from Procter & Gamble)

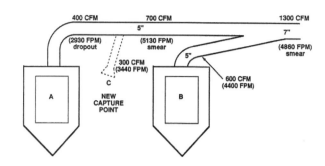

FIGURE A9-14. Effects of adding a new hood (Reprinted with permission from Procter & Gamble)

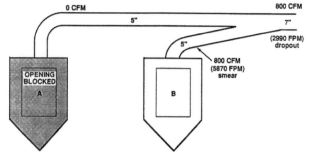

FIGURE A9-15. Effects of blocking or altering hood opening (Reprinted with permission from Procter & Gamble)

In a second example, one of the lines is blocked to increase the airflow to the second line (see Figure A9-15). The results are the same.

- The airflow for Hood A is blocked.

- Airflow increases through Hood B. High velocity could cause the 5-inch duct to plug if dust is sticky or to wear out elbows.

- Low velocity in the 7-inch duct causes dropout and eventual plug.

As these examples show, changing the airflow at any point in the duct network can change the conveying velocities and airflows in all parts of the network. Blocking the air at one sta-

tion might affect the network on a completely different floor. For this reason, the person responsible for maintaining the system must evaluate all change ideas for the dust control system. Again, making a small change without adjusting the rest of the system can degrade service everywhere in the plant.

It does not take much to disrupt the performance of a functioning local exhaust ventilation, even under normal operation. Changes need to be made thoughtfully, with the help of a competent ventilation engineer. See Chapter 8 for further information and examples of how changes affect local exhaust ventilation operation and explanations of the right way to make the change.

INDEX